The practice of soil reinforcing in Europe

The practice of soil reinforcing in Europe

Proceedings of the symposium *The practice of soil reinforcing in Europe* organised by the Tenax Group under the auspices of the International Geosynthetics Society, and held at the Institution of Civil Engineers on 18 May 1995

Edited by Dr T. S. Ingold

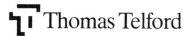 Thomas Telford

Symposium organised by the Tenax Group under the auspices of the International Geotechnics Society, and held at the Institution of Civil Engineers, 18 May 1995.

Published by Thomas Telford Services Ltd, Thomas Telford House, 1 Heron Quay, London, E14 4JD

First published 1995

Distributors for Thomas Telford books are
USA: American Society of Civil Engineers, Publications Sales Department, 345 East 47th Street, New York, NY 10017-2398
Japan: Maruzen Co. Ltd, Book Department, 3–10 Nihonbashi 2-chome, Chuo-ku, Tokyo 103
Australia: DA Books and Journals, 648 Whitehorse Road, Mitcham 3132, Victoria

A CIP catalogue record for this book is available from the British Library.

ISBN: 0 7277 2082 X

This book is published on the understanding that the authors are solely responsible for the statements made and opinions expressed in it and that its publication does not necessarily imply that such statements and/or opinions are or reflect the views or opinions of the organizers or publishers.

Printed and bound in Great Britain by Cromwell Press Ltd, Melksham, Wiltshire.

Preface

This volume contains the proceedings of the symposium *The practice of soil reinforcing in Europe*, which was held at the Institution of Civil Engineers on 18 May 1995. The proceedings comprise the seventeen papers and discussions presented at the symposium together with five post symposium papers.

The symposium was organised by the Tenax Group under the auspices of the International Geosynthetics Society. Thanks are due to them and the Technical Committee comprising Steve Corbet of Maunsell & Partners, Dr Shiram Dikran of Tenax Plastics Limited, Professor Colin Jones of the University of Newcastle-upon-Tyne, who is the current President of the International Geosynthetics Society, Dr Piero Sembenelli of Piero Sembenelli Consultants and Dr Terry Ingold.

Thanks are also due to the session chairmen, Steve Corbet and Colin Jones, for the smooth running of the presentations, as well as the discussion reporters, Chris Lawson of Terram Limited and Chris Jenner of Netlon Limited for their prompt, accurate reporting.

Last but by no means least, thanks are due to the authors, from Austria, France, Germany, Italy, Switzerland, The Netherlands and the United Kingdom, who have unstintingly shared their knowledge of the practice of soil reinforcing in Europe.

Dr T. S. Ingold
Consulting Engineer

Contents

Post Symposium Papers

The development and use of polymeric reinforcements in reinforced soil

C .J.F. P. JONES, Department of Civil Engineering,
University of Newcastle upon Tyne, United Kingdom

SYNOPSIS
The paper considers the use of polymeric materials as reinforcement in permanent reinforced soil structures. The behaviour characteristics of the materials are described with respect to their long-term inclusion in soil with an emphasis on durability. The influence of the selection of polymer reinforcement on the design of reinforced soil is considered and details are given indicating how long-term reinforcement properties are selected. Recent developments and some current research into the development of polymers is described. Finally the inherent durability and safety of polymeric reinforced soil structures are illustrated by their survival in the Kobe earthquake.

INTRODUCTION
The concept of earth reinforcement is not new. The basic principles are demonstrated in nature by animals and birds and in the action of tree roots. In the past, reeds and vines were used extensively to reinforce clay bricks and granular soils in the construction of many large earth structures. The earliest remaining examples of soil reinforcement are the Ziggurat in the ancient city of Dur-Kurigatzu now known as the Agar-Quf and the Great Wall of China. Reinforcing techniques for military earthworks appeared common up to the last century although there is little reference in published texts. A notable contribution was made in 1822 when the British Army introduced a form of reinforced soil for military construction, Pasley (1922). Pasley used brushwood, wooden planks and canvas as his reinforcement. Arguably this was the first application of geotextile reinforcement to reinforced soil structures, although the resultant structures would probably have had a short life.

The use of geotextiles for permanent reinforcement could not be contemplated until the development of synthetic polymer based materials. Synthetic fabrics were known prior to 1940 but it was not until the late sixties and early seventies that the advances in synthetic fabric and geotextile developments produced materials whose longevity could be assured. Geotextiles can be divided into two categories, conventional geotextiles and specials. *Conventional geotextiles* are products of the textile industry and include nonwoven, woven, knitted and stitched bonded textiles.

Nonwoven geotextiles consist of a random arrangement of fibres bonded together by heat (melt bonded) or physical entanglement (needle punched). The fibres used can be in the form of either stable (short lengths) or continuous filaments. The structure of non-woven geotextiles is illustrated in Figure 1(a). Woven geotextiles consist of fibres arranged essentially at right angles to one another in varying configurations; the general structure is shown in Figure 1(b). Alternative configurations are identified on the basis of the cross sectional shape of the constituent fibres. Monofilament wovens are manufactured from fibres with circular or elliptical cross sections. Multi-filament and fibrillated tape wovens result from a gathering of fibres in parallel arrays along the length and across the width of the geotextile. Tape wovens are made from fibres with a flat cross-section. Knitted geotextiles consist of fibres which are inter-looped. This process produces two different structures, weft knitted and warp knitted geotextiles. Stitch bonded geotextiles are formed by the stitching together of fibres or yarns, Figure 1(c). Fabric reinforced retaining walls have proved to be economic but are often utilitarian in appearance and the larger use of geotextile fabrics has proven to be in the areas of separation, filtration and drainage. Knitted geotextiles in the form of open grids are used extensively for reinforcement.

  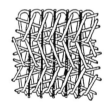

1a) Nonwoven structure   1b) Woven structure   1c) Stitch-bonded structure

Figure 1:   Different geotextile constructions

Special geotextiles are not usually produced in a textile process. There are two major types of special geotextiles, geogrids and geocomposites. Geogrids are formed either by the cross laying of strips which are subsequently bonded together at their cross over points or by the punching and drawing of polymer sheets. It is common practice for the cross laid strips to consist of *geocomposite* strips formed from high strength filament fibres in a polymer matrix. Geogrids are open structures frequently presenting over 50 per cent open area, Figure 2.

Geocomposites, in a soil reinforcement context, generally consist of high strength fibres set within a polymer matrix or encased within a polymer skin. The fibres provide the tensile properties for the material while the matrix or

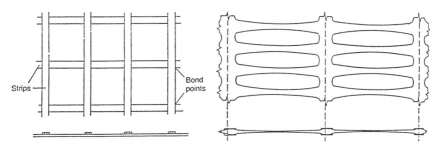

Figure 2:   **Two different geogrid structures**

skin provides the geometrical shape and protects the fibres from damage. There are two common types of geocomposite structures, strips and bars, Figure 3. In addition to these special geotextiles, knitted grid structures are also encased within a polymer skin used to provide protection for the tensile members. Advanced geocomposite materials are being developed; some of these are considered later.

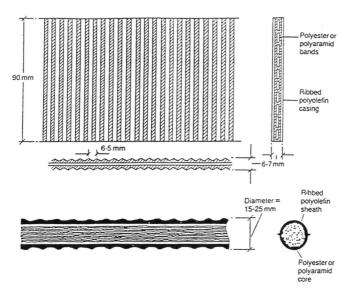

Figure 3:   **Composite strip and bar structures**

The form of any geotextile required to reinforce a structure depends upon the nature and life of the structure itself. The properties required for permanent reinforcements are likely to be different from those required for temporary structures. In order to achieve maximum reinforcement efficiency the load carrying elements of the geotextile are laid flat and in a highly directional alignment within the geotextile structure; in this manner the tensile characteristics of the load carrying elements determine the tensile characteristics of the material as a whole. Typical properties of polymer reinforcements currently available are listed in Table 1. The established uses of polymeric reinforcement are illustrated in Figures 4 and 5.

REINFORCEMENT MATERIAL PROPERTIES

Polymer materials used as soil reinforcement have four main requirements. They must be strong, relatively stiff, durable and bond with the soil. Of critical importance is that the strength of the reinforcement is sufficient to support the force required to achieve stability of the structure. The magnitude of the required force will vary depending upon the application.

Table 1 Representative properties of geosynthetics

Geotextile construction	Tensile strength kN/m	Extension at max. load %	Apparent opening size mm	Water flow litres/m²/sec *	Unit weight g/m²
Conventional					
Nonwovens					
Melt-bonded	3 - 25	20 - 60	0.01 - 0.35	25 - 150	70 - 350
Needle-punched	7 - 90	50 - 80	0.03 - 0.20	30 - 200	150 - 2000
Wovens					
Monofilament	20 - 80	9 - 35	0.07 - 2.5	25 - 2000	150 - 300
Multifilament**	40 - 800	9 - 30	0.20 - 0.9	20 - 80	250 - 1350
Flat tape	8 - 70	10 - 25	0.07 - 0.15	5 - 20	90 - 250
Knitteds					
Weft	2 - 5	300 - 600	0.2 - 1.2	60 - 2000	
Warp	20 - 120	12 - 15	0.4 - 5	100 - 2000	
Stitch-bonded	30 - 1000	8 - 30	0.07 - 0.5	30 - 80	250 - 1200
Special					
Geogrids					
Cross-laid strips	25 - 200	3 - 20	50 - 300	NA	300 - 1200
Punched sheets	10 - 200	11 - 30	40 - 150	NA	200 - 1100
Geocomposites					
Strips	20 - 150#	3 - 20	50 - 300	NA	300 - 1200
Bars	20 - 500#	0.5 - 20	NA	NA	NA
Link structures	100 - 4000	3 - 20	NA	NA	600 - 4500

*	normal to the plane of the geotextile with 10 cm constant head
**	fibrillated tapes are included in this category
#	measured in kN (not kN/m)
NA	not applicable

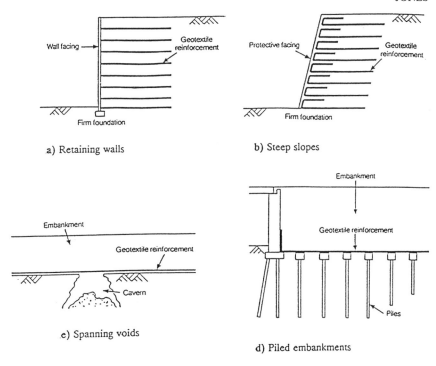

a) Retaining walls

b) Steep slopes

c) Spanning voids

d) Piled embankments

Figure 4:   **Permanent applications of reinforced soil**

In a steep slope strengthened by a geotextile reinforcing layer each reinforcement might have to support a force of 10 - 40 kN/m; alternatively a single geotextile reinforcing layer at the base of an embankment on soft soil may be required to support a tensile force of 100 - 400 kN/m to ensure stability. The tensile strength required to provide support of structures in areas of subsidence can be significantly greater with long term strengths in excess of 1,000 kN/m.

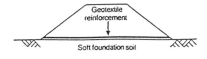

Embankments on soft soil

Figure 5:   **Short term application of reinforced soil**

The requirement of the geotextile to be stiff is so that the required force can be mobilised at a tensile strain which is compatible with the deformation of the soil. The concept of strain compatibility between the reinforced soil and

5

the soil is implicit in any reinforced soil structure, Jewell (1992). The allowable tensile strain depends on the application and in the case of a reinforced slope on soft soil the allowable extension can vary from 5 - 10 per cent. In the case of a reinforced soil wall the design *allowable* tensile extension of the reinforcement is unlikely to exceed 2 - 4 per cent, with a limitation of <1 per cent strain occurring after construction. The *actual* extension is likely to be <2 per cent in total.

Durability of the polymeric reinforcement is influenced by time and has to be considered together with the environment conditions. With permanent structures durability is the dominant consideration of the designers.

The mechanical requirement for bond between the reinforcement and the soil is important but often a function of the form of the polymer reinforcement. Geogrids and conventional geotextiles in the form of sheets provide good bond with the soil either due to the large surface offered by the geotextile or, in the case of geogrids, by soil/reinforcement interlock. In the case of strip or bar reinforcement, bond can become a critical consideration particularly in the top of a reinforced soil structure, Hassan (1992).

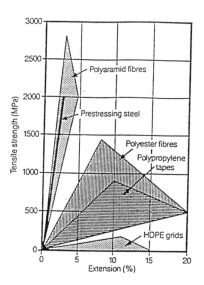
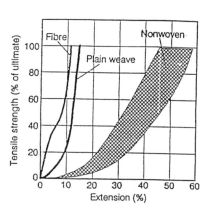

a) Tensile strength/extension characteristics
of various geotextile load carrying elements
and that of prestressing steel

b) Effect of geotextile construction
on resulting extension characteristics using polyester fibres

**Figure 6:   Load/extension characteristics of geotextiles
and influence of construction**

Strength-stiffness of the polymer

The tensile strength and extension characteristics of geotextiles are a function of the tensile properties of the constituent materials and the geometrical arrangement of the elements within the geosynthetic material.

The tensile characteristics of a range of geosynthetics are shown in Figure 6(a) which shows that the strength of polyaramide fibres can be greater than that of prestressed steel tendons. Polyaramide fibres are seldom used for

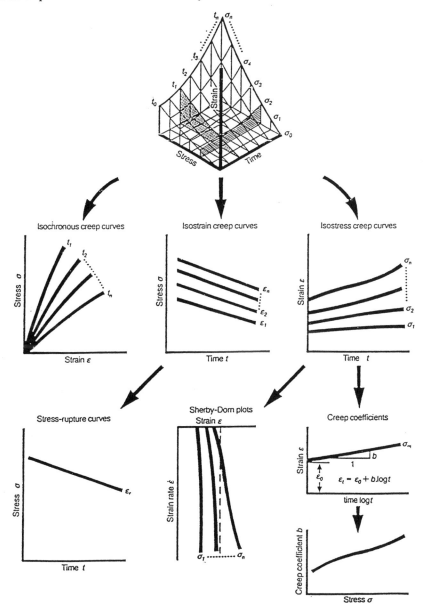

Figure 7:   **Various ways of representing creep data (at constant temperature) (After Lawson, 1991)**

7

geosynthetic reinforcement because of cost; alternatives are available from polyester fibres, polypropylene tapes and high density polyethylene (HDPE) grids which all exhibit good tensile characteristics at relatively low costs. All of these materials have been shown to be well suited for reinforced soil applications. High density polyethylene grids can be manufactured in a form which is immediately suitable for use as reinforcement, whilst polyester fibres can be produced in a form which is easy to install. The influence of geometrical structure on the resultant geotextile stress-strain characteristics is shown in Figure 6(b). For maximum efficiency it is desirable that the geosynthetic reinforcement be able to reproduce as closely as possible the characteristics of the constituent load carrying elements. Reference to Figure 6(b) indicates why woven, stitch-bonded, geogrid and geocomposite structures are preferred for reinforced soil applications.

Effect of long-term loads on strength-stiffness

For many polymeric based materials, ambient operating temperatures coincide with their visco-elastic phase, thus creep becomes a significant consideration in assessing their long-term load carrying capacity. Creep is the increase in extension of a material under a constantly applied load. The stress-strain time characteristics (at constant temperature) of geotextile reinforcements can be visualized in terms of a three-dimensional body with stress, strain and time comprising the three axes, Figure 7, Lawson (1991). By projecting the three-dimensional body into each of three phase planes, three sets of curves are obtained which can be used to describe creep behaviour:

- isochronous creep curves (projecting onto the stress-strain plane)
- isostrain creep curves (projecting onto the stress-time plane)
- isostress creep curves ((projecting onto the strain-time plane)

The creep curves of most practical use for geosynthetic reinforcements are the stress-rupture curves, the isochronous creep curves and the creep coefficient curves. The stress-rupture curves are used to predict the lifetime over which the geotextile reinforcement can carry a specific load. The isochronous creep curves and the creep coefficient curves are used to estimate both the total extension and the creep extension of the geotextile reinforcement over different design lives and stress levels. In order to describe the creep behaviour of geotextiles it is necessary to present both the stress-rupture curve for the material and either the isochronous creep curve or the creep coefficient curve. Figure 8(a) shows the isochronous creep curves for a commercially available high modulus polyester fibre based geostrip. The shape of the curve indicates that there is little change in the load extension curve with time for load levels below 40 per cent of the initial tensile strength (less than 1 per cent creep extension). The difference in behaviour of a polypropylene geotextile is shown in Figure 8(b).

At a working stress level of 20 per cent for the initial ultimate tensile strength in the material, long term creep extensions could be expected to be 5-6 per cent. Creep coefficients provide a convenient means of comparing the rate of creep of different polymeric materials. Figure 8(c) shows the distribution of creep coefficients for various structural materials used in geotextile reinforcements. It can be seen that the creep coefficient increases for increasing applied load for all polymers, although processing techniques can alter significantly the rate of creep of a particular polymer.

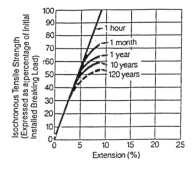

a) Isochronous creep curves for high modulus polyester fibre geostrips at 23 °C (After ECGL, 1989)

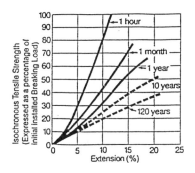

b) Isochronous creep curves for high modulus polypropylene tape woven geotextiles at 23 °C (After ECGL, 1989)

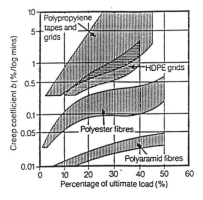

c) Creep coefficient versus percentage applied load for various geotextile reinforcing elements at 23 °C (After Hollaway, 1990)

Figure 8: **Isochronous creep curves for two commercially available geotextiles and comparison of the rate of creep of various geotextile reinforcements**

Effect of temperature on strength and stiffness

The temperature at depth within a soil mass remains constant; however, near the surface the ambient temperature may vary depending on the external temperature and the environment, Figure 9. At depth the constant soil temperature may range from 10°C in temperate climates to 20°C in tropical climates. The temperature profile of a reinforced soil structure in a desert environment is shown in Figure 10 which shows that the temperature of the soil immediately behind the concrete soil reinforcing units could reach 35°C during the summer months.

For those polymeric materials whose operating temperatures coincide with their visco-elastic phase, a change in operating temperature can affect their

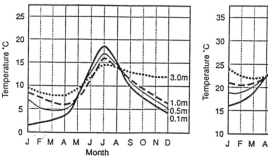

Mean monthly in-soil temperatures at different depths in Britain (Murray and Farrar, 1988)

Mean monthly in-soil temperatures at different depths in Hong Kong (based on data from Royal Hong Kong Observatory, after Howells and Pang, 1989)

Figure 9:   In-soil temperatures in the United Kingdom and Hong Kong

strengths/stiffness characteristics particular in relation to creep, Table 2. At operating temperatures below its glass transition temperature a material behaves in an elastic manner with a relative small plastic (creep) component. At operating temperatures between the glass transition temperature and its melting point a material behaves in an essentially visco-elastic manner with a significant creep component when load is applied. If changes in operating temperature are confined to a region below the materials glass transition temperature there is an insignificant change in the materials behaviour under load. Thus for polyester reinforcements, changes in ambient operating temperatures in the range 10 - 40°C would not be expected to alter the creep characteristics. However, changes in the same temperature range would be expected to alter the creep characteristics of polypropylene tapes and high density polyethylene (HDPE). This increase in the rate of creep with temperature has been used by researchers to provide accelerated creep data at ambient temperatures for specific products, Bush (1990).

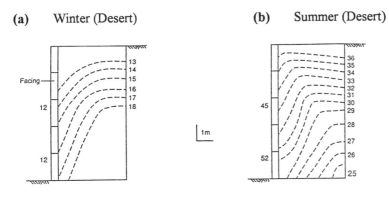

(a)   Winter (Desert)

(b)   Summer (Desert)

(c)   Air temperature in Phoenix, Arizona, USA

	J	F	M	A	M	J	J	A	S	O	N	D
Max.	24	27	31	36	40	44	45	43	41	37	31	26
Mean	10	12	16	20	25	30	33	32	29	22	15	11
Min.	-1	1	3	6	11	16	20	21	17	8	2	0

Figure 10 Temperature conditions in desert environment (a) and (b) show in-soil temperatures (°C) for a reinforced soil wall near Tuscon, Arizona

Table 2 Glass transition temperatures and melting points for various geotextile elements

Geotextile element	Glass transition temperature T_g °C	Melting point T_m °C
Aramid fibres		370
Polyester fibres	90 to 110	260
Polypropylene tapes	-20	170 to 180
High density polyethylene	-120 to -90	130

As temperature affects the rate of creep and the stress-rupture characteristics of many polymer reinforcements, this should be taken into account if the creep data to be used in design is obtained at different operating temperatures from that occurring in service. Where the creep data has been derived at higher ambient temperatures than those expected in

11

service conservative predictions will result if the data is used in the calculation of long-term design strength and extensions. Alternatively, if the creep data has been derived at lower ambient temperatures than those expected in service, unsafe predictions may result. In the majority of tests for creep a test temperature of 20 - 23°C has become the industrial standard; reference to Figure 9 shows that the majority of this information is directly applicable to many reinforced soil structures.

DURABILITY

The durability of the reinforcement is of primary importance to designers and owners of structures. In the context of polymeric reinforcements, durability can be considered under the following headings:

(i)   degradation of polymers
(ii)   mechanical damage
(iii)   influence of outside agencies (ie fire)

Polymer degradation

Modern polymer reinforcements used in reinforced soil are composed of highly durable polymers. However, polymeric materials will eventually degrade as a result of a number of different actions; these include ultraviolet light, high energy radiation, oxidization, hydrolysis and chemical reaction. Biological degradation is not considered an issue for polymeric reinforcements formed from high molecular weight polymers, Koerner et al (1992).

While each of the actions which can result in polymer degradation are usually assessed individually, they are complicated by temperature, stress and synergism between one another. With respect to temperature, it is established that elevated temperature increases all the listed types of degradation in a predictable manner. Regarding stress, one must identify the type and the relative magnitude. In terms of reinforced soil, stress is associated with tension. The influence of synergism in reinforced soil structures is complicated.

While the actions leading to degradation are complicated and difficult to quantify, the overall impact on polymeric reinforcement is well established. Degradation is associated with chain scission, side chain breaking and cross linking, Grassie and Scott (1985). Each of these actions cause the polymer to become aggressively more brittle thereby decreasing from its original elongation to gradually lesser values.

Effect of ultraviolet light

The influence of ultraviolet light on polymeric reinforcements can be eliminated by burying the reinforcement in the soil. However, in some reinforced soil applications the geosynthetic elements are required to remain exposed to sunlight for extended periods, as in the case of geotextile face slopes and walls. In these cases the geotextile must be adequately resistant to the effects of UV light exposure. Ultraviolet light causes degradation by reaction with the covalent bonds of organic polymers causing yellowing and embrittlement. All polymers are susceptible to varying degrees of degradation by this method, with polyester being the least susceptible and polyethylene and polypropylene being the most. In addition to the type of polymer, the structure of the geotextile influences the rate of ultraviolet degradation. Geotextiles with large diameter structural members such as some geogrids or thick and bulky materials exhibit a higher degree of resistance than thin fibrous materials.

Polyester used as a reinforcement has a good resistance to UV light and will retain approximately 80 per cent of its original strength after exposure of continuous sunlight in an aggressive environment. Polyethylene and polypropylene do not have the same UV resistance as polyester and to provide UV resistance it is normal practice to provide a UV stabilizer into the polymer during manufacture.

There are two types of UV stabilizers used for polyethylene and polypropylene, passive stabilizers and active stabilizers. Passive stabilizers work by shielding the polymer molecules from UV radiation. The most common passive stabilizer is carbon black which has been shown to be an effective barrier for UV absorbed by polyethylene. The carbon black type and the dispersion characteristics are crucial to performance. To ensure extended UV protection the carbon black must be a channel type with a particle sizes of less than or equal to 20 nanometres (20×10^{-9} m); a minimum concentration of 2 per cent is required and it must be well dispersed. The result of the addition of carbon is to render the polymer black in colour. Carbon black stabilizers are often used in conjunction with active stabilizers which absorb the high UV radiation energy and release lower non-destructive energy. In converting the high energy UV radiation into low energy the active stabilizer is consumed and hence the UV resistance life of the stabilized polymer depends upon the quantity of stabilizer originally added during the manufacturing process.

The effect of oxidation on polyolefins: polyethylene (PE) and polypropylene (PP)

Degradation due to oxidation occurs due to heat (thermo-oxidation) and exposure to ultraviolet light (photo-oxidation) as considered above. Oxidation is not considered a problem with polyester but can have an effect on polyethylene and polypropylene. The application of oxygen and heat cause a breakdown and cross-linking of the molecular chains resulting in embrittlement of the polymer.

Controlling the oxidation of polyethylenes is a well developed science supported by long term experience and a range of applications in the telecommunications cable insulation field. Antioxidants are added to the polymer to prevent oxidation during processing and use. Antioxidant packages calculated to provide over 250 year life have been designed for specific polypropylene geotextiles, Wisse et al (1990). In addition to the use of antioxidants changing the molecular structure through orientation inhibits degradation. In the case of high density polyethylene (HDPE) geogrids the degree of orientation required by the manufacturing process has been shown to provide significant resistance to oxidation.

Effect of hydrolysis on polyester: polyethylene-terephthalate (PET)

Hydrolysis occurs when water molecules react with polymer molecules, resulting in chain scission, reduced molecular weight and strength loss. Of the polymeric reinforcements used for permanent reinforcement only polyester is susceptible to hydrolysis. For hydrolysis to proceed water must be present. In reinforced soil applications it is assumed conservatively that 100 per cent relative humidity can exist. Therefore hydrolysis needs to be considered in reinforced soil. As with all chemical reactions raised temperatures affect the rate of hydrolysis, with an increase of 3 - 400 per cent occurring with an increase in temperature from 20° to 30°C.

Chemical agents can act as catalysts in the hydrolysis reaction. In an acid environment (pH < 2) hydrogen ions increase the reaction rate. In an alkaline environment the OH⁻ can also influence the reaction, and when polyester fibres are directly exposed over long periods of time at pH > 11 the presence of OH⁻ can have a detrimental and destructive effect. Thus direct exposure of polyester fibres to environments such as curing concrete can initiate hydrolysis. This is of potential concern in some modern forms of reinforced soil constructions using modular concrete block facings and to which the reinforcement is connected by trapping the material between the vertically adjacent blocks.

To protect polyesters from highly alkaline environments robust coating of polyethylene or PVC are used. Both of these coatings need to ensure that, although water vapour can migrate through the casing, the PE of PVC acts as a barrier to the migration of inorganic ions. Thus the environment inside the casing remains neutral. If the barrier is punctured during installation protection can be lost.

The molecular weight of the polyester affects the rate of hydrolysis. Advances in polyester manufacture since the 1940s have enabled heavier molecular weight polyesters to be produced with a consequent increase in resistance to hydrolysis. High molecular weight polyesters (average molecule M_n > 30000) should be specified for technically demanding applications such as reinforced soils.

The type of processing performed on polyester also affects the rate of hydrolysis, and partly drawn polyester film exhibits worse behaviour than highly drawn polyester fibres. The effect of drawing the polymer during processing causes orientation (strengthening) to the molecular structure with the result that the molecular chains are aligning much closer together. This makes in more difficult for water molecules to penetrate the molecular structure of the polymer. It can be concluded that hydrolysis is not significant in reinforced soil if well engineered materials are used as the reinforcement.

Mechanical degradation

The tensile characteristics of polymer materials are measured in the laboratory under ideal conditions. When used as reinforcement it is necessary to consider the possibility of mechanical damage. The placing and compaction of soil directly against the polymer reinforcement may reduce its tensile properties. The amount of damage inflicted on the reinforcement depends on the actual construction of the geotextile, the size and type of soil being placed

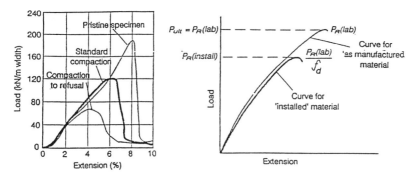

(a) Effect of compaction on strength/ extension properties of a woven polyester geotextile (After Watts and Brady, 1990)

(b) Representation of effect of installation damage by use of a partial factor

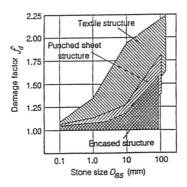

(c) Variation in damage factor according to stone size and geotextile structure (After Lawson, 1991)

Figure 11: **Effect of installation damage on geotextile reinforcements**

and the compaction effort. The effect of installation damage on geotextile reinforcements is to reduce the tensile strength but the modulus (stiffness) is not affected, Figure 11. Figure 11(a) shows the loss of strength of woven polyester directly exposed to the compaction of 30 mm diameter crushed limestone.

The effects of installation damage to the tensile strength of polymeric reinforcement is considered in design by the use of a partial factor applied to the tensile strength of the "as manufactured" material, Figure 11(b). The partial factor is determined by recovering the geotextiles from test sites and comparing the tensile properties with undamaged material, BS 8006 (1994).

Influence of outside agencies

In addition to mechanical damage occurring to the geotextile during construction, polymeric reinforcements can be damaged or destroyed during their life by unforeseen actions or accidents. The action of fire has been known to completely destroy structural facing formed from polymers and the use of unprotected polymer materials on the face of critical structures is not permitted in the United Kingdom. Similarly, protection of the polymer material from the action of vandals should be provided.

BOND

There are two types of interaction between geotextile reinforcement and the soil. The first is bond, which determines the load transfer between the reinforcement and the adjacent soil, Figure 12(a). The assessment of bond is required when the critical failure plane crosses the geotextile reinforcement. The second form of interaction is direct sliding resistance which is important for wide width reinforcement materials, Figure 12(b). The assessment of direct sliding is required when the potential failure plane coincides with the surface of the polymeric reinforcement.

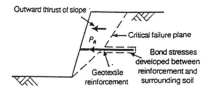 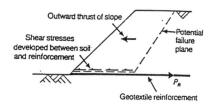

(a) Application of bond between geotextile reinforcement and surrounding soil

(b) Application of direct sliding along surface of geotextile reinforcement

Figure 12: **Situations where the geotextile reinforcement interacts with the adjacent soil**

The tensile stress in the reinforcements are transferred to the soil by means of the development to bond between the geotextile and the adjacent soil. For reinforced soil there are two types of bond mechanisms, friction and bearing. Friction between the reinforcement and surrounding soil occurs along a surface in a direction parallel to the reinforcement, whereas end bearing between the geotextile reinforcement and the surrounding soil occurs along the surface normal to the plane of the reinforcement. Conventional strip materials develop bond by friction, whereas polymeric anchors develop bond by end bearing and geogrids develop bond by a combination of friction and end bearing. It is possible to increase the bond between the soil and a geosynthetic by electrical means; this is considered later.

MATERIAL DEVELOPMENT

The successful development of many innovative technologies depends uponthe active support of influential "champions". In the case of geosynthetic reinforced soil structures in the United Kingdom, the active support of the Department of Transport (DTp), the Transport Research Laboratory (TRL), the Highway Authorities and the Universities has been essential. In addition, the material manufacturers have been a major influence

Table 3 Main geosynthetic reinforcing materials developed in the United Kingdom during 1973-83

Material (name)	Form	% extension at working load	Load capacity or characteristic tensile strength kN/m^2 or kN	Manufacturer (approx. date of introduction to the market)
Glass reinforced plastic (Fibretain)	strip §	0.2	16 - 80	Pilkington plc (1973)
Molecularly orientated grid (Tensar)	grid (2D or 3D)	< 3 *	varies (typically 97)	Netlon (1978)
Woven fabric (Terran RF12)	fabric	< 3 *	varies #	Imperial Chemical Industry (ICI) plc (1975)
Linear composite strip (paraweb)	tape	< 2	10 - 100	ICI/Linear Composites (1976)
Linear composite grid (paragrid)	grid	2 - 5	varies (300 - 1000+)	ICI/Exxon Chemical Geopolymers Ltd (early 1980s)

*   Extension at working load is usually in range 1 - 2 %
\#   Depends upon structure and weight per square metre
§   Normal width 40 - 160 mm

in initiating research and development.Different forms of high quality geosynthetic reinforcement materials providing the essential properties detailed above have been developed by a number of manufacturers. Brief details of the main geosynthetic materials developed in the United Kingdom during the ten year period 1973-83 are shown in Table 3. Several of these are the subject of continuous development and improvement. Most of these materials are now established, the main exception being glass reinforced strip (Fibretain) which, due to the structure of the market rather than the technology, is not in general use. Developments of polymeric reinforcing materials have occurred in other parts of the world, notably in Europe, Japan and the United States. Nearly all are associated with different forms of grid materials or geotextiles in the form of needle-punched, heat-bonded or woven/knitted. One exception which is unique is the use of continuous single polymeric thread in the Texsol method developed by Leflaive et al (1986). The quantity of reinforcing material used is in the region of 0.15% by volume of the sand fill using a 167 dtex thread. The result is to impart "cohesion" to the soil and to permit the construction of very stable near vertical structures. Similar cohesive effects are developed using small grid reinforcing elements and short fibres mixed randomly into the soil. These latter applications are mostly used to provide soil stability/reinforcement to turf such as at race courses. Details of the potential "cohesion" which can be developed in a sand by such inclusions are shown in Table 4, which also includes the nature of the soil-reinforcement interaction assumed.

Table 4 Values of cohesion and soil-inclusion interaction types in sand reinforced with synthetic inclusions

INCLUSIONS	FIBRES		GRID TYPE PLATES	CONTINUOUS FILAMENTS
	50mm	150-200mm	60 x 40mm	
Cohesion kN/m^2	10	100	50	200
Types of interaction	Friction Extensibility		Friction Extensibility Entanglement Interlocking	Friction Extensibility Entanglement Curvature effect

BENEFITS OF POLYMERIC REINFORCEMENT

The initial development of polymeric reinforcement was to address the potential problem of corrosion of steel reinforcing elements. Polymeric materials do not corrode, although durability has to be assured as described previously. A second major incentive to the use of polymeric reinforcement is the possibility of using indigenous and waste fills which can provide significant savings in construction costs. The use of pulverised fuel ash as a fill is now established in the UK and can provide benefits not only in cost savings but also in the technical benefits arising from the cohesive nature of many of these fills which produce a lighter and inherently stronger structure. The use of indigenous (cohesive) fill in steepened slopes is common and this is the application where the majority of polymeric reinforcement is used.

The acute lack of suitable frictional fill in parts of Japan has lead to the use of cohesive soils being used in major reinforced soil structures, notably those developed for the widening of railway embankments supporting the Shinkan-Sen railway network. Extensive research by Japan Railways including the construction of full scale trial walls has established that geosynthetic reinforced soil structures formed using cohesive or cohesive-frictional fill are potentially more stable than structures formed from purely frictional fills, Tatsuoka et al (1992), Tatsuoka (1992). The form of construction developed for these structures is shown in Figure 13. It is noticeable that this form of construction was the only retaining structure to survive the Kobe earthquake.

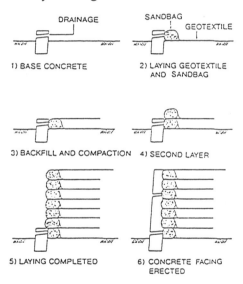

Figure 13:   Construction procedure for rigid faced polymer reinforced soil structure - Japan Railways (After Tatsuoka, 1992)

In France the development of geosynthetic reinforced structures has been continuing for over twenty years. A major argument advanced for the use of geosynthetic reinforcements is that on site material can be used for construction, whatever its nature. This concept has been demonstrated in the Lezat experimental wall where on site silt was used in the works. One of the largest structures built in France to date is a 21 m high structure, formed in three 7 m tiers with two 3 m berms, Gourc and Matichard (1994).

In Italy permanent geosynthetic reinforced soil walls have become an accepted and widely used technique. The low cost of the constituent materials forming the structures, the speed of construction and the possibility of developing alternative solutions are quoted as primary reasons for their success, Cazzuffi et al (1994).

INFLUENCE OF POLYMERIC REINFORCEMENT ON DESIGN AND ANALYSIS

Rowe and Ho (1992), in their review of the behaviour of reinforced soil walls comment on the design method used for reinforced soil structures. The methods identified by Rowe and Ho are mainly associated with the design of structures using proprietary reinforcements and do not cover the methods used in the general design of reinforced soil in parts of Europe, the United States and the United Kingdom. These latter methods can be classified as those based upon the coherent gravity hypothesis or the tie-back hypothesis, Jones (1985). The coherent gravity method is an empirical technique which has been described by Mitchell and Villett (1987) and the Ministeres des Transports (1979). It was developed to cater for structures reinforced with steel strip (inextensible) reinforcements. The tie-back method was developed by the United Kingdom Department of Transport in 1978 and was revised in 1986. It is based upon limit equilibrium methods and it is independent of the reinforcement material used with both inextensible and extensible reinforcements and with anchors being covered. In this context polymeric reinforcements are identified as being extensible.

The most recent innovation in the design of reinforced soil structures in the United Kingdom has been the introduction of the Draft British Standard BS8006 (1994). The British Standard (BS8006) is written in a limit state format which covers all forms of reinforced soil identified as internally stabilized systems with the exception of soil dowels, reticulated micro-piles and special materials. Hybrid systems included tailed gabions, tailed masonry and also the gravity faced soil retaining structures described by Tatsuoka (1992) are covered by the new Code of Practice, as are the design of reinforcements over voids and as support systems over piled embankments and soil nailing, Figure 4.

The two limit states considered in BS8006 are the Ultimate Limit State and the Serviceability Limit State, which are defined as:

Ultimate Limit State at which collapse mechanisms form in the ground or the retaining structure or when movement of a retaining structure leads to severe structural damage in other parts of the structure or in nearby structures or services.

Serviceability Limit State at which movements of the retaining structure affect the appearance or efficient use of the structure or nearby structures or services which reply upon it.

Being a *Code of Practice*, BS8006 reflects past/established methodologies. It does not cover the most advanced analytical procedures which have been developed recently using the concept of Limit Modes, Jones (1992), Masterton and Mair (1995).

The limit states are identified in terms of Limit Modes. Six Limit Modes are considered, Figure 14. Of particular interest is Limit Mode 6 covering deformation which is used to check the serviceability of any structure and which is also used to determine the stress-state applicable in the analysis. The analytical model used in the new analysis method is sensitive to the form of reinforcement used in that an extensible reinforcement will lead to greater structural deflection during and post construction than if inextensible (stiff) reinforcement is specified. The use of stiff reinforcement can result in additional stress being attracted to the reinforcement, a point implicitly acknowledged in the coherent gravity hypothesis where the Ko stress rate is used in the analysis.

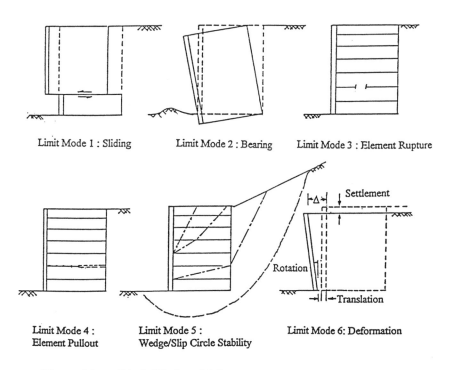

Figure 14: **Limit Modes of failure of reinforced soil structures**

In the Limit Mode method the correct stress-state of the soil for use in the analysis is obtained by adopting the following analytical sequence;

(i)   The geometry of the structure is chosen.

(ii)   The stress-state of the soil K_{des}, is assumed equal to Ka (the active condition).

(iii)   Limit Modes 3 and 4 are checked and the quantity of reinforcement needed to satisfy these conditions identified.

(iv)   Limit Mode 6 is checked.

$$\text{If } \Delta \geq 0.0001H$$

the selection of K_{des} = Ka is considered to be justified and the design proceeds with consideration of the remaining Limit Modes, Figure 14.

$$\text{If } \Delta < 0.0001\ H$$

$K_{des} \neq$ Ka and consideration of Limit Modes 3 and 4 is repeated with K_{des} = Ko (at rest pressure).

   The Limit Mode method is unique in providing a general analytical method which acknowledges the concept of strain compatibility, the importance of reinforcement stiffness and the role of structural deformation, Jewell (1992), O'Rourke and Jones (1990). The benefits to be gained using polymeric reinforcement can be demonstrated through the use of lower design stresses.

   Limit Mode 6 requires the estimation of deformation. Deformation can be difficult to analyze although methods have been developed which cater for polymeric reinforcement, Jewell and Milligan (1989). A simple method of estimating deformation based on the United States FHWA design memorandum, DoT (1989), is shown in Figure 15.

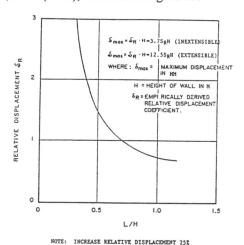

NOTE: INCREASE RELATIVE DISPLACEMENT 25%
        FOR EVERY 20 kN/m² SURCHARGE

Figure 15:   Deformation characteristics of reinforced soil retaining walls

CONSTRUCTION

The construction of any reinforced soil structure must be of a form determined by theory and in keeping with the assumed idealization and analysis. The theoretical form of the structure may be different from an economical prototype and attention has to be paid to the method of construction throughout the design process.

The use of soil deposit in layers to form the structure results in settlement within the soil mass caused by gravitational forces. These settlements within the soil result in the reinforcing elements positioned on discrete planes moving together as the layers of soil separating the planes of the reinforcement are compressed. Construction techniques capable of accommodating this internal compaction within the soil are required, Jones (1985). Failure to accommodate differential movement can result in loss of serviceability and even collapse, Lee et al (1994).

Rigid facing systems

Tatsuoka (1992) and Jones (1992) have identified the benefits of the use of rigid facings for reinforced soil walls and shows that the inherent additional structural stability of these structures is greater than structures formed using elemental facing systems. The structural advantage obtained from the use of rigid facings is clearly illustrated by the Limit Mode method of analysis for vertical reinforced soil walls and bridge abutments. Limit Mode 5 covers external failure mechanisms which, in a reinforced soil structure, can pass through any elevation in the structure. In the case of structures erected with rigid facings, the potential failure planes are reduced and must pass below the toe of the structure. Experience shows that retaining walls, including reinforced soil walls, seldom fail on a plane passing through the toe. The usual critical failure plane passes through the face of the structure at a point 1/3 above the toe, and in the case of structures formed from element facing units and masonry structures occurs when the facing distorts to a point where mechanical stability is lost at which point failure is inevitable and usually very rapid, Lee et al (1994).

One point not covered by Tatsuoka (1992) is the potential increased stability provided by the use of polymeric reinforcement. Laboratory studies using metallic reinforcements have shown that the failure of model reinforced soil walls can be sudden if the failure mechanism is due to the rupture of metallic reinforcement, Limit Mode 3, Figure 14, Bolton and Pang (1982). With metallic reinforcement, rupture of one reinforcement leads to rapid load shedding and potential overstress of adjacent reinforcements leading directly to further rupture which in turn leads to more load shedding and hence structural instability. The use of polymeric (extensible) reinforcement, able to creep, may be immune to this mechanism with stress redistribution being accomplished without reinforcement rupture, Jaber (1991).

An electrical analogy can be used to describe the different potential failure methods of inextensible and extensible reinforcements. The rupture and subsequent rapid failure with metallic reinforcement can be identified as being a *series system* failure where failure of one element leads directly and immediately to failure of the whole. Extensible reinforcement can be identified as being equivalent to a *parallel system*, in which total failure occurs only when all the reinforcements fail simultaneously, Figure 16. If any reinforcement is overstressed, creep will occur leading to limited load shedding, but not reinforcement rupture.

It can be concluded that the most stable reinforced soil structural form uses a rigid facing and is reinforced with a *geosynthetic reinforcement.*

$$\longleftarrow\!\!-\!\!-\!\!-\text{X}\!\!-\!\!-\text{//}\!\!-\!\!-\text{X}\!\!-\!\!-\!\!-\text{X}\!\!-\!\!-\!\!-\text{X}\!\!-\!\!\longrightarrow$$

a) Series failure (inextensible reinforcement)

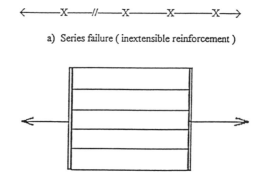

b) Parallel failure (extensible reinforcement)

Figure 16:   Analogy of reinforced soil failure mechanisms

Anchored earth

The construction of anchored earth is the same as for other forms of reinforced soil structures, the only difference being that the reinforcing element differs. Anchored earth is a well established method of construction in Japan and to a certain extent in the United States and the United Kingdom. The usual form of anchor is manufactured from steel elements. Polymer reinforcements have successfully been used to produce anchored earth, Figure 17.

The first use of anchored earth in the United Kingdom was associated with the use of waste tyres, Figure 17(c). The facing was formed from tyres with one side wall and the anchor was formed from a tyre filled with soil. The connecting strips between the anchor and the facing tyres was a polyester strap. Embankment structures as high as 18 m have been constructed using this system.

More formal faced structures can be constructed using the Austrian method, Figure 17 (d). In this system the anchor is held in place by a loop of polymeric tape with the anchor consisting of a precast concrete unit. A recent development in anchored earth is the introduction of a polymer anchor, Figure 17(e). The use of a polymeric anchor offers a reduction in the total quantity of reinforcing materials whilst still satisfying the design requirements of existing Codes of Practice. With the new polymeric anchor, material savings up to 40 per cent are possible, Jones and Hassan (1992).

Hybrids

Hybrid systems have been developed whereby conventional construction systems are improved with the addition of reinforcement. The resultant structure combines the benefits of conventional externally stabilized structures with those of internally stabilized structures. The result is often a more stable

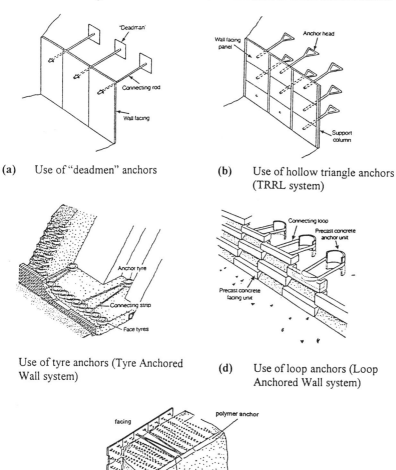

(a)   Use of "deadmen" anchors

(b)   Use of hollow triangle anchors (TRRL system)

(c)   Use of tyre anchors (Tyre Anchored Wall system)

(d)   Use of loop anchors (Loop Anchored Wall system)

(e)   Polymer anchor

Figure 17:   **Anchored soil retaining wall systems**

structural form and is coupled with a significant reduction in cost. The first true hybrid reinforced soil system is the tailed gabion introduced in 1980, Figure 18(a), Jones and Templeman (1979). A number of proprietary walling systems based upon the use of elemental blocks have been developed both in the United Kingdom, United States and parts of Europe. These systems are used to provide low height gravity structures often associated with landscaping works associated with low rise housing or light industrial development. The use and effectiveness of these walling systems can be extended by the use of reinforcement added to the gravity structure. The addition of reinforcement improves the stability of the gravity wall and permits the structure to be built to higher levels than would normally be possible. This technique was initially established with the tronderblock system in Norway, Figure 18(b). The method has now been developed extensively, particularly in the United States with the reinforcement normally being formed from a polymer grid.

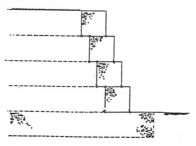

Figure 18(a): Tailed gabion reinforced soil structures

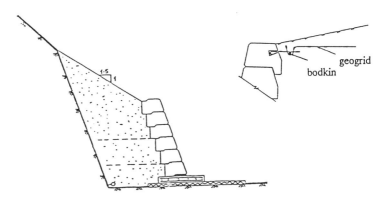

Figure 18(b): Tronderblock wall system

The design of the system follows that of conventional reinforced soil structures but the construction does not adhere strictly to that used for reinforced soil, as no allowance is made for differential settlement between the facing and the fill. This presents a potential problem in that high structures built on soft soils are at risk from differential settlement between the facing panels and the fill, O'Rourke and Jones (1990).

Connections

The connection between the reinforcing member and the facing of a permanent wall is a critical part of the design. With polymer reinforcements a full strength connection is assumed and the tensile performance of the reinforcing element is limited to the capacity of the connection. A number of connection techniques have been developed which ensure full strength at transfer, a typical example being the toggle connection used with polymeric tape, Kempton et al (1985). Wherever possible reinforcement should be provided as a single element without connections along its length. However, in some applications such as the use of elemental precast concrete facings connection between starter elements embedded in concrete facing and the reinforcement are required. With high density polyethylene geogrids a bodkin connection has been shown to provide near full strength capacity. However, the nature and form of the bodkin chosen is critical to performance and it has been demonstrated that the use of circular steel bodkins can reduce the carrying capacity at the junction by a factor of 35 per cent. This is a result of stress raisers resulting from the use of the circular stiff connecting element. A more efficient connection providing approximately 95 per cent capacity is provided by a flat polymeric strip, Figure 19, Jones et al (1993). Connections between geotextile sheets must be undertaken in an approved manner, BS8006 (1994).

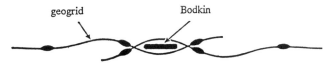

Figure 19:   Bodkin connections for geogrids

In the majority of cases the durability of the polymeric connection is equal to that of the polymer reinforcing material; however, under certain circumstances the connection detail can influence durability. It is accepted that polyester can be adversely affected in a highly alkaline environment, see above. Accordingly it is not good practice to embed polyester reinforcing elements into concrete and polyester reinforcement should be isolated from direct contact with concrete facing elements.

RECENT DEVELOPMENTS

The development of polymeric materials has been rapid and polymeric reinforcements are now accepted as being suitable for use in permanent reinforced soil structures.

Developments in material technology are continuing with all of the producers of proprietary materials producing regular improvements in the performance of their materials. New forms of reinforcement are also being explored; in the United Kingdom these include the development of materials offering the *combined functions* of drainage and reinforcement and the introduction of a new generation of materials known as *electro-kinetic geosynthetics* (EKG) which are electrically conductive.

Composite geosynthetics

Most vertical reinforced soil structures are constructed using good quality fill; however, it is accepted that poor quality fill in the form of material found on site can be used for steepened embankments. In parts of the world good frictionless fill is not available; as a consequence the full economic benefits inherent in reinforced soil construction may not be achieved. The solution is to adopt the construction to accept poor quality fine grained soils. The use of such material could lead to difficulties associated with bond between the reinforcement and the soil and the possibility of excessive creep of the fill resulting in unacceptable distortion of the structure, Elias and Swanson (1984). A method of overcoming these problems is to ensure the drainage of the fill material; this can be achieved using drainage geotextiles and some proprietary methods used to construct steepened slopes rely upon the drainage properties of the geotextile.

Geotextiles providing a drainage function are frequently non woven materials having little inherent tensile strength, Table 1. A logical approach is to provide two geosynthetic materials, one providing the drainage function and the other providing the reinforcement. It has been found that this approach can have an *inherent weakness* with the resultant shear strength of the composite material being *less* than if the drainage or reinforcing materials are used singly, the reason being that the presence of the drainage geotextile can reduce the bond of the reinforcing material. The solution is to structure the combined material such that this cannot occur, Heshmati (1994).

Electro-kinetic geosynthetics

It is now possible to create an electrically conducting geosynthetic. Such a material offers a number of technical possibilities including the ability to provide electro-kinetic remediation of contaminated soils and electro-osmosis which can be used to produce rapid reduction in the moisture content of the fill. Accompanying this reduction in moisture content is an increase in the bond between the charged geosynthetic and the adjacent soil. This bond develops rapidly when the geotextile is given an electric charge and can be retained once the charge is removed.

CONCLUSIONS

The use of polymeric reinforcement for reinforced soil was initially greeted with some reluctance but after 20 years these materials are now accepted as providing economic reinforcements for permanent structures. The remarkable performance of polymeric reinforced soil structures during the Kobe earthquake emphasises their inherent durability and safety.

Polymer technology is developing rapidly and advanced forms of polymeric reinforcement are already being developed. The challenge is to develop analytical and marketing tools which will permit their early application.

REFERENCES

Bolton, M D & Pang, P L R , 1982, *Collapse limit states of reinforced earth retaining walls*, Geotechnique 32, No.4 ,349-367.

British Standards Institution, 1994, *BS8006 Code of Practice for Strengthened/Reinforced Soils and Other Fills*.

Bush, D I , 1990, *Variation of long term design strength of geosynthetics in temperatures up to 40°C*, Proceedings Fourth International Conference on Geotextiles, The Hague, Balkema, Vol.2, 673-676.

Cazzuffi, D, Rimoldi, P & Sembenelli, P 1994, *Italian experience in geosynthetic reinforced soil structures*, 7th Italian Conference on Geosythetics, Bologne, pp.29-40, L'ingegnere e l'architetto.

Department of Transport, 1978, *Reinforced earth retaining walls and bridge abutments for embankments*, Technical Memorandum BE3/78, UK.

ECGL Designing for soil reinforcement, Exxon Chemical, UK, 1989.

Elias, V & Swanson, P , 1984, *Cautions of reinforced earth with residual soils*, Transportation Research Report 919, 21-26.

Federal Highway Authority, 1989, *Reinforced soil structures, Vol.1, Design and construction guidelines*, FHWA-RD-89-043, p.287, National Technical Information Service, Virginia, USA.

Gourc, J-P and Matichard, Y, 1994, *French experience in geosynthetic reinforced structures*, 7th Italian Conference on Geosythetics, Bologne, L'ingegnere e l'architetto, 29-40.

Grassie, N and Scott, G, 1985, *Polymer degradation and stabilization*, Cambridge University Press.

Hassan, C A, 1992, *The use of flexible transverse anchors in reinforced soil*, PhD Dissertation, University of Newcastle upon Tyne, UK.

Heshmati, S, 1993, *The action of geotextiles in providing combined drainage and reinforcement to cohesive soil*, PhD Dissertation, University of Newcastle.

Hollaway, L C , 1990, *Polymers and polymer composites in construction*, Thomas Telford Ltd, London.

Howells, D J and Pang, P L R , 1989, *Temperature considerations in the design of geosynthetic reinforced fill structures in hot climates*, Proceedings Symposium on Application of Geosynthetics and Geofibres in South East Asia, Petaling Jaya, Malaysia, 1.1-1.7.

Jaber, M , 1989, *Behaviour of reinforced soil walls and centrifuge model tests*, PhD Dissertation, University of California, Berkeley, 239 p.

Jewell, R A, 1992, *Strength and deformation in reinforced soil design*, Fourth International Conference on Geotextiles, Geomembranes and Related Products, Balkema, 913-946,.

Jewell, R A & Milligan, G W E, 1989, *Deformation calculations for reinforced soil walls*, Proceedings 12th ICSMFE, .1257-1262.

Jones, C J F P, 1985, *Earth reinforcement and soil structures*, Butterworths Advanced Series in Geotechnical Engineering, 192p. (Revised Reprint 1988)

Jones, C J F P, 1992, *Discussion: slope and excavation*, Proceedings Earth Reinforcement Practice, Kyushu, Vol.2, Balkema, 972-975.

JONES, C J F P & HASSAN, C A, 1992, *Compression movements within reinforced soil structures*, Paper presented at Geotropika Conference.

Jones, C J F P, Lomax, C D & Paul, J, 1993, *The efficiency of geogrid connections and the effect of temperature*, In Geosynthetics '93, IFAI Vancouver, 431-442.

Jones, C J F P & Templeman, J, 1970, *Soil structures using high tensile plastic grids (tailed gabions)*, UK Patent No. 7941627.

Kempton, G T, Enwistle, R W & Bonlay, M J, 1985. *An anchored fill harbour wall using synthetic fabrics*, Proceedings Institution of Civil Engineers, April, Part 1, Vol. 78, 237-347.

Koerner, R M, Hsuan, Y & Lord, A E, 1992, *Remaining technical barriers to obtain general acceptance of geosynthetics*, The 1992 Mercer Lecture, Institution of Civil Engineers, p.47.

Lawson, C R, 1991, *Use of geotextiles in reinforced soil retaining structures*, Sydney Technological University, Australia, 44p.

Lee, K, Jones, C J F P, Sullivan, W R & Trolinger, W, 1994, *Failure and deformation of four reinforced soil walls in eastern Tennessee*, Geotechnique 44, No. 3, 397-426.

Leflaive, E & Liansu, P L, 1986, *The reinforcement of soils by continuous threads*, Proceedings 3rd Int. Conf. on Geotextiles, Vienna, Vol. 4, 1159-1162.

Masterson, G G T & Mair, A J, 1995, *Aspects of limit state design of reinforced soil*, 11th ECMFE, p.17.

Murray, R T & Farrar, D M, 1988, *Temperature distributions in reinforced soil retaining walls*, International Journal of Geotextiles and Geomembranes, Vol. 6.

O'Rourke, T D & Jones, C J F P, 1990), *Overview of retention systems 1970-1990*, Design and Performance of Earth Retaining Structures, Lambe and Hansen (eds), ASEC Geotechnical Special Publication No. 25, New York, .22-51.

Pasley, C W, 1822, *Experiments in revetments*, Vol.2, Murray, London.

Risseeuw, P & Schmidt, H M, 1990, *Hydrolysis of HT polyester yarns in water at moderate temperatures*, Proceedings Fourth International Conference on Geotextiles, The Hague, Balkema, Vol.2, 691-696.

Rowe, R K & Ho, S K, 1992, *A review of the behaviour of reinforced soil walls*, In Earth Reinforcement Practice, Balkema, Vol.2, 299-828.

SETRA, 1979, *Les ouvrages en terre armée, recommendations et regles de l'art*, Direction des Routes et de la Circulation Routier, Laboratoire Central des Ponts et Chassées, Paris, September.

Tasuoka, F, Murata, O & Tateyama, M, 1992, *Permanent geosynthetic-reinforced soil retaining walls used for railway embankments in Japan*, Geosynthetic-Reinforced Soil Retaining Walls, Wu (ed), Balkema, 101-130.

Tatsuoka, F, 1992, *Roles of facing rigidity in soil reinforcing*, In Earth Reinforcement Practice, Balkema, 831-870.

Watts, G R A & Brady, K C , 1990, *Site damage trials on geotextiles*, Proceedings Fourth International Conference on Geotextiles, The Hague, Balkema, Vol.2, 603-608.

Wisse, J D M, Broos, C J M & Boels, W H, 1990, *Evaluation of the life expectancy of polypropylene geotextiles used in bottom protection structures around the Ooster Schelde Storm Surge Barrier*, Proceedings Fourth International Conference on Geotextiles, The Hague, Balkema, Vol.2, 697-702.

Flexible or stiff geogrids - state-of-the-art

W. VOSKAMP, Akzo-Nobel Geosynthetics bv, The Netherlands

SYNOPSIS
With the advent of BS 8006 and independent certification of product characteristics by the British Board of Agrément, a sound base for the use of reinforcing products, whether flexible or stiff, is now available. Many geogrid products offer a reliable range from which users can select the product best suited to their purpose. However, it should be emphasized that the proper selection of design parameters must be applied. The allowable design strength should clearly be specified for a design life and the design conditions which influence the various partial factors should also be listed. Alternatively, the factors used for the different polymers must be listed and verified by the supplier.

INTRODUCTION
The first geogrids appeared on the market in the late seventies. They were made of HDPE and, after intensive research on product characteristics and design methods, have since been increasingly adopted for civil engineering applications. The first products came from an UK supplier who must be honoured for his bright view on the potential of the application. The strength of the geogrids varied between 20 and 110 kN/m and they were used in both road construction slope reinforcement.

At the time, only strong PET fabrics were used commercially for basal embankment reinforcement and they were in fact too strong for slope reinforcement, which typically requires strengths of < 100 kN/m. The only other materials then available were various types of nonwovens and lightweight wovens. Due to the unique structure of the geogrid, and the strength range in which it was available, it was highly suitable for use in slope reinforcement applications and for bearing capacity improvement applications in roads. The success of the product since its introduction proved its usefulness.

As with all products developed for specific applications, other types of products came on the market as the market became more mature. Nowadays, we can choose from a variety of stiff geogrid products and flexible geogrid products.

The history of flexible geogrids differs from that of the stiff types, since polyester fibres had already been used for quite some time in soil reinforcement applications, mainly for basal reinforcement of embankments. The first commercial application of these reinforcing fabrics goes back to 1977 when a highway embankment was built near Muiden in the Netherlands. Although in the early eighties, this material, Stabilenka, was used for several other projects, it was not commercially successful. The reinforcing mat was simply too strong and therefore too expensive.

It was technically impossible to make a reinforcing fabric with a strength less than 150 kN/m in the traditional fabric form. A leap forward was made in 1985 when an open-fabric mesh, coated with PVC, was developed. Now it was possible to use PET yarns with their superior properties as well as to make a grid type structure with the required lower strength. Further, the PVC coating provided an excellent protection against mechanical damage which made the product even more attractive. So, at the end of the eighties more geogrids appeared on the market and this increased competition between the products. Geogrids can be divided into two groups:

♦ Stiff geogrids, mostly HDPE with a monolithic mesh structure

♦ Flexible geogrids, mostly PET with PVC or acrylic coating with mechanically connected longitudinal and transverse elements

Over the past years many advantages and disadvantages have been claimed for the various products. It is the intention of this paper to make a general comparison between the two groups of products on the basis of specific properties. The purpose is to eliminate commercially biased technical arguments and to give the necessary background information to allow engineers to judge for themselves if any special requirement is needed.

MAIN DESIGN PARAMETERS

The main design requirements for the use of geogrids in soil structures result from the mechanical design. This includes the calculation of different failure modes resulting in requirements for:

♦ allowable design strength of the geogrid

♦ maximum strain requirements

The practice is to design for the ultimate limit state (strength requirement) and to check for the serviceability state (strain level and deformation). In BS 8006 (1994) different requirements are formulated for the design of reinforced walls, abutments and reinforced slopes.

MAXIMUM ALLOWABLE STRENGTH

As outlined by Jewell (1990a), soil reinforcement designs have separate requirements for maximum allowable strength and for stiffness or maximum allowable deformation of the structure. Both criteria must be checked for the entire lifetime of the structure. For some years, Voskamp (1988), the maximum allowable strength has been calculated from the general equation :

$$P_{all} = (P_{char} [t,T]) / (f_m \cdot f_e \cdot f_e)$$

where

P_{all} is the allowable design strength

P_{char} is the characteristic tensile strength for the design lifetime, t, and design temperature T

f_m is the partial factor for extrapolation and accuracy of test data

f_e is the partial factor for environmentall aspects

f_d is the partial factor for mechanical damage

For tensile rupture failure a similar formulation has been embodied in BS 8006 (1994) :

$$T_D = T_C / f_m$$

where:

T_D is the design strength

T_C is the characteristic strength above which the material fails in tension from peak loading during the design life of the structure

f_m is a material factor $f_m = f_{m1}.f_{m2}$ where $f_{m1} = f_{m11}.f_{m12}$ and $f_{m2} = f_{m21}.f_{m22}$

The values of the above parameters differ for flexible and stiff grids. Various load factors f_f are used in the design to complete the ultimate limit state design. $P_{char, t, T}$ or T_C for HDPE grids is derived from a creep deformation limit of 10% during a design life, Jewell & Greenwood (1988). In the case of polyester (PET) grids, this value is obtained from stress-rupture data produced by tests on yarns, running to more than 10 years and tests on actual products running

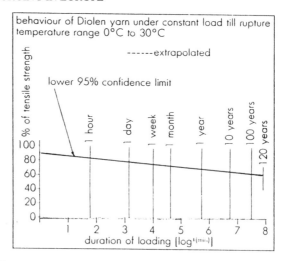

Figure 1 Tensile strength against time for PET yarn

for more than 4 years. All these data are summarized in one stress-rupture graph, which is normalized as a percentage of the short term ultimate tensile strength, to give the so-called stress-rupture graph, in which a 95% confidence limit indicates the characteristic levels, Voskamp (1990). Later testing at 40° and 60°C confirmed the normalized stress-rupture graph by time temperature superposition. Detailed comparison of the creep data for the yarns and for the product made of these yarns made it is possible to combine the data to confine the extrapolation to one decade of time.

The mechanical damage factors are product and application related. Most products have been tested under controlled field conditions and specific factors are quoted by manufacturers. With a view to, for example, BBA certification, independent checks have been made to certify these values. The values are typically in the range 1.05 - 1.5 depending on the type of fill and the type of geogrid, BBA (1992).

A chemical environment factor must also be applied. All polymer materials are vulnerable to certain specific chemical conditions. It is therefore useful to determine whether these conditions will occur in the design case and what the concentration of chemicals will be. Polyester, for example, is sensitive to an alkaline environment with pH levels higher than 9.5 combined with a temperature above 50°C. Under normal soil conditions the phenomena of hydrolysis will not have an impact on the allowable strength, BBA (1992), Schmidt et al. (1994). Special high-alkaline conditions, continuing for most of the design life of the structure, must be evaluated more closely. Thermo-oxidation is a process which influences the ductile behaviour of polyolefins like HDPE and PP. Also this item must be evaluated if the lifetime conditions include the existence of chemicals that may lead to

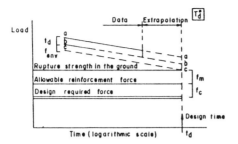

Figure 2 Reinforcement strength against time

dissolving of additives. These plasticizers or other additives in the polymer composition are evaporated or slowly washed away from the polymer. Extensive testing in various laboratories has shown that the reduction in strength and other properties of the geogrids is negligible when the material is used in normal soil conditions. Also the CEN committee TC 189 is developing standard test methods as index tests for chemical attack. HDPE material is sensitive to environmental stress cracking. However, extensive studies by ERA, Small & Greenwood (1993), have not revealed such a sensitivity in the HDPE geogrids tested.

Resistance to fungi and other biological attack has to be evaluated. As far as known, all geogrids are capable of withstanding this type of attack without loss of strength.

The material factors cover uncertainties in extrapolation, accuracy of testing etc. First introduced by Jewell & Greenwood (1988), they are now modified and incorporated in BS 8006. Figure 2 summarises the relationship between the rupture strength and allowable reinforcement force, the design strength, which is a function of the design life, t_d , and the design temperature, T_d .

STIFFNESS

As stated earlier, the second design requirement is stiffness. Most soil reinforcement structures will deform to a certain extent only. This design requirement can be translated into a maximum strain requirement for the geogrids, BS 8006 (1994). In such a case, the requirement limits the strain during construction as well as the additional strain occurring during the service life of the structure. These strain requirements can in some cases be more restrictive than the strength requirements. The values for the strain in the products can be obtained from isochronous curves, which are available for most geogrids.

It should be emphasized that stress-rupture and creep-strain data are product specific. Even with flexible geogrids made of PET, knowing that they are made of PET is not enough. In such a case, details about the type of yarn used should be supplied and verified.

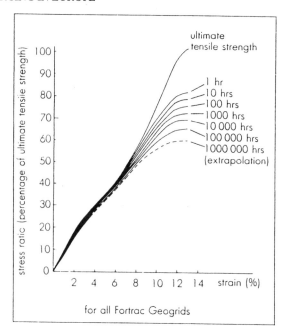

Figure 3 Isochronous curves for PET yarn

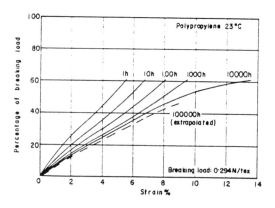

Figure 4 Isochronous curves for polypropylene yarn
after Jewell & Greenwood (1988)

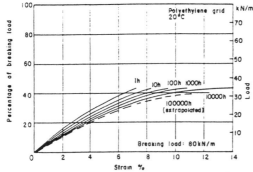

Figure 5 Isochronous curves for polyethylene grid
after Jewell & Greenwood (1988)

COMPARISON OF DESIGN METHODS IN USA AND EUROPE

There is a distinct difference between the USA and Europe in the approach to the subject. For one thing, as described in the GRI-GG4 test method, in the USA a fixed partial factor for creep is applied in the calculations of the allowable strength, but no partial factor for extrapolation of test data and uncertainties. The main difference, however, is that overlap joints are allowed in the loaded direction of the geogrid. The effect of the joint strength must be factored into the design strength. This factor FS_{jnt} should be taken as the ratio of the unjointed specimen strength to the joined specimen strength. Testing in accordance with GRI-GG5 is required at a load level equal to the allowable strength. Sustained tension tests of 1000 hours minimum duration should be conducted on mechanically connected joints.

In Europe, the allowable strength is calculated without a fixed factor for creep, but the design is based on the characteristic strength derived from the stress-rupture line for a specific design life. In general, overlaps in the direction of the primary tensile load force are not allowed. Therefore no partial factor for joints or overlaps is used.

SOIL-REINFORCEMENT INTERACTION

Failure of a reinforced structure, specifically the reinforcement, can take place in two ways; tensile rupture of the geogrid or pullout of the grid. These potential failure modes are assessed separately.

To determine the pullout resistance of a geogrid mainly pullout tests are used in which either the coefficient of interaction between the geogrid and soil is determined or the minimum anchor length, Voskamp (1992). Oostveen et al. (1994) conducted an extensive study of the pullout behaviour of geogrids and executed many tests in a 100 by 200 cm pullout box, comparing extensible geogrids, both stiff and flexible, with non-extensible, steel, grids. This study revealed that the behaviour of flexible grids differed completely from that of steel grids, with regard to the load transfer between the grid and surrounding soil.

Unlike stiff, non-deformable steel mesh, extensible geogrids do not have a constant load transfer by shear. This also means that the coefficient of interaction is not a constant value. The total anchor length required, however, is no more than that calculated with a constant value for the coefficient of interaction. Further research is being conducted. Whichever method is chosen, pullout or maximum anchor length, the load is transferred by the maximum mobilized number of junctions in the anchor zone eg anchor length x width.

Not once during the pullout tests that were executed on flexible geogrids, Fortrac, under various test conditions and with various fill materials, was a junction failure observed. This proves that the junction strength under confined conditions is always sufficiently high.

If an anchor length of 1 m is assumed, the number of junctions over this length is approximately 1600 if 40 rib junctions occur over a 1 m.

As the load is always transferred over a certain anchor length, the requirement of a high junction strength, sometimes specified as 90%, is not necessary. Such a requirement is clearly biased as it strongly favours monolithic junctions.

Further, the junction strength has no influence on the strength of the geogrid and should therefore not be related to a safety consideration for the strength of the geogrid as suggested by Task Force 27 in *Design guidelines for the use of extensible reinforcements*, AASHTO (1989). Layer design guidelines, such as published by the Federal Highway Administration in 1992, no longer specify this. This document contains requirements for geogrid pullout such as:

♦ quick effective stress pullout tests and through-the-junction creep testing of the geogrid per GRI-GG3a Test Method; or

♦ quick effective stress pullout tests of the geogrid with severed transverse ribs; or

♦ quick effective stress pullout tests of the entire geogrid structure if the summation of the strengths of the joints occurring in a 300 mm (12") long grid sample is equal to or greater than the ultimate strength of the grid element to which they are attached; or

♦ long-term effective stress pullout tests of the entire geogrid structure

Research on long term effective stress pullout of four flexible grids and one stiff grid, Wilson-Fahmy & Koerner (1995), showed that for practical purposes the pullout strength of the geogrids tested is independent of time within the observed 1000 hours test duration. Whenever a safety factor is required for pullout it should be related to the anchor length or grid length in the embankment and not the allowable strength as suggested and used in the USA, AASHTO (1989).

In the design method developed by Jewell (1990b) the effect of the junction strength or anchor length is taken into account in the calculation of the bond length. Even with very low values, it shows that the effect is minimal. The bond factor has a very limited effect on the anchor length. Together with the findings of recent research work, Oostveen et al. (1994), especially the extra safety in the anchor length due to the fact that the design is for an allowable strength compared to the available rupture forces, it is concluded that a separate factor of safety for junction strength is not correct and therefore not applicable. BS 8006 does not require such a factor either but uses a partial factor in the calculation of the anchor length instead.

SUMMARY

The availability of data relating to stress-strain curves, long term stress rupture against time and stiffness, together with the basis for definition of junction strength, are summarised in Table 1 for flexible and stiff geogrids. Data determined by direct testing is classified as *available* and data derived from graphical construction is classified as *Sherby-Dorn plots.*

Table 1 Availability of load/strain/time data

Load/strain/time data	Flexible	Stiff
Stress-strain curves	Available	Available
Long term stress rupture	Available	Sherby-Dorn plots
Stiffness (strain-v-time)	Available	Sherby-Dorn plots
Junction strength	Minimum strength	Unlimited strength

Typical values for partial factors for mechanical damage, chemical attack, hydrolysis, thermo-oxidation and environmental attack are summarised in Table 2.

Table 2 Partial factors

Partial factors	Flexible	Stiff
Mechanical damage	1.05-1.5	1.1 - 1.5
Chemical attack	N/A - 1.0	N/A - 1.0
Hydrolysis	pH>9, T >50°	N/A
Thermo-oxidation	N/A.	In special cases
Environmental attack	1.0	1.0

CONCLUSIONS

With the present BS 8006 and independent certification of product characteristics as carried out by BBA, a sound base for the use of these products is now available. The many geogrid products offer a reliable range from which specifiers and contractors can select the product best suited to their specific purpose. However, it should be emphasized that the proper design parameters must be accurately specified to enable the selection of the correct geogrid.

The allowable design strength should be clearly specified for a design life while the design conditions which influence the various partial factors should also be listed. Alternatively, the factors used for the different polymers must be listed and verified by the supplier.

The manufacturers should supply the appropriate stress-rupture line and certification of the partial factors applicable for the stated design conditions. Alternatively, they should supply independently verified test reports for the site conditions mentioned. Requirements for material or extrapolation factors must be clearly specified.

Further, the stiffness must be specified in the form of a strain requirement either as maximum level after a certain lifetime, or as a maximum value during construction and a maximum value for creep during a certain number of years after construction.

When specifications are compiled in this way, there need not be discussions about applicability and product specific parameters. Instead, a straightforward calculation can be made to prove whether or not a product fulfils the design requirements. Thus, competition between the products will be used to maximize the benefits for designers and contractors alike.

REFERENCES

AASHTO-AGC-ARTBA, 1989, *Design guidelines for use of extensible reinforcements for mechanically stabilized earth walls in permanent applications*. Task Force 27 Report.

BBA CERTIFICATE 92/69 (1992), Road and Bridges Agrément Certificate for Fortrac Geogrids, British Board of Agrément, UK.

BS 8006, 1994, *Code of Practice for Strengthened/Reinforced Soils and other Fills*. (Draft), BSI

Jewell R.A., 1990a, *Strength and deformation in reinforced soil design*. Proceedings 4th International Conference on Geotextiles, Geomembranes and Related Products, The Hague, Vol. 3, 913-947.

Jewell, R.A., 1990b, *Revised design charts for steep reinforced slopes*. Reinforced Embankments, Thomas Telford, 1-30.

Jewell R.A. & Greenwood, J.H., 1988, *Long-term strength and safety in steep soil slopes reinforced by polymer materials*. Geotextiles & Geomembranes, Vol 7, Nos 1 & 2, 81-118.

Oostveen, J.P, Maas, K.C. & Hendikse, C.S.H., 1994, *The coefficient of interaction for geogrids in non cohesive soil.* Proceedings 5th International conference on Geotextiles, Geomembranes and Related Products, Singapore, Vol. 1, 427-432.

Schmidt, H.M., the Pas, F.W.T., Risseeuw, P. & Voskamp, W., 1994, *The hydrolytic stability of PET yarns under medium alkaline conditions.* Proceedings 5th International conference on Geotextiles, Geomembranes and Related Products, Singapore, Vol 3, 1153-1159.

Small, G.D. & Greenwood, J.H., 1993, *A review of the phenomenon of stress rupture in HDPE Geogrids*. Geo Report 19, Geotechnical Engineering Office, Civil Engineering Department, Hong Kong.

Voskamp, W., 1986, *Maximum allowable load, bond and other specific design parameters for high modulus polyester reinforcing Mats*. Proceedings seminar on Soil Reinforcement, Hong Kong Inst. of Engineers, Hong Kong.

Voskamp, W., 1990, *Determination of allowable design strength of polyester reinforcing mats*. Reinforced Embankments, Thomas Telford, 67-81.

Voskamp, W., 1992, *Determination of maximum allowable load and anchor length of polyester geogrids*. Proceedings of Kyushu '92, Earth Reinforcement Practice Kyushu, Balkema Rotterdam, 173-178.

Wilson-Fahmy, R.F. & Koerner, R.M., 1995, *Long term pullout behaviour of polymeric geogrids*. GRI report.

Reinforced soil and soil nailing for slopes - Advice Note HA68/94

J.P. LOVE, Geotechnical Consulting Group, United Kingdom

SYNOPSIS

The new DOT Advice Note, HA68/94 (1994), offers a simple and economic method for the design of both reinforced soil slopes and soil nailing. It is based on the two-part wedge mechanism and is now supported by state-of-the-art software.

INTRODUCTION

In 1994 the DoT published an Advice Note covering the design of reinforced slopes, HA68/94 (1994), which now forms part of the Design Manual for Roads and Bridges in the UK. The Document, HA 68/94, entitled *Design methods for the reinforcement of highway slopes by reinforced soil and soil nailing techniques*, fulfilled an obvious need in the guidance available on the subject of strengthened slopes. The advice note provides the DOT preferred approach to design. Tenderers for highway projects, especially motorway widening schemes, will presumably have an easier time generally if their design approach conforms to that given in the document. This paper aims to set out what is new about the advice note and to give a brief overview of the method.

THE TWO-PART WEDGE MECHANISM

The underlying philosophy of the advice note is based closely on existing design methods. The first paper which set out the method on which the note is based was that of Jewell et al. (1984) which contained a comprehensive set of design charts for steep reinforced embankments. The theory was based on limit equilibrium of a two-part wedge failure mechanism, Figure 1, which proved particularly well suited to the analysis of reinforced soil, and the charts have become widely used. The note takes this paper as its starting point and extends the analysis.

A revised set of design charts, Jewell (1990a), based on a log-spiral mechanism of failure and, although more complicated and less intuitive than the two-part wedge method, provided significant savings in the amount of reinforcement required over the earlier charts. During the preparation work for the advice note it was found that the simplicity of the two-part wedge method in Jewell et al. (1984) could be combined

The practice of soil reinforcing in Europe. Thomas Telford, London, 1995

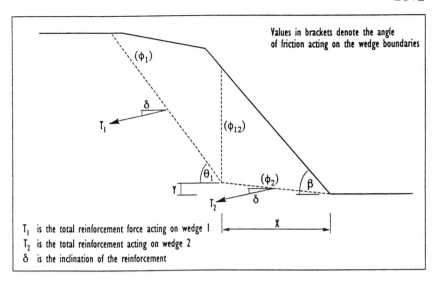

Figure 1   Two-part wedge mechanism

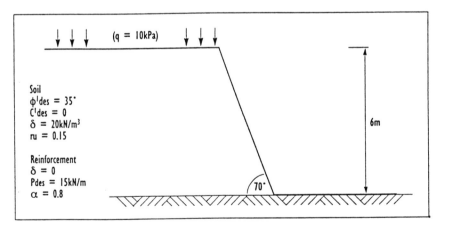

Figure 2   Design example for reinforced soil

with the economy of the second method by introducing friction along the interwedge boundary of the two-part wedge. By careful calibration with established solutions for earth pressure, Caquot & Kerisel (1948), it was determined that the angle of interwedge friction could be safely set at $\frac{1}{2}\phi'$. It was found that this gave comparable answers to the second design method in terms of both the spacing and length of the reinforcements.

The original two-part wedge theory was extended to soil nailing and lead to a program, *Nail-Solver*, Jewell (1990b), which incorporates essentially the same theory as provided in the 1984 paper for reinforced soil, but is extended to allow for inclined reinforcement. The German design method for soil nailing and reinforced soil is also based on the two-part wedge, Gässler (1988), as is the *Textomur* method for reinforced soil, Rüegger & Steiner (1992), and the Californian DpT software for soil nailing, *Snail*, Caltrans (1992). Therefore the decision to opt for the two-part wedge mechanism in the advice note was founded in established practice both in the UK and abroad.

What is new about the advice note is that, firstly, one single simple design method is offered which applies equally to both reinforced soil and to soil nailing. However, despite being simple, it is powerful, providing solutions which compare favourably with those of other design methods for both techniques. Later in this article, solutions are compared against Jewell (1990a) and *ScanSlope*, Leshchinsky (1992) for the case of reinforced soil, and against Nail-Solver and Clouterre (1991) for the case of soil nailing, later in this article.

Secondly, designers are no longer confined to a set of design charts, although charts for standard cases are provided in the document, nor are they confined to using software which is not wholly explanatory. Designers are provided with the understanding and the tools with which to derive solutions from first principles: there are no hidden steps. Simple spreadsheets may be written for a PC based on the formulae provided in the document, and hand checked. But AGS-validated software is also available for this job. *ReActiv* follows the advice note method, step by step, and is available from the Transport Research Laboratory (TRL). The program allows the designer to explore at speed the effect of a large number of variables. In addition to the usual variables (slope angle, slope height, r_u, ϕ' and surcharge), the advice note also allows the incorporation of soil cohesion; the definition of the geometry of the upper slope; variation of the interwedge friction; the application of the reinforcement force to either wedge; and variation of the interface sliding coefficient between the reinforcement and the soil.

Thirdly, unlike many other methods available, the advice note is a *design* method rather than a *calculation* method. ie. it leads the designer to a unique, optimised solution, rather than offering a trial-by-error calculation based on a guessed initial layout. Thus different designers should achieve the same solution using the Advice Note.

THE DESIGN METHOD

In its simplest form the method can best be described by way of example as follows. Consider a 6 m high embankment slope, with a front face angle of 70° and a horizontal crest. The embankment is founded on competent ground and is to be built from well compacted granular fill ($\phi'_{pk} = 42°$, $\phi'_{cv} = 35°$, $\gamma = 20$ kN/m³). The porewater pressure parameter, r_u is set conservatively at 0.15. The reinforcement chosen is a geotextile having a long term factored design strength, P_{des}, of 15 kN/m and a coefficient of interface sliding, α, of 0.8 . There is a surcharge of 10 kPa acting on the crest of the slope. The example is summarised in Figure 2.

For preliminary design, it will be assumed that the angle of interwedge friction, ϕ'_{12} is zero. Because of the surcharge the design height of the slope, H_{des}, is set at 6.5 m. The design angle of friction for the soil, ϕ'_{des}, is set at the large displacement value, ϕ'_{cv}, of 35°. Because large displacement soil strength parameters are used, combined with a long term factored design strength for the reinforcement and a conservative value of r_u , no additional overall factor of safety is necessary.

The first step is to identify the two-part mechanism which requires the maximum reinforcement force. This is called the T_{max} mechanism in the Advice Note, and can be found by searching systematically varying X,Y and θ_1 on Figure 1. The T_{max} mechanism for this example is found to lie at X=1.3 m, Y=0.0 m, $\theta_1=58°$, see Figure 3a, and the reinforcement force required for this mechanism to be 118 kN/m.

The T_{max} mechanism provides two things. Firstly, the total *number* of layers of reinforcement required; N is defined by 118 kN/m divided by 15 kN/m, which is 8 (to the nearest integer). Secondly, it determines the required *length* of reinforcement at the top of the slope. The top layer of reinforcement has to extend far enough beyond the T_{max} mechanism to mobilise its full design strength in pull-out (and if the top layer is satisfactory for pull-out, then so will all the other layers). The required pull-out length for the top layer is given by:

$$L_{e1} = P_{des}/(2 \, \alpha \, \sigma'_v \, \tan\phi'_{des})$$

where
$$\sigma'_v = \gamma \, z_1 \, (1 - r_u)$$
$$z_1 = 0.5 \, H_{des} / \sqrt{N}$$

Hence the pull-out length on the top layer (L_{e1}) needs to be 0.7 m. This fixes point A in Figure 3a.

The second step is to determine the length of reinforcement required at the base of the slope. This is done by searching along the baseline until a 2-part wedge mechanism is found which just doesn't require any reinforcement. This mechanism is called the T_{ob} mechanism, and fixes point B, see Figure 3b, in this example at X = 3.8 m. This is effectively

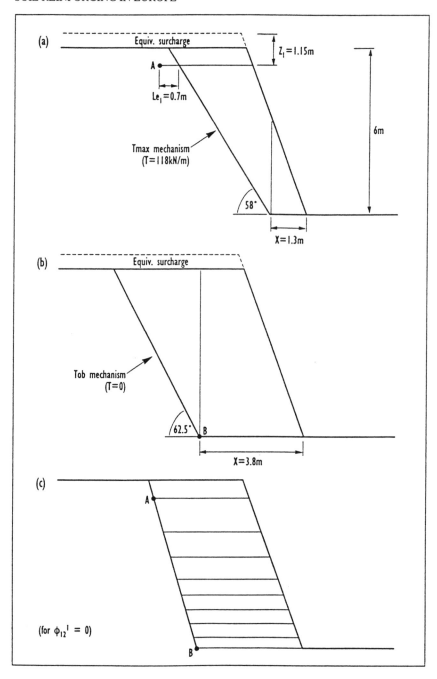

Figure 3   Worked example for reinforced soil

the same calculation which would be used to determine the base width of an equivalent gravity retaining wall.

The final step is to join A to B and put in the remaining layers of reinforcement according to the following relationship, see Figure 3c:

$$z_i = H_{des} \sqrt{([i-1]/N)}$$

The basis of this expression is given in the Advice Note. It should be appreciated that by using this expression an extra layer is automatically introduced at the bottom of the slope, thus giving a total of 9 in the example.

The preliminary design is now complete. However, it is advisable that designers should try and shoot down the design by choosing several trial mechanisms and checking whether the design layout always provides adequate available force. It was found during the preparation of the Advice Note that the trial design layouts were always satisfactory. Soil nailing solutions are arrived at by exactly the same method. For example, the slope in Figure 4 can be designed as shown in Figure 5.

A comparative exercise, Boden & Love (1994), was undertaken to compare the solutions given by the Advice Note to other design methods. The two examples given in this article (Figures 3 and 5) were included in the study. Figures 6 and 7 summarise the results of the comparison. *ReActiv* was used to provide the advice note solutions, both for a frictionless interwedge boundary (ie. $\phi'_{12} = 0$) and a frictional interface ($\phi'_{12} = \frac{1}{2}\phi'_{des}$). The comparison shows that the Advice Note provides economic solutions, especially when the latter assumption regarding interwedge friction is made.

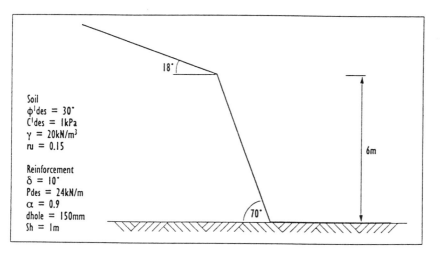

Figure 4 Design example for soil nailing

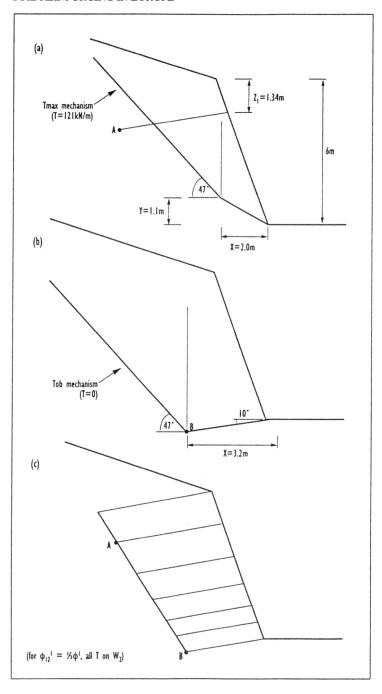

Figure 5 Worked example for soil nailing

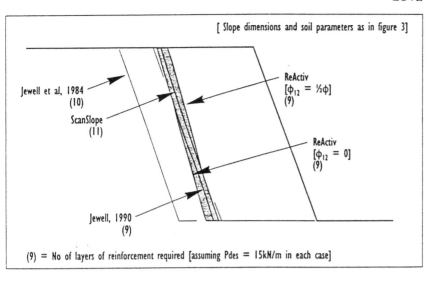

Figure 6   Comparison of desing solutions for reinforced soil example

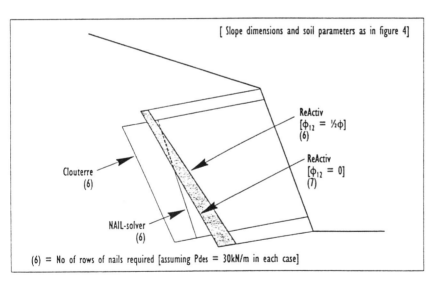

Figure 7   Comparison of design solutions for soil nailing example

In summary, the method is both simple and powerful. It may be used equally for reinforced soil and for soil nailing problems. Computer output may be checked simply by hand calculation, and it is compatible with existing design methods used in the UK.

COMPUTER SOFTWARE

The advice note is now supported by a computer program, Bond et al. (1994), which closely follows the method given in the advice note, contains some additional features such as an extensive soil data base and runs under Microsoft Windows. All the necessary output is provided for hand checking, so there is no black box ethos. There is also an extensive soils library within the program which the user may make use of, if so desired. Figure 8 shows a typical screen shot from the program.

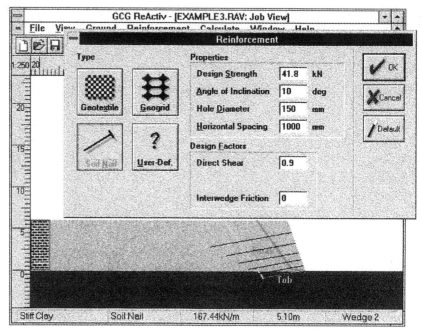

Figure 8   Typical screenshot from *GCG ReActiv*

CONCLUSIONS

The advice note fulfils an obvious need in the guidance available on reinforced slopes and this will be of immediate use in motorway widening schemes. The advice note expresses the DOT preferred design method. The underlying theory is based on well tried limit equilibrium analysis of a two-part wedge failure mechanism and is compatible with existing design methods used in the UK and elsewhere.

The method is both simple and powerful. It may be used equally for reinforced soil and for soil nailing problems. To improve the economy of the solution, partial friction can be assumed to act on the interwedge boundary. The method is based on two simple mechanisms; the T_{max} mechanism and the T_{ob} mechanism.

Designers are not confined to a set of design charts which may only cover a limited set of cases. Nor are they confined to using software which is not wholly explanatory. There are no hidden steps, and computer output may be checked simply by hand calculation. In addition to the normal range of variables (slope angle, slope height, r_u, ϕ' and surcharge), the method allows the incorporation of soil cohesion; definition of the geometry of the upper slope; the variation of the interwedge friction; the application of the reinforcement force to either wedge; and variation of the interface sliding coefficient between the reinforcement and the soil.

The advice note offers a *design* method rather than a *calculation* method, ie. different designers should arrive at the same solution. A comparative exercise, Boden & Love (1994), has shown that the Advice Note method and other currently available methods provide similar solutions. The Advice Note is now supported by ReActiv which is available from the TRL.

The views expressed in this article do not necessarily reflect those of the Highways Agency.

REFERENCES

Boden, D.G. & Love, J.P., 1994, *Design software for soil nailing and reinforced earth slopes.* TRL Project Report, PR/GE/2/94.

Bond, A.J, Love, J.P. & Milligan G.W.E., 1994 *GCG ReActiv.* Reinforced Slope Design Program and manual, TRL.

Caltrans, 1992, *Snail.* Program for soil nailing and manual available from California Department of Transportation, USA.

Caquot, M.A. & Kerisel, J., 1948, *Tables for the calculation of passive pressure, active pressure and bearing capacity of foundations.* Gauthier-Villars, Paris.

Clouterre, 1991, *Soil nailing recommendations for designing, calculating, constructing and inspecting earth support systems using soil nailing.* French National Research Project, Ecole Nationale des Ponts et Chaussées, Paris. English translation, July 1993, US Department of Transportation, Federal Highway Administration, FHWA-SA-93-026.

Gässler, G, 1988, *Soil Nailing - Theoretical basis and practical design.* International Geotechnical Symposium on Theory and Practice in Earth Reinforcement. Fukuoka, Japan pp 283 - 288.

HA 68/94, 1994, *Design Methods for the Reinforcement of Highway Slopes by Reinforced Soil and Soil Nailing Techniques.* Design Manual for Roads and Bridges, Vol. 4, Section 1, Part 4. HMSO.

Jewell, R.A, Paine, N. & Woods, R.I., 1984, *Design methods for steep reinforced embankments.* Symp. Polymer Grid Reinforcement in Civ. Eng, ICE, London, March 1984. Thomas Telford. pp 70 - 81.

Jewell, R.A., 1990a, *Revised design charts for steep reinforced slopes.* Proceedings of Symposium on Reinforced Embankments - Theory and Practice in the British Isles. Thomas Telford, London.

Jewell, R.A., 1990b, *NAIL-Solver.* Computer program and unpublished paper, Oxford Geotechnical Software.

Leshchinsky, D., 1992, *SCANSLOPE.* Slope stability analysis program, Strata Technology Ltd.

Rüegger, R. & Steiner, P., 1992, *The Textomur retaining system - Elements of calculation.* Textomur technical literature, Comtec, Switzerland.

The STRU method of design for reinforced soil

P. Newman, Comtec (UK) Limited, United Kingdom and
P.Steiner, Ruegger AG, Switzerland

SYNOPSIS

In early 1993 the Highways Agency published HA 68/94, *Design methods for the reinforcement of highway slopes by reinforced soil and soil nailing techniques.* This has brought a welcome degree of standardisation to the subject and has increased the interest in reinforced soil in all applications. In Europe reinforced soil has been widely used and in Switzerland the Textomur system has been successfully constructed for up to ten years using the STRU design method. Comparisons are made between this design method and the recently adopted HA 68/94.

INTRODUCTION

The use of reinforced soil continues to grow in the UK, encouraged by the Highways Agency which can see the economic benefits of moving away from hard retainment solutions like piles and reinforced concrete walls. Textomur is a reinforced soil system using a steel form to aid compaction and ensure a smooth front face. It has enjoyed considerable technical and economic success across Europe, the Far East and Canada; and in the past two years this has been repeated in the UK. However the design method used in Switzerland and across the world is not yet fully accepted in the UK where Textomur is currently being built to the guidelines laid down in HA 68/94. The STRU method was devised as a result of fundamental work done at the University of Stuttgart and of research carried out in Switzerland in the 1980s

Both HA 68/94 and STRU are both limit equilibrium approaches based on a two-part wedge mechanism. One of the differences between the two systems is the positioning of the inter-wedge boundary between the disturbing and retaining wedges. HA 68/94 places the boundary at the back of the bottom reinforcement rising at 90° until it outcrops. The STRU method hypothesises that the inter-wedge boundary rises at the same angle as the front face, normally 60°, and the whole reinforced block is treated as the retaining wedge, Figure 1.

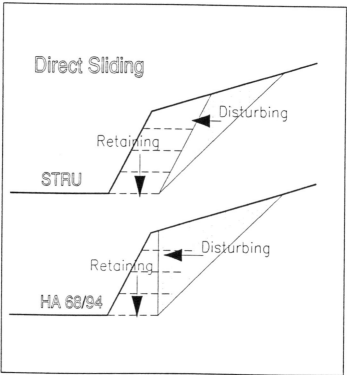

Figure 1 Comparison of two wedge mechanisms of STRU and HA 68/94

DESIGN RATIONALE

The Textomur reinforced soil system was developed through the combined efforts of an environmental engineer, a geotechnical engineer and a geotextile manufacturer. With the basic elements and geometry of the system defined and its buildability proved there came a desire to improve the efficiency of reinforced soil design based on the practical experience that reinforced soil structures show a much higher failure resistance than one expects when using a classical dimensioning process. Together with the numerous measurements taken on reinforced soil structures historically and new scale models, designers set about supporting the hypothesis put forward.

The theory was that the soil stress transferred to the reinforcing elements results in a higher apparent combined shearing strength of the soil and geotextile than expected classically. This stiffening of the soil is applied across the whole block and hence the assumption that the inter-wedge boundary is at the back edge of the reinforced block. A safety factor is applied to the re-compacted fill reducing the friction angle within the reinforced fill; this is usually a tangential factor of 1.2

TESTS

A large number of measurements have been done on geotextile-reinforced slopes, including the monitoring of constructed reinforced steep slopes and the results have been as expected; that is, there are small deformations and they occur mainly during construction. Since the design is connected to the failure of the slope no direct input into the dimensioning process can be expected. In an attempt to get failure large loads have been placed on top the construction. However, besides the fact that total failure hardly ever occurs the simulated load pattern does not relate to realistic failure mechanisms. To understand the mechanisms involved small scale tests have been undertaken together with calculation modelling and field monitoring, Overall the following has been carried out:

- Small scale tests on geotextile reinforced soil structures (1988). The results showed the big stiffening influence of even a very weak reinforcement. The soils, a rounded sand, showed a big plastic reserve.

- Comparison work of different assumptions concerning partial safeties and of different calculation models was done (1992).

- Pullout tests on different reinforcing geotextiles and different soils are being undertaken to understand the complex soil geotextile interaction.

- All these investigations show that the STRU calculation method gives appropriate dimensioning results by being conservative in the assumption of considering the reinforcement as single forces and by taking into consideration the overall stiffening effect of the geotextile by changing the inter wedge boundary.

COMPUTER PROGRAM

The computer program calculates the *geotextile efficiency* and thus the internal stability of the reinforced soil slope. The input allows for most types of geometry and includes up to three soil types and a water table. Safety factors can be set for all the input soil strength parameters, φ' and c', as well as any surcharge loads and the allowable strength of the reinforcing elements. The standard safety factors are shown below in Table 1:

Table 1 Partial safety factors used in design

Influence			Partial Safety
Density:			
	Subsoil	γ_u	1.0
	Fill Material	γ_s	1.0
Friction Angle:			
	Subsoil	φ_u	1.0
	Fill Material	φ_s	1.2
		$(\tan\varphi_s/\tan\varphi_{scal})$	
Cohesion:			
	Subsoil	c	1.5
	Fill material	c	1.5
Loads, p, P:			1.0
Geotextiles (for permissible tensile force Zg)			2.0

The allowable force for the reinforcing elements is assumed to be 1/3 - 1/4 the short term reinforcement strength, i.e. a factor of safety of 3.0 - 4.0. This allows for stability with time (creep, environment etc..), installation damage and general calculation safety factor. This can be compared with the combined effect of partial safety factors suggested by HA 68/94 which is similar to the rationale provided by BBA (1992) certification of reinforcing geogrid, Table 2.

Table 2 Comparison of partial safety factors for allowable geotextile strength

HA 68/94	STRU
$P_{des} = P_c/(f_d . f_e . f_m)$	$P_{des} = P_{ult} / 3.0 - 4.0$
where P_c = characteristic strength, dependent on design life f_d = factor for mech. damage f_e = factor for environmental effects f_m = factor for uncertainties in material strength inc. extrapolation	
Worst case: $P_{des} = P_{ult}$ x 60% /(1.3 x 1.4 x 1.15) Hence if P_{ult} = 35kN/m then $P_{des} = 10kN/m$	Hence if P_{ult} = 35 kN/m then $P_{des} = 8.8 -11.6 kN/m$

The computer program calculates the geometry and weight of the disturbing and retaining wedge including any surcharge load which is input. The corresponding disturbing and retaining forces are then calculated for each layer. By varying the geometry of the disturbing wedge the program searches for the maximum disturbing force by taking into consideration the exact geometry of the surface and the soil layers, up to three different types, and any ground water influences. The retaining forces are supplemented by the addition of reinforcing elements, in 500 mm layers. If layers closer are required then intermediates are placed 250 mm above the primary reinforcing layer. This can sometimes result in more geotextile being used than necessary but the offset in buildability more than compensates in economic terms. The output is provided in both graphical and numerical form and provides proof of both the direct sliding stability and the internal stability. The direct sliding stability is the factor of safety against failure below the base layer of reinforcing and should always exceed 1.5. The internal stability is satisfied as long as the geotextile efficiency does not exceed 100% , Figures 2 and 3.

EXAMPLES OF REINFORCING WIDTHS

Table 3 below shows the reinforcing widths required for different scenarios based on the STRU method and comparing those reinforcing widths dictated by HA 68/94. All designs are for a 3m high slope at 60° with, in the case of embankment, a 20 kN/m^2 surcharge. In all examples r_u is assumed at zero.

COMTEC (UK) Ltd.	Order: 1 994 001	Append.
	Example - Highway embankment	

Date: 31.01.95 Time: 14: 9:14 Quant. of points: 20 Quant. of calculated sliding surf.: 331	**TEXTOMUR CALCULATION** Mecanism of two solids by lamella, procedure STRU © 1993 Computer program by P.Steiner, Rüegger Ltd.

NUMERIC RESULTS

Version: H = 5.0m; B = 4.0m

TEXTOMUR no. 1

Soil characteristics:	Upper section:	TEXTOMUR section:
Specific gravity:	20.0 kN/m³	20.0 kN/m³
Inner friction angle:	32.0 °	32.0 °
Cohesion:	0.0 kN/m²	0.0 kN/m²
Friction security:	1.00	1.20
Cohesion security:	1.00	1.50

Reinforcing geotextile in layers of 0.5 m

Service strength: z_a = 10.0 kN/m
Geotextile security: F_a = 2.00

1. force: Spread load: beginning = 6.00 m end = 11.00 m

Amount: p = 20.0 kN/m²

Geotextile layer	Height of cut [m]	Weight subsoil [kN/m]	Weight TEXTOMUR [kN/m]	Earthpressure subsoil [kN/m]	Earthpressure TEXTOMUR [kN/m]	Geotextile available [kN/m]	Geotextile required [kN/m]	Efficiency of Geotextiles [%]
1	0.00	206.40	450.36	46.97	-234.52	0.00	-187.54	0.00
2	0.50	179.20	430.36	40.37	-163.93	5.00	-123.56	0.00
3	1.00	153.79	410.36	34.22	-111.24	10.00	-77.02	0.00
4	1.50	128.76	390.36	28.51	-71.25	15.00	-42.74	0.00
5	2.00	107.07	370.36	23.25	-40.59	20.00	-17.34	0.00
6	2.50	87.16	350.36	18.43	-16.99	25.00	1.44	5.76
7	3.00	65.55	356.63	14.09	1.22	30.00	15.31	51.02
8	3.50	46.76	336.63	10.31	16.19	35.00	26.50	75.71
9	4.00	33.06	316.63	7.18	27.53	40.00	34.71	86.78
10	4.50	21.26	296.63	4.55	35.90	45.00	40.45	89.89
11	5.00	0.00	237.60	0.00	46.96	50.00	46.96	93.91

Maximum geotextile efficiency factor: 93.9 %

Sliding security: F_{a1} = 4.99

Program V3.2 Peter Steiner

Figure 2   Tabular output from STRU computer program

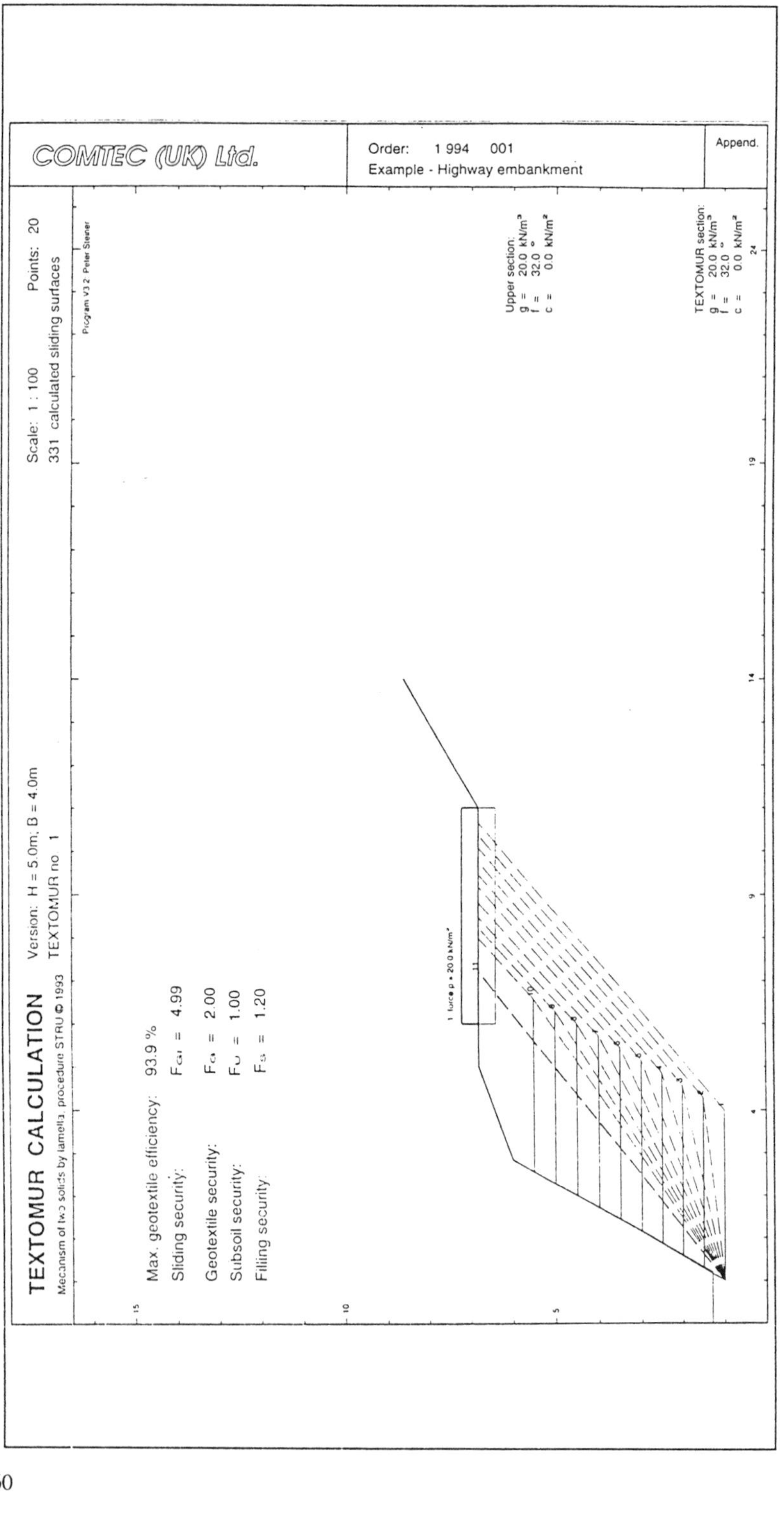

Figure 3   Graphical output form STRU computer program

Table 3   Reinforcing widths for various scenarios

Scenario	Soil Type	φ'	c'	γ	Reinforcing Width		
					STRU	HA68/94	
						$\varphi'_{12}=0$	$\varphi'_{12}=\frac{1}{2}\varphi'$
Cutting 1:3.5	Clay	23	1	18.5	2.5	3.3	2.8
Cutting 1:2	Sand	32	0	20.0	1.8	2.6	2.1
Embankment	silty sandy Clay	26	0	19.0	2.3	3.0	2.6
Embankment	Sand	30	0	20.0	1.8	2.4	2.1

There are two HA 68/94 values shown, one with inter wedge friction and one without. The STRU method assumes no inter wedge friction between the disturbing and retaining wedge. The reinforcing width using STRU is less, in the above cases between 11 and 14%. The main reason is that the reinforcing width depends a great deal on the length required to ensure direct sliding stability. It is this mechanism that benefits most from the assumption that the inter wedge boundary lies at 60° in the case of the STRU method. Hence, although more layers may be proposed using STRU, their width is less. This still yields savings however, since most reinforced soil applications require excavation and re-compaction. It is easier and less costly to place 10 layers of reinforcing at 3 m width then 6 layers at 4 m width when excavation and muck handling costs are taken into account.

MEASUREMENT OF DEFORMATION
Various projects across the world have been the subject of tests using extensometers to measure the deformation of the front face with time.

Aosta Valley, Italy
   The conforming design of a large reinforced concrete viaduct for a six lane autostrada through the Alps was replaced by a reinforced soil embankment. At its highest point the slope was 25 m high with a maximum reinforcing width of 13 m. This point was chosen for the placement of 6 extensometers to measure the front face deformation during and after construction. The results showed the maximum deformation all occurred during the construction period and was approximately 0.06% of the total length of reinforcement, corresponding to a front face deformation of approximately 70 mm, Figure 4. This particular construction was of further interest since the embankment was temporarily overloaded by approximately 250,000 cubic metres of spoil during construction. This was not considered during the design. The fill material used was crushed stone from the tunnel excavations nearby.

Auto-route 73, Quebec
   The fill material was glacial till and of a sandy nature. The total height varied between 5 and 9.5 metres. Extensometers were utilised to measure the deformation with anchor points at 1.5, 2.4, 3.1, 5.2, and 7.2 metres from the reference point. The last anchor point was behind the back face of the

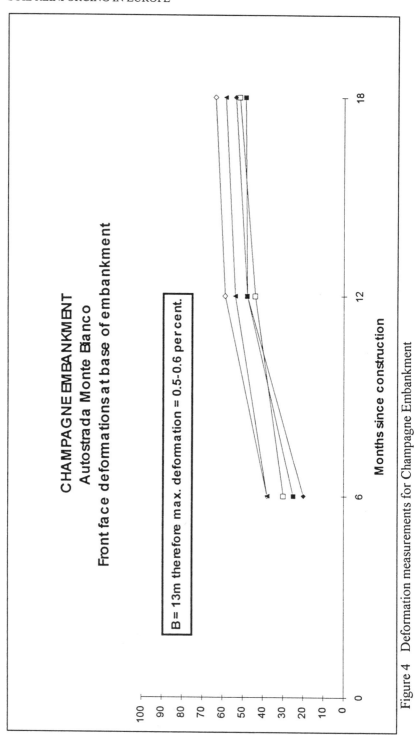

Figure 4   Deformation measurements for Champagne Embankment

reinforced block. The deformation was measured during and after construction. The following conclusions were drawn:

- The deformation was very small, a maximum of 0.6%
- The deformation increases towards the front face
- Almost all the deformation occurs during construction
- The deformations are principally caused by the internal stability of the slope which results in a small increase in tension in the reinforcing geotextile.

From the stress-strain graph of the geotextile used a deformation of 0.6% represents a stress of 0.52 kN/m. The general arrangement of the extensometers with respect to the slope is shown in Figure 5 and the deformation results in Figure 6. Further results were collected later in the spring and it was found that the deformations had decreased slightly. This was due to the fact that the earlier increase measured in January and February were as a result of moisture in the topsoil layer expanding when frozen. Temperatures in Quebec in January 1994 were the lowest that century, down to -45°C !

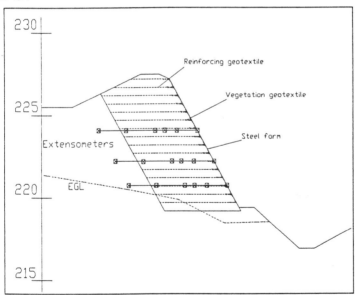

Figure 5   Auto-route 73, General arrangement of extensometers in slope

CONCLUSIONS

The STRU design has been shown to be representative and indeed conservative with respect to the actual behaviour of reinforced soil structures. As with all reinforced soil design methods it relies on the accuracy of soil data. In the future, with improved monitoring of existing structures and further research using scale models, it may be possible to quantify the assumption that all the reinforced block acts as a retaining force. This

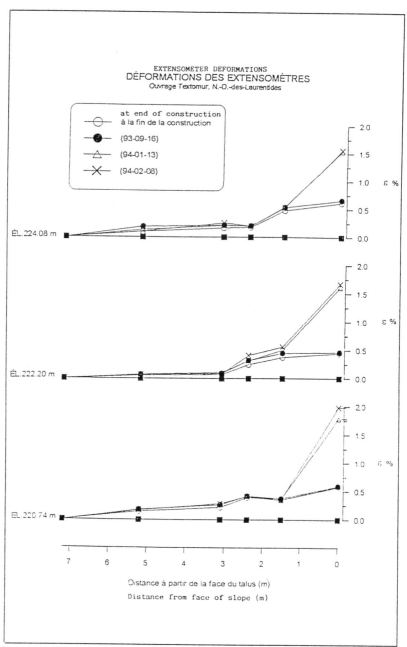

Figure 6 - Quebec, Auto-route 73, Front face deformations

assumption can lead to the conclusion that if the interaction between the soil and geotextile can be better understood then ultimately designers could utilise an increased φ' for the reinforced block to simulate reinforcing and thus greatly simplify design procedures.

Continued research is planned both in Switzerland and in the UK to further our understanding of the interaction between the soil and reinforcing geotextile. Of special interest is the idea that non-woven geotextiles, although exhibiting high creep when tested in isolation actually out perform stiffer reinforcing elements when in confinement. Currently pullout tests are being done on non woven geotextiles designed with the Textomur system. Their drainage properties can provide a substantial advantage over other geotextiles in cohesive fill where, in the case of non-draining reinforcing, the interface between soil and geotextile can be an area of positive pore pressure.

REFERENCES

BBA , 1992, *Roads and Bridges Agrément certificates No 92/69 - Fortrac Geogrids.* British Board of Agrément, pp 10.

DOT, 1994, *Design methods for the reinforcement of highway slopes by reinforced soil and soil nailing techniques* . Design Manual for Roads and Bridges, Vol 4, Section 1, Part 4, HA 68/94, pp 111.

Gouvernement du Quebec - Ministere des Transport, 1993, *Mesures des déformations effectuées sur l'ouvrage TEXTOMUR construit en bordure l'autoroute 73 Notre-Dame-des Laurentides.* Report No 0132-19-090(19)91.

Ruegger, R., Steiner, P. & Eugster, M., 1988, *Statische Modellversuche an schlanken, geotextilbewehrten Verkleidungskonstruktionen.* German Society for Soil and Underground Construction. Proc. 1st Congress Plastic Materials in Geotechnics K-GEO, Hamburg 1988, 157-166.

Sembenelli, G. & Sembenelli, P., 1988, *Displacements and strain measured on a high reinforced soil structure.* Proc. X European Conference on Soil Mechanics and Foundation Engineering, Firenze 1991, 153-158.

Steiner, P., 1992, *Steilboschungen aus geotestilbewehrtern Erdmaterial: Vergleich verscheidener Sicherheiten und Bemessungsmodelle* K-GEO 92, Luzern, 163-171.

A review of methods of slope stability analysis

I. M. MORRISON, Consulting Geotechnical Engineer, and
S. S. DIKRAN, Tenax Plastics Limited, United Kingdom

SYNOPSIS

There are a large number of calculation methods for analysing the stability of slopes, both with and without reinforcement. Generally, these methods are based on assumptions made for mathematical reasons and either simplify the problem by ignoring some of the variables or introduce additional variables to obtain a solution. A complete method of solving the limit equilibrium slope stability problem with the soil strength expressed in terms of the Mohr Coulomb failure criterion was discovered some 15 years ago. This paper describes the commonly used methods of slope stability analysis by reference to the implied physical assumptions, explains the complete method, and reviews the methods of calculation adopted in slope stability computer programmes available in the U.K.

INTRODUCTION

A review has been carried out of the commercial software available within the United Kingdom for use in the design of reinforced soil structures and the analysis of associated slope stability and foundation problems. This paper presents the results of the review and explains the criteria expected from a modern method of slope stability analysis. As a result of the review a computer programme using a comprehensive and mathematically rigorous method of slope stability analysis has been developed for commercial use.

Many reviews of methods of slope stability analysis have been published in the technical literature, e.g. Sarma (1979) and Fredlund et al. (1981). In these reviews the author has typically classified the calculation methods by the assumptions made to obtain a mathematical solution. For example, does the method consider force or moment equilibrium or both, and how many unknowns and equations are available. No such review will be attempted in this paper.

Why are there so many different methods of slope stability analysis? The conceptual model used for engineering design is relatively simple. For a complete solution of the model all the forces must be considered and the number of equations and unknowns must balance, preferably without the introduction of additional variables. If these conditions are met a rigorous mathematical solution can be obtained and there would be few, possibly only one, method of solution. It is obvious that in the past these conditions had not been achieved and as a result a large number of approximate methods were developed.

METHOD OF CALCULATION - LIMIT EQUILIBRIUM METHOD

The vast majority of slope stability calculation carried out in the United Kingdom are made by the method of slices. In this method the slide mass is divided into a set of vertical sided wedges or slices. The analysis is then carried out by the limit equilibrium method, Atkinson (1981). The main assumptions of the limit equilibrium method may be summarized as

(a)   the equilibrium of a slope may be analysed as a series of blocks forming a mechanism

(b)   equilibrium is independent of the stresses and strains within the blocks

(c)   the forces acting on the boundaries of the blocks are known.

The first two assumptions cause little practical difficulty though not all arbitrarily chosen series of blocks can form a mechanism, Morrison (1988). The third assumption causes difficulty as the forces on the boundaries of the blocks depend on the proportion of the available strength mobilized and on the forces on the other blocks in the mechanism.

The proportion of strength mobilized is normally represented by the factor of safety which when applied to the Mohr Coulomb failure criteria leads to

$$\tau_{mob} = c'/F + (\sigma_n - u)(\tan \phi')/F$$

where τ_{mob} is the mobilized shear strength

c' and ϕ' are the effective stress shear strength parameters

σ_n and u are the normal total and pore water pressures

By definition, a limit equilibrium analysis seeks to find the forces acting on the boundaries of the blocks when the strength available is fully mobilized, i.e. the factor of safety F = 1 and the mechanism is in equilibrium with the applied forces. The introduction of another variable, the factor of safety F ≠ 1, is an addition to the basic assumptions and will complicate the analysis. The complication is increased as the factor of safety has no direct physical meaning and can not be measured by any field or laboratory test.

Because of the introduction of the additional variable, the factor of safety, the number of equations and unknowns do not balance and the conventional limit equilibrium model in which the main disturbing force is due to gravity, can not be solved. To overcome this difficulty a number of further assumptions have been used to obtain a solution. The resulting approximate methods of calculation may be classified by the additional assumptions made. By rearrangement of the basic stability equations, the physical assumptions implied by the mathematical assumptions used to obtain a solution can be demonstrated, Morrison and Greenwood (1989).

Simplified Methods

The simplified methods do not consider all the forces on the slice boundaries. In particular the stability of the failure mechanism is assumed to be independent of the effective stresses on the interslice boundaries, i.e. independent of strain within the slide mass. In addition a pore water pressure distribution within the slide mass is assumed. This distribution does not necessarily correspond to the real or specified pore water distribution in the slope.

In the U.K., the most widely used simplified methods are those by Bishop (1955), Janbu (1973) and the Simple method, Greenwood (1983). The methods by Bishop and Janbu are similar, the first satisfying moment equilibrium and the second horizontal force equilibrium.

The pore water pressure distributions implied by Bishop and Janbu are functions of the factor of safety, and the weight, geometry and shear strength of the slide mass. They do not correspond to any real pore water regime but ensure that no effective stresses can develop on the interslice boundaries.

The forces acting on the slice boundaries considered by the simplified methods are summarized in figure 1(a). The simplified methods calculate a factor of safety and may be used with a wide range of slip surfaces both circular and non-circular.

Rigorous Uncoupled Methods

The rigorous uncoupled methods consider all the forces present on the wedge boundaries. To obtain a solution they introduce an additional unknown parameter which effectively uncouples the interslice shear force from the effective stresses on the slip surface. A variety of different mathematical techniques are used to uncouple the interslice forces. Well known methods using this technique to obtain a solution are those by Morgenstern & Price (1965), Spencer (1967) and Sarma (1973).

A solution is obtained by iteration of the interslice effective stresses so that moment and force equilibrium are satisfied and hence the methods are mathematically rigorous. However, the interslice stresses found by iteration are often less than allowed by the failure criterion, i.e. the factor of safety on the interslice boundaries is higher than that on the slip surface and generally can not be specified.

The forces acting on the slice boundaries considered by the rigorous uncoupled methods are summarized in figure 1(b). The methods calculate a factor of safety and may be applied to a wide range of slip surfaces.

In the U.K. Department of Transport Advice Note HA68/94 *Design methods for the reinforcement of highway slopes by reinforced soil and soil nailing techniques* a two wedge mechanism is recommended for design use. This method is not a *simplified method* as the interwedge forces can be considered. In order to obtain a solution the effective interwedge forces are uncoupled from those on the slip surface and the method is similar to the rigorous uncoupled methods described above. However in contrast to those methods, the shape of the slip surface which can be studied by this method is restricted and the method is of limited general use.

For routine design use, HA68/94 recommends that the interwedge shear force is set to zero and that the interwedge line is vertical. This recommendation effectively reduces the two wedge mechanism to a *simplified method*.

The forces acting on the slice boundaries considered by a typical 2 wedge mechanism are summarized in Figure 1(c). As formulated in HA68/94, the method calculates the total force to achieve stability with the specified factor of safety or minimum conceivable soil strength parameters. No factor of safety is calculated.

Complete Multiple Wedge Method

In a real slope which is about to fail, the strength of the failure mechanism is fully mobilized. If such a condition does not exist, we need to vary the mechanism, and or the external forces acting on the mechanism, to create a limiting condition. An obvious force to vary is the horizontal force acting on the slide mass, Figure 1(d). This force has direct physical meaning as it may represent either a dynamic earthquake force or the total reinforcing force required to stabilize the slide. If the horizontal force is expressed as a proportion of the weight of the slide mass, the number of unknowns and equations balance and all the forces acting on the boundaries of the blocks may be calculated without iteration or additional assumption. In principle, this procedure is similar to that adopted in the analysis of reinforced concrete and other engineering structures to calculate an allowable load.

In structural analysis the strength of the material is specified by the user often in the form of an allowable strength. Different allowable strengths will result in different allowable loads. In soil mechanics, the allowable strength is the limiting strength of the soil divided by a factor of safety, i.e. the mobilized strength given by equation (1). A series of calculations with different factors of safety will provide a relation between the factor of safety and the horizontal force applied to the slide mass, see Figure 2. The allowable horizontal force for the specified factor of safety or alternatively, the factor of safety for the applied horizontal force may

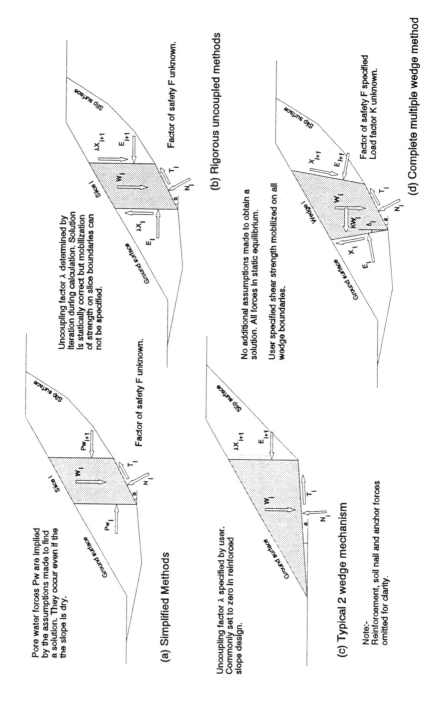

Fig. 1 SUMMARY OF FORCES CONSIDERED IN ANALYSIS

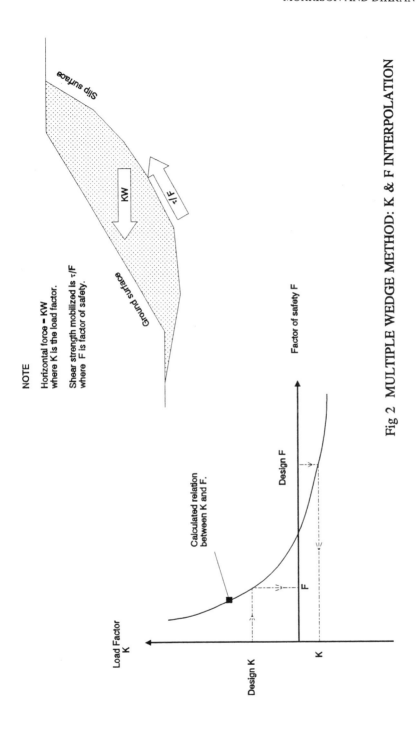

NOTE

Horizontal force = KW
where K is the load factor.

Shear strength mobilized is τ/F
where F is factor of safety.

Fig 2 MULTIPLE WEDGE METHOD: K & F INTERPOLATION

then be obtained by interpolation. The first interpolation provides the reinforcing force required and the second the conventional factor of safety of the slope. The shapes of the blocks forming the failure mechanism may be varied to find either the maximum reinforcing force or the minimum factor of safety whichever is required. In general these two critical mechanisms will not be the same.

The important point about the complete multiple wedge method is that the calculation of the forces acting on the blocks is made without any assumptions additional to those of the basic limit equilibrium method. No boundary forces are ignored, no factor of safety is calculated and no iterative uncoupling parameter is required. The calculation is a complete and rigorous solution of the limit equilibrium problem.

REVIEW OF COMMERCIALLY AVAILABLE SLOPE STABILITY COMPUTER PROGRAMMES

A literature search and personal communications were made to identify all computer programmes currently available in the U.K., which involve the use of geosynthetics in geotechnical engineering. Some 29 programmes were found dealing with the various applications in geotechnical engineering, such as filtration, drainage, river and costal erosion, unpaved roads, embankment basal reinforcement, and reinforced earth slopes and walls. Out of the 29 programs, only 12 deal directly with the stability of reinforced earth slopes, and of these only seven programmes are known to be available commercially, the rest are either for academic or in-house use and not for sale. The following review summarizes the scope, user friendliness, method of calculation, data verification and use of graphics and, where available, the cost of each of these programmes. The detailed information has been obtained largely from the relevant advertising literature and or user manuals. It is hoped that the following summaries are fair despite the difficulty in obtaining all the information required.

(1)   *Programme Name:-* SLIP4
        Supplier:-   Travers Morgan, Nottingham, U.K.
        Cost:-   Not specified, but low cost.

Slip4 is a slip circle programme developed from a hand calculation procedure for determining the factor of safety of a single slip surface by three simplified methods, Bishop's Simplified Method, Janbu's Simplified Method and the Swedish Simplified Method, Fellenius (1936). The programme is intended as a basic analytical tool enabling experienced engineers to design reinforced soil slopes. The increase in the factor of safety provided by the reinforcement, is calculated by the Simple Method. The slope must be drawn by hand first and then slices from the failure mass are selected to suit the slope geometry and strata. Slice dimensions are measured and strength parameters assigned as appropriate. Selection of the centre of rotation of a critical surface is determined by conventional trial and error methods. The programme does not provide any graphical output.

(2)   *Programme Name:-* STABLE
      Supplier:-   I.T.C. Division, Mott MacDonald Group, Croydon, U.K.
      Cost:-   circa £1200

A programme for assessing the stability of circular and non-circular slip surfaces in slopes and embankments. Four methods of analyses are included; Bishop's Simplified Method, Morgenstern & Price's Uncoupled Method, the Multiple Wedge Method, and the Simple Method. When the programme was last used by the authors, only the latter method could model soil reinforcement. For users familiar with CAD drawing programmes, STABLE is user friendly with pop-up menus and on-line help files. The slope geometry, including any layers of reinforcement, is prepared either in a separate CAD programme or in a specially formatted text file, the former being recommended. The slope geometry is obtained automatically by the stability programme from a CAD data exchange file. The programme calculates the factor of safety of the slope against sliding and tabulates detailed information derived from the analysis. Graphical output is obtained from the CAD programme by reversing the input data procedure. For circular surfaces using Bishop's Simplified Method, the minimum factor of safety may be found by calculating the factor of safety on a grid of points and using the familiar contouring technique, Bishop (1955).

(3)   *Programme Name:-* SLOPE
      Supplier:-   Geosolve Ltd., London, U.K.
      Cost:-   circa £1800

SLOPE is a programme for assessing the stability of both circular and non-circular failure surfaces, including the stability of reinforced soil slopes and embankments. Five methods of analysis are available. For circular failure surfaces, the Swedish Simplified Method and Bishop's Simplified Method. For other failure surfaces, Spencer's Uncoupled Method, and Janbu's Uncoupled and Simplified Methods, Janbu (1973). Janbu's Simplified Method is the only method available in the programme when soil reinforcement is specified. The programme output gives a summary of the input data followed by a list of the slip surfaces analysed, including in each case the factor of safety. A graphical output of data and results is also provided.

(4) *Programme Name:-* STABGM
     Supplier:- Virginia Polytechnic and State University, Department of Civil Engineering, Blacksburg, Virginia, U.S.A.
     Cost:- approx. £200

STABGM is a computer programme developed in 1985, for the stability analysis of reinforced embankments and slopes. The programme uses the Swedish Simplified Method or Bishop's Uncoupled Method, Bishop (1955) to calculate the factor of safety for circular slip surfaces. Up to thirty layers of reinforcement, with the force in the reinforcement layers varying along their lengths, may be considered in the analysis. The input data are typed one after another, separated by commas. The programme does not provide a graphical output and is generally considered difficult to use.

(5) *Programme Name:-* TALREN
     Supplier:- Terrasol, France
     Cost:- £3000

TALREN is a slope stability analysis programme developed by Terrasol over a 12 year period starting in 1980. The programme considers hydraulic and seismic data, in addition to various types of soil reinforcements such as soil nails, anchors, braces, reinforced soil strips, geosynthetic reinforcement, piles and mini-piles. The calculations are based on the Swedish and Bishop's Simplified Methods of analysis specially modified and presented as the Perturbation Method to avoid the numerical difficulties found in the original methods, Raulin et al (1974). The programme is user friendly and provides an impressive graphical output which can be readily included in a geotechnical report.

(6) *Programme Name:-* ScanSlope
     Supplier:- STRATA Technology Ltd.
     Cost:- £190.00

The programme is used to determine the required reinforcement layout (length and strength) for a known steep slope geometry to obtain a prescribed factor of safety. The calculation assumes that the slope rests on a competent foundation, which limits the use of the programme for general slope stability analysis. Approximate analysis of potential foundation failures is carried out by Bishop's Simplified Method. The reinforcement design is made using the log spiral method for internal stability calculations which, for homogeneous reinforced earth structures, results in a statically determinate problem, Leshchinsky & Boedeker (1989). Hence for the limited case considered the method of analysis requires no additional unknowns for a solution and is a complete and mathematically rigorous calculation. Direct sliding of the reinforced earth mass over the foundation is checked using the simplified two wedge mechanism with a vertical interwedge line along which the full soil strength is mobilized. The programme is user-friendly and graphical output and data verification are provided.

(7)   *Programme Name:-*   ReACTIVE
        Supplier:-   Transport Research Laboratory, Crowthorne, U.K.
        Cost:-   £1000.00 (single-user licence)

The programme ReACTIVE was produced by the Geotechnical Consulting Group for the Transport Research Laboratory. The programme is based on the Department of Transport's Advice Note HA 68/94 *Design methods for the reinforcement of highway slopes by reinforced soil and soil nailing techniques*. The user enters the slope geometry, soil properties, water regime, surcharge, and reinforcement properties, and the required factor of safety. The programme uses the simplified two wedge mechanism to calculate the stabilising force required from the reinforcement. As with ScanSlope, the design assumes a competent foundation for the reinforced earth mass and hence the programme is not suitable, and is not intended, for general slope stability analysis. The results are presented in spreadsheet and graphical format, but unfortunately it is not possible to print-out a paper copy of the graphics. Otherwise, the programme is easy to use.

CONCLUSION

There are many attempts in the engineering literature to demonstrate that one method of slope stability analysis is superior to another. These attempts frequently show that the method being considered agrees with known field failures. The agreement is often claimed to be good enough' for engineering purposes. In a multi variate problem such as slope stability, it is not surprising that there are a number of approximate methods of calculation which appear to give reasonable results. If there are enough variables within the calculation, the errors are unlikely to be additive. As an example, the pore water pressures implied by the Bishop Simplified Method of analysis are similar to those observed in many relatively shallow slopes with near surface ground water levels. Under these conditions, the effective stresses on steep surfaces within the slide are low. Hence setting the interslice shear forces to zero is a reasonable approximation and does not cause significant error in the calculated factor of safety. These conditions are typical of the slope failures which were used to verify the method. However, the same calculation method yields unreasonable results when the slope is steep and the ground water levels are high, Turnbull & Horslev (1967).

The main basis for recommending the complete multiple wedge method is that it solves the limit equilibrium model of slope failure reliably. No additional uncertainties are introduced due to the method of calculation. Reinforcement and anchors forces are easily incorporated. The method can analyse accurately all feasible multiple wedge failure mechanisms in slopes and foundations and calculate passive and active pressures on retaining walls, and the forces required from reinforcement to provide the required factor of safety.

The complete multiple wedge method of calculation was discovered by Dr Sarma at Imperial College and first published 15 years ago, Sarma (1979). Development, professional acceptance and commercial use of the method is overdue. As the method of calculation is easy to understand, numerically simple and less complex than many of the approximate methods, there is no practical reason for its lack of use. The method of calculation has been described in the technical literature both by the author and others, Hoek (1983).

As shown by this review of commercially available slope stability programmes, none of the user friendly programmes implement the complete multiple wedge method with reinforcement. As even the simplest commercial design tends to be done on a computer, this has obviously hindered the development of the method. In order to encourage the development of the method and improve the commercial design of reinforced slopes, the Authors have developed a suitable programme which will shortly be available.

REFERENCES

Atkinson, J.H., 1981, *Foundations and slopes*, Maidenhead: McGraw-Hill.

Bishop, A.W., 1955, *The use of the slip circle in the stability analysis of slopes*, Géotechnique **5**, Nº 1, 7-17.

Fellenius, W., 1936, *Calculation of the stability of earth dams*, Trans. 2nd Int. Congr. Large Dams, Washington D. C., **4**, 445-462.

Fredlund, D.G., Krahn, J. & Pufahl, D.E., 1981, *The relationship between limit equilibrium slope stability methods*, Proc. 10th Int. Conf. Soil Mech., Stockholm **3**, 409-416.

Greenwood, J.R., 1983, *A simple approach to slope stability*, Ground Engng **16**, N° 4, 45-48.

HA 68/94, 1994, *Design Methods for the Reinforcement of Highway Slopes by Reinforced Soil and Soil Nailing Techniques*, Design Manual for Roads and Bridges, Dept. of Transport, U.K.

Hoek, E., 1983, *23rd Rankine Lecture: strength of jointed rock masses*, Géotechnique **33**, N° 3,187-223.

Janbu, N., 1973, *Slope stability computations*. In *Embankment dam engineering*. Hirschfield, R. C. & Poulos, S. J. (eds), New York: Wiley.

Leshchinsky, D. & Boedeker, R.H., 1989, *Geosynthetic reinforced earth structures*, J. Geot. Engng, Am. Soc. Civ. Engrs. **115**, GT10, 1459-1478.

Morgenstern, N.R. & Price, V.E., 1965, *The analysis of the stability of general slip surfaces*. Géotechnique **15**, N° 1, 79-93.

Morrison, I.M., 1988, *Discussion on Sarma, S. K. (1987) A note on the stability analysis of slopes*, Géotechnique **38**, N° 1, 157-159.

Morrison, I.M. & Greenwood, J.R., 1989, *Assumptions in simplified slope stability analysis by the method of slices*, Géotechnique **39**, N° 3, 503-509.

Raulin, P., Rouques, G. & Toubol, A., 1974, *Calcul de la stabilité des pentes en rupture non circulaire*, Report de recherche n 36, L.C.P.C., Paris.

Sarma, S.K., 1973, *Stability analysis of embankments and slopes*, Géotechnique **23**, N° 3, 423-433.

Sarma, S.K., 1979, *Stability analysis of embankments and slopes*, J. Geot. Engng, Am. Soc. Civ. Engrs. **105**, GT12, 1511-1524.

Spencer, E., 1967, *A method of analysis of the stability of embankments assuming parallel interslice forces*, Géotechnique **17**, N° 1, 11-26.

Turnbull, W.J. & Horslev, M.J., 1967, *Special problems in slope stability*, J. Soil Mech. Engng, Am. Soc. Civ. Engrs. **93**, SM4, 499-528.

Geotextile reinforced walls and slopes - Austrian experience

G. MANNSBART and G. WERNER, Polyfelt GmbH, Linz, Austria

SYNOPSIS

Geotextiles are able to complement the properties of soil as construction material in an ideal manner. They are used as reinforcements in the construction of dams, retaining structures and foundation layers. The system behaviour of reinforced soil and the requirements for reinforcing elements are described, and an overview of the existing design methods is given and illustrated by examples of practical applications. In these examples both nonwovens as well as high-strength geo-composite materials were successfully used.

PRINCIPLES OF DESIGN AND INPUT PARAMETERS

Soil parameters

Soil properties have a marked influence on the behaviour of a reinforced soil structure. In theory any soil may be used, but for practical purposes only a limited range of soils are used. The choice of a particular soil is dependent upon the reinforced structure, eg steep embankment, wall, and the type of reinforcement, eg strip, sheet or grid. A site investigation is a key parameter for success and it is generally necessary to perform a comprehensive subsurface exploration program. Carefully obtained design values for particle size distribution, friction, cohesion and unit weight are the basic requirements for any calculation. As the loads must be transferred between the soil and reinforcement the soil to fabric friction angle is important.

The water content of soil affects its strength. At higher water contents a lower undrained strength, Figure 1b, and at lower degrees of saturation a higher residual friction angle, Figure 1a, Brandl (1993). Granular fills are preferred due to their ability to transfer shear stresses more effectively. However, where such materials are not readily available, the use of poor quality fills may be considered. Cohesive soils may be used with an appropriate layer thickness and drainage capacity of the reinforcing elements. If poorly draining backfills are used with non-draining reinforcing elements, eg grids or wovens, there may be a considerable amount of pore water pressure during and immediately after construction. The acting effective stress σ' has to be calculated. For non saturated conditions the relation u/σ depends mainly upon the degree of saturation of the soil.

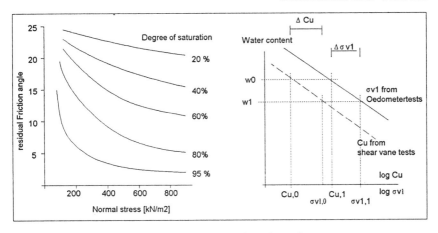

Figure 1 Strength properties as a function of water content

Geotextile tensile strength

Strip tensile tests still have their significance as index tests, however, the in-situ behaviour of geotextiles is considerably different from that observed in *isolated* tests, Werner & Resl (1986). Especially with nonwoven geotextiles not only a stiffer force-elongation behaviour but also a considerably increased rupture force and reduced creep deformations were observed. In any case not only stability, but also serviceability have to be checked. This means that project-specific requirements concerning load, at say 2% or 5% strain, have to be fulfilled. Usually there is no strain compatibility between the soil and reinforcement. The relationship between force and strain in the reinforcing geotextile is quite different from the force-strain relationship for soil. Only at large strains is there some compatibility between the two. As large deformations are not generally acceptable, the strains in the geotextiles are normally limited by using only a small proportion of the geotextile maximum strength. This is achieved by the application of partial factors of safety and by imposing strain limits on the geotextile. Existing geosynthetic products have a wide range of different stress strain curves, which shows that in any case the user has to define exactly the desired load-elongation behaviour for his specific requirements.

Geotextile drainage capacity

During installation and compaction, especially of fine grained cohesive soils, excess pore water pressures may develop which reduce the transferable shear stress of the soil and thus contribute to a reduction in stability. Therefore the use of drainage elements in wet soils has the effect of stabilisation, Delmas et al. (1992). Thus not only a high tensile strength, but also a good drainage capacity is important for the performance of geotextile reinforcing elements. Nonwoven geotextiles with a certain thickness and a certain permeability are particularly suited in applications where the fills are poor draining materials.

Due to their transmissivity these geotextiles have a draining effect on the adjacent soil layers thus increasing the shear strength of the soil. Consolidation of the soil is accelerated and a higher total safety factor of the whole structure can be obtained, Delmas et al. (1992)

Geotextile robustness and survivability

Geotextiles have to withstand so-called installation stresses caused by the falling fill material and by compaction. These requirements have been established mainly for the application of geotextiles in unpaved roads, but they are presented here to illustrate the importance of survivability. Many different approaches exist concerning design for survivability. In the German FGSV recommendations, FGSV (1994), nonwoven geotextiles are classified according either to their CBR-puncture strength, according to prEN 776 or BS 6906 - Part 4, or for wovens, their maximum tensile force determined by the wide width tensile test to ISO 10319 . Five different types of fill material and four different levels of installation stress are defined. For each combination of fill material and level of installation stress a certain *geotextile robustness class - GRK* is required, Table 1. Multifilament wovens usually have much lower deformabilities and their resistance to installation damage is defined by the maximum tensile strength to ISO 10319, Table 2.

Table 1 Robustness classes for nonwoven geotextiles (FGSV, 1994)

Robustness-class	CBR-puncture Resistance [N]	Minimum weight
GRK 1	500	80 g/m^2
GRK 2	1000	100 g/m^2
GRK 3	1500	150 g/m^2
GRK 4	2500	250 g/m^2
GRK 5	3500	300 g/m^2

Table 2 Robustness classes for multifilament wovens (FGSV, 1994)

Robustness-class	max. Tensile strength [kN/m]	Minimum weight
GRK 1	60	230 g/m^2
GRK 2	90	280 g/m^2
GRK 3	150	320 g/m^2
GRK 4	180	400 g/m^2
GRK 5	250	550 g/m^2

The Swiss standard, SVG (1991), designs to 5 classes of subsoil bearing capacity. The decisive geotextile parameter is the *rupture resistance* which is defined as the product of rupture strength and rupture elongation. So, a geotextile with lower elongation must have an accordingly higher tensile strength to be equal. Figure 2 is an example of the curves for the required rupture-resistance. These diagrams have been obtained empirically and do not include different site traffic loads or subsoil conditions. Depending on the type fill material there is an additional survivability requirement defined by the hole diameter obtained in the cone drop test to prEN 918 or BS 6906 - Part 6.

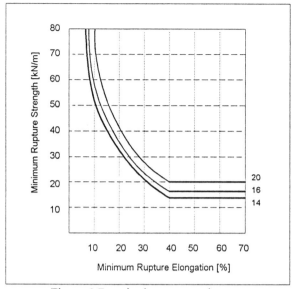

Figure 2 Required rupture resistance

The Finnish system of geotextile specification, Rathmayer (1993), is based mainly on empirical methods. The mechanical requirements depend on the methods of Installation and compaction , the material installed above the fabric and site access traffic during the construction period.

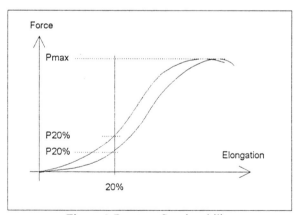

Figure 3 Rupture Surviveability

It is assumed that compaction of the layer above the fabric occurs and that there will be construction traffic. For areas where the mechanical stress is limited, lower demands may be made on the geotextile and its selection reflects the actual case. The rupture surviveability P_{srr}, after 20% initial tension, Figure 3, is regarded as the decisive parameter for the resistance against installation damage.

This criterion is used to judge the capacity of a geotextile for differential load take-up in the range of deformation between $\varepsilon = 20\%$ and ε at P_{max} so leading to $P_{srr} = P_{max} - P_{\varepsilon 20}$

Frictional behaviour

For the design of geotextiles the composite behaviour between the geotextile and soil is important. The value of the coefficient of friction is depends on the type of reinforcement and the type of fill material to be used. In direct shear tests, as well as in pullout tests, either the soil to fabric friction angle or an adequate reduction factor for the internal friction angle of the soil is determined. Sometimes it may be important that friction is not a constant for a particular combination of soil type and reinforcement, but also a function of the overburden pressure.

Ideally it would be useful to perform tests with on site soil types to obtain adequate and reliable input parameters for the calculation. Koerner (1990) found the following friction angles and efficiencies for frictional soils, sand, in contact with a nonwoven needle punched fabric, Table 3.

Table 3 Frictional efficiencies

Internal peak friction angle	30°	28°	26°
Soil to fabric friction angle	30°	26°	25°
Efficiency	1	0.92	0.96

GEOSYNTHETICS USED IN SOIL REINFORCEMENT

A wide range of geosynthetics, such as geogrids, woven and nonwoven geotextiles and polymeric strip may be used as reinforcement, however, of particular interest are those which are more suited to poorly draining fills.

Nonwovens - For lower structures, or upper sections of higher structures, nonwoven geotextiles have been successfully used for many years. There are two main reasons for this success. The actual in-soil stress-strain behaviour of polypropylene nonwovens shows an increase in modulus of the order of ten and significantly lower creep behaviour, Werner & Resl (1986). Secondly the drainage properties lead to better mechanical properties especially of fine-grained cohesive soils. Thus the effect of nonwovens in steep slopes and walls is not only reinforcing but also strengthening of the soil. The maximum tensile strength of nonwovens is typically around 30 kN/m.

Composite materials - The above mentioned criteria have lead to the development of geosynthetic materials which fulfil these requirements in an ideal way. Composite geotextiles combine both the reinforcing properties of grids and wovens with the good hydraulic performance of needlepunched nonwovens. With such composite materials tensile strengths up to 200 kN/m may be achieved. Additionally the nonwoven component protects the reinforcing yarns against installation and compaction damage.

DESIGN METHODS

General considerations

Generally it can be stated that all existing design methods are conservative which has often been shown by large scale and model loading tests. Two primary forms of stability must be investigated in any design of reinforced soil structures:

- external stability
- internal stability

Simply it may be stated that the internal stability concerns all cases for which the sliding surface intersects the geotextile reinforcing elements. Regarding external stability, the geotextile reinforced soil mass is considered to behave as a rigid body. Most methods require a sufficient margin of safety against the occurrence of a limit equilibrium state, Werner & Resl (1986), FHWA (1990). These methods are easy to handle and quickly give reliable results.

External stability checks

For the mechanisms of external stability failure, surfaces lying completely outside the reinforced soil mass are assumed. The decisive cases of failure are sliding along the base, bearing capacity failure and failure in deeper sliding surfaces. The design has to be carried out according to the methods for conventional earth retaining structures.

Internal stability checks

Internal stability has to cover all possible failures for which the assumed sliding surfaces intersect the reinforced soil mass. Sufficient factors of safety against rupture and pullout of the geosynthetic reinforcing element have to be proved.

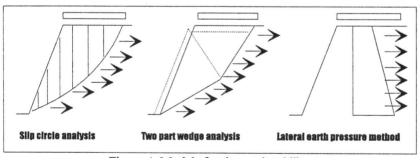

Figure 4 Models for internal stability

Two methods are mostly used for design at the moment; the lateral earth pressure method and the displacement method. With the lateral earth pressure method the design is done by calculating the total active earth pressure, which then has to be taken up by the tensile forces in the reinforcing geosynthetic layers. The total earth pressure E is divided by the number of layers, resulting in a required tensile force T_{des}.

In the displacement method it is assumed that a deformation occurs along a certain failure surface, which makes it possible to correlate local displacements of the geotextiles with the displacements at the top. The determination of these gives the degree of mobilisation of each single reinforcing layer, taking up a certain amount of retaining tensile force. Thus for each single layer the required design tensile strength may be calculated.

For both design methods the minimum value obtained, T_{des} has now to be reached by the ultimate tensile strength T_{ult} of the specific geotextile T_{des} .

Rupture of each single reinforcing layer - From the design calculation a required tensile force is obtained. This design force T_{des} has to be multiplied by several safety factors to define the required tensile strength of the geotextile:

$$T_{ult} = T_{des} * F_d * F_{geot} * F_{Cr} * F_c$$

where

T_{ult}	Ultimate Tensile Strength of Geotextile
T_{des}	Design Tensile Force
F_d	Partial Factor of Safety for Environmental Influences
F_{geot}	Partial Factor of Safety for Material Influences
F_{Cr}	Partial Factor of Safety for Creep
F_c	Installation Damage Factor

At the moment many different partial reduction factors are recommended. Two groups of recommendations do exist:
• Official (independent) national guidelines (US, UK, France, Germany, ...)
• Factors suggested by manufacturers
Comparing these two groups there is a significant difference between their order of magnitude: Whereas the official recommendations in general give values of > 5 for the product of all partial reduction factors, the values given by the manufacturers are between 2.5 and 3.0.

The values in Table 4 are from official guidelines or from draft versions of these and may give an idea of the range of variation these values still have.

Table 4 Reduction Factors for Tensile Strength

Guideline	F_d	F_{geot}	F_{cr}		F_c	
			PET	PP	not crit.	crit.
FHWA (USA)	1,1-2	1,5	2,5	5	1,25	3
CFGG (F)	1,1	1,2	2,5	4,5	1,1	1,5
DGGT (D)	1,1	1,75	2,5	4	1,3	1,5
Polyfelt PEC	1,1	1,2	2	4	1,1	-

Four partial factors of safety must be considered. These are :

F_D Environmental reduction factor - In general it seems, that there is an agreement for a value between 1.0 and 1.1 as all recommendations give values within this range (except FHWA guideline).

F_{geot} Overall material safety factor - This reduction factor is the most general one. In the draft of the German guideline this value has been reduced to 1.4 (from 1.75) recently. Values are typically between 1.2 and 1.5. Due to the accurate design and manufacturing of some fabrics, it is reasonable to take the lower boundary of the range for this factor.

F_{cr} Creep reduction factor - Tests have to be performed according to existing standards. Normally it will not be necessary to perform creep tests for very long times, *eg* 1000 hours, which is 42 days will be sufficient, as the deformation will increase linearly with time. However it is important to have creep tests done at four different load stages, to be able to predict a time of serviceability. Two different test methods are used to define tensile creep strain and tensile creep rupture of geosynthetics.

F_c Construction damage reduction factor - At the moment there is no test standard available to determine this factor. Full scale tests are performed at the moment at the technical University of Munich. Additionally site-specific surviveability testing may always give useful information about reduced properties due to installation. Typical values are in the range between 1.1 and 1.5 (except FHWA guideline). The protection function only is of crucial importance, where the grain diameter of the fill material is larger than fine gravel. Except for hydraulic application or unsorted blasted rock, most slopes will use granular or cohesive frictional material.

Safety against pullout of the reinforcing layer - The required reinforcement length may be controlled by pull out or sliding failure. Traditionally the minimum length has been empirically set to 0.8 H. Current research shows that walls on firm foundations which meet all external stability requirements can be safely constructed using length as short as 0.5 H, FHWA (1990). In any case each single geotextile layer has to be designed against pullout failure. Special tests have to be performed to determine the frictional properties between the soil and geotextile. The required anchoring length is given as :

$$L_e = T_{des} * FS / [2 * (\gamma * h) \tan (\phi_{soil-geot})]$$

where

FS	Factor of Safety
γ	Unit weight of soil
h	Height of fill material above the geotextile layer
$\phi_{soil-geot}$	Friction Angle between soil and the geotextile

Figure 5 gives the required minimum anchoring length for a pullout failure mode as a function of the design strength T_{des}, normal stress $\gamma^* \Sigma h$, and the effective friction angle of the soil. The suggested factor of safety for the pullout resistance in this case is 1.5, Koerner (1990).

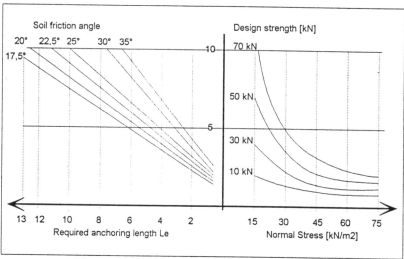

Figure 5 Pullout resistance and anchoring length

Note that the value of L_e has to be added to the non-acting lengths of the reinforcing layers between the face and the failure surface, to obtain the total fabric length. As a rough guidance the Rankine failure surface may be assumed to define active and passive zone of the reinforcement for steep slopes and walls.

TYPICAL APPLICATIONS

Usually geometry and the soil parameters are given. First an initial design and an internal stability check is done according to the lateral earth pressure method. The external, and global, stability check may be done using the common computer programs *eg* Cartage, LCPC (1991).

Application of needle punched nonwovens

In Vienna a railway bridge crossing the river Danube had to be elevated by 3.0 m in the course of the construction of the Wien-Freudenau hydro-electric power plant.

To only interrupt rail traffic during the elevation itself, one lane was closed and the ramp towards the bridge was constructed in advance. The bridge lifting (heaving), Figure 6, was done and then the second half of the railway embankment was constructed.

The steep slope between the two railway tracks was reinforced by 10 layers of Polyfelt TS800 during construction. The static design was to the lateral earth pressure method. Traffic load was assumed to be 52 kN/m^2 at a level of

0.5 m under the sleeper. The results of the internal stability calculation were the following:

- Rupture: 5   Pullout: 1.5

The installation was done by a series of L-shaped steel angles with a continuous wooden brace board running along the face of the wall. The fill material was compacted to 96 % d_{Pr}.

At the portal of a tunnel in Austria, Figure 6, a 10 m high geotextile reinforced slope with an inclination of 50° had to be erected. The reinforcement was achieved by 20 layers of Polyfelt TS 800. Also in this case the design was done in the best co-operation between the owner, consulting engineer and geotextile manufacturer. Due to the flat inclination of the slope a special vegetation felt was used for covering the structure to obtain a green appearance of the slope.

Geotextile retaining walls with nonwovens provide economic solutions for potentially expensive applications. They can also be used as permanent structures by covering with special vegetation felts and with topsoil and encouraging plant growth.

High strength composite geotextiles

For a road construction project in southern France a vertical geotextile reinforced wall had to be constructed. Geometry and the soil parameters were given, the total height of the wall is 19 m, which makes it the highest geotextile reinforced wall in Europe. First an initial design and an internal stability check were carried out in accordance with the lateral earth pressure method. The external, and global, stability check were done using the Cartage computer program. Both calculations were done together with independent geotechnical engineers and in close contact with the contractor and geotextile manufacturer. Fabric with different rupture strengths were used in the upper and lower part of the construction. The structure was divided by two berms, the front of the geotextile was covered by large prefabricated concrete slabs.

In course of the repair of a local landslide, along the S31 road near Sieggraben in Austria, special measures were necessary to stabilise the slope. One of the alternatives in question was the reinforcement with layers of Polyfelt PEC, a high strength composite geotextile. After comparing the economic and technical parameters of each variant, the local authorities decided to carry out the works using Polyfelt PEC. Due to the local situation it was necessary to install reinforcement with low extensibility, which should guarantee that the design forces were activated at low deformations of the structure. A working tensile strength of 14 kN/m at 2% elongation was specified, which means a safety factor > 7 against rupture of the geotextile. High strength nonwovens offer a number of technical benefits and latent safety-factors:

- Increase of stability due to the drainage effect of the nonwoven component
- Optimum stress-strain relation which guarantees the stability of the structure, even with extremely high loads
- Better compaction of the soil by layer-wise installation.

87

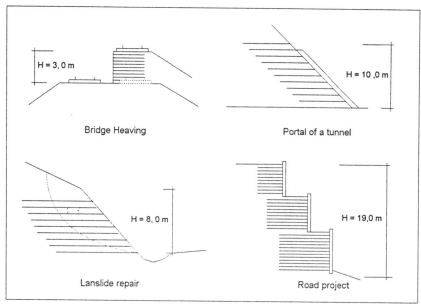

Figure 6   Sketch of completed projects

SPECIFICATION GUIDELINES

To ensure the installed product is able to fulfil the specified requirements, product description and specification are crucial. Therefore the following items should be included in any reinforced soil specification, FHWA (1990) :

Materials:
    Facing elements
    Reinforcing elements
    Connection and alignment devices
    Joint materials
    Reinforced backfill

Construction:
    Excavation
    Foundation preparation
    System Erection
    Backfill placement
    Measure and payment

The specification must define the raw material of the geotextile, its hydraulic properties and resistance to installation damage. The material shall be free of defects and tears. Grade and production batch number shall be marked at regular intervals along the length of each roll. The contractor shall submit to the engineer a manufacturers certificate of compliance which includes the manufacturer's name and address, full product name, geotextile polymer type. Due to different national codes different test methods have to be referred when specifying the geotextile. These are given in the data sheets.

Tensile strength
In-plane permeability
Weight

Maximum tensile strain
Vertical permeability
Thickness

The supplier must provide certification that the above requirements are completely satisfied by the product provided. The supplier must provide a quality assurance /quality control plan for the manufacturing process.

REFERENCES

Brandl, H., 1993, *Geotechnische Maßnahmen zur Sicherung von Rutschhängen*. 8. Christian Veder Kolloqium, TU Graz, April.

Delmas, P., Gotteland, Y., Gourc, J.P. & Haidar, H., 1992, *Soil reinforced by geotextiles - study of deformations on two full size structures*. Proc. Conference on Ground Improvement, ASCE.

FGSV, 1994, *Merkblatt für die Anwendung von Geotextilien und Geogittern im Erdbau des Straßenbaus*, FGSV, Köln.

FHWA, 1990, *Reinforced soil structures*. Report RD-89-043, FHWA, Springfield, Virginia.

Koerner, R. M., 1990, *Designing with geosynthetics*. Prentice Hall, Englewood Cliffs, N.J.

LCPC, 1991, *Cartage*. Computer program, Laboratoire Central des Ponts et Chausses, Paris.

Rathmayer, H., 1993, *Nonwoven geotextiles in road construction - The VTT geotextile specification*. Helsinki.

SVG, 1991, *Geotextilien*. Swiss Standard SN 640 552, Zürich.

Werner, G. & Resl, S., 1986, *Stability mechanisms in reinforced earth structures*. Proc. 3 Int. Conference on Geotextiles, Vienna , Vol. 4.

Four case studies of the use of polymer grid reinforced soil in Europe

C. G. JENNER, Netlon Limited, United Kingdom

SYNOPSIS

There are a number of design methods adopted for the design of reinforced soil structures, some of which form the basis of Approval Certification in European countries. Two of these methods are described with examples of the resultant structures along with two other applications :

a) Reinforced soil bridge abutments carrying major road traffic.

b) Steep reinforced soil slopes carrying high speed rail traffic.

c) A geocell mattress under a motorway embankment.

d) A reinforced unpaved access road carrying construction and future maintenance traffic for overhead power line construction.

INTRODUCTION

The benefits which can be gained by using reinforced soil are more generally appreciated as these structures become part of the standard range of options open to engineers. The design of vertical reinforced soil walls and bridge abutments has been the focus of the legislators in European countries and approval is required for reinforcing materials. In the UK and Germany the approval of the reinforcing material for this type of structure is also linked to a prescribed design method.

REINFORCED SOIL BRIDGE ABUTMENTS IN THE UK

In the United Kingdom approval of materials for use in structures for the Department of Transport is assessed by the British Board of Agrement, The approval certification indicates which characteristics of the reinforcing material have been examined and assessed and gives the design strength values that should be used in the calculations. These strengths are derived to be compatible with the design assumptions of the design method and include all the necessary material factors of safety required to satisfy the performance criteria required for the final bridge abutment structure.

In order to ensure that the approved materials are produced consistently and to the quality that has been assessed, a system of random inspection of the manufacturing plant forms an important part of continuing approval.

The design method is defined in the Department of Transport Technical Memorandum BE3/78 (Revised 1987), DOT (1987), which, at the time of writing this paper, is the only official standard document which describes how to design reinforced soil walls and bridge abutments in the UK. An example of the application of BE3/78 and BBA certification is the design and construction of the reinforced soil abutments for two bridges on the Banbury By-Pass in Oxfordshire.

Project details

A section of the Banbury By-Pass required the construction of two new bridges, one over the River Cherwell and another over the Oxford Canal. These bridges were designed as lightweight continuous span steel composite construction by Oxfordshire County Council and therefore a decision was made to investigate the construction of the bridge abutments using relatively light weight materials as a consistent approach to the design. Pulverised fuel ash was selected as fill for the embankment and reinforced soil abutment and therefore due regard to its corrosive nature was taken in the selection of the soil reinforcement. The durability of reinforcement materials is one of the major points of assessment in the BBA certification and guidance is given as to whether the more extreme conditions that can occur in soils and some construction materials are a cause for concern. In this case the reinforcement selected was Tensar SR110 geogrids which are the subject of a BBA certificate, BBA (1988)

Design

The design method follows the normal basic principles of design for any retaining structure in that it treats the design in two sections, the external stability and the internal stability of the reinforced soil block, DOT (1987). In the case of a bridge abutment the externally applied loads from the bridge bankseat carrying vertical and horizontal line loads also form part of the two design sections.

The soil shear strength is taken to be the peak value where a peak value is appropriate. With PFA, as in this project, a value of $\phi'=30°$ can be adopted for initial design and this should be confirmed by testing for final design. A value of c' up to 5 kN/m^2 may be used provided that it is also confirmed by testing.

a) External stability

The criteria for external stability are that the factors of safety against sliding and overturning should be greater than, or equal to, 2 and that the applied bearing pressure should not exceed the allowable bearing capacity of the underlying soil assuming a trapezoidal pressure distribution under the reinforced soil structure, Figure 1. The adoption of a trapezoidal pressure distribution under the reinforced soil block is one that has been the subject of discussion and it is likely that a uniform distribution over a portion of the base width, i.e. Meyerhoff distribution, will be adopted in the future.

In this project the external stability calculations carried out by and for Oxfordshire County Council resulted in reinforcement lengths of 5 m.

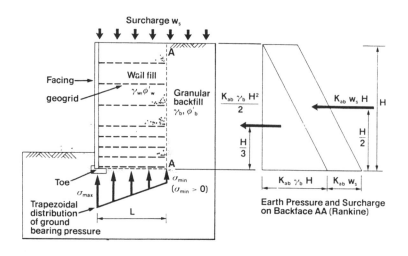

Figure 1

b) Internal Stability

The determination of the amount of soil reinforcement required within a structure is carried out to satisfy two criteria, Figure 2 .

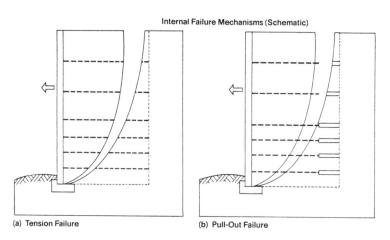

Figure 2

1) There must be enough reinforcement strength across any potential failure plane to resist the horizontal tensile forces across that plane.

2) The reinforcement must extend far enough beyond the potential failure plane to be able to mobilise the design strength in anchorage or, if this is not the case, a lower strength should be used in the wedge anchorage check. A factor of safety of 2 is required for anchorage resistance.

The calculation of the horizontal stress at any level within the structure is carried out by summating the stresses caused by the effects of:

1) Height of reinforced fill above the reinforcement layer.

2) Uniform surcharge on top of the wall.

3) Vertical load from the bridge structure via the bankseat.

4) Horizontal load from the bridge structure via the bankseat.

5) External moment applied to the reinforced soil by the unreinforced retained fill.

In this case horizontal loads were taken by layers of polymer geogrid reinforcement cast into the back of the bankseat ballast wall and hence these loads were not included in the reinforced soil abutment design.

Bridge loading on the two structures were taken as:

	Spiceball Bridge (Canal Bridge)	Cherwell River Bridge	
	Both Abutments	N. Abutment	S Abutment
Vertical Dead Load	100 kN/m	30 kN/m	90 kN/m
HA & HB Live Load	365 kN/m	155 kN/m	210 kN/m
Braking / Traction	155 kN/m	64 kN/m	0
Temperature and Shrinkage	50 kN/m	6 kN/m	2 kN/m

The effects of the vertical soil load and the surcharge give direct vertical stress and the additional vertical stress from the bankseat loads are distributed as shown in Figure 3.

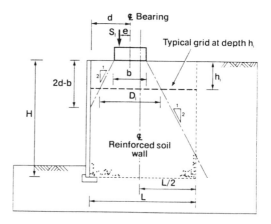

Figure 3

The effect of the external moment is to increase the vertical stress at the structure face and to produce the trapezoidal vertical stress distribution at the level being considered. An active stress condition is assumed within the reinforced soil block to determine the horizontal stresses that need to be resisted by the reinforcement.

The resultant layout of reinforcement for the Spiceball bridge abutments is shown in Figure 4.

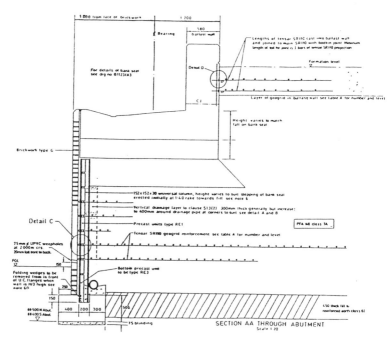

Figure 4

CONSTRUCTION

The construction method selected is termed the *Dewsbury wall system* which is named after the place where it was first used. This involves the use of a facing comprising steel stanchions set at 1.2 m spacings and concrete facing panels spanning between to contain the fill, whilst the geogrid layers provide the structural stability within the pulverised fuel ash, PFA. A detached brick facing was then added to give a structure whose aesthetics were in sympathy with the surroundings.

Details in the construction of interest were the use of stainless steel for the anchor bars, around which the reinforcing grids were anchored at the face, and the anchor slots and wall ties which provided the connection between the structural face and the architectural face. These precautions were particularly required because of the use of PFA fill. The steel stanchions, which have no structural duty post-construction were given a bitumen paint treatment.

The bridge has now been open to traffic for more than three years during which time the performance of the structure has been as excellent.

STEEP REINFORCED SOIL SLOPES IN GERMANY

Approval for soil reinforcing materials in Germany can be granted by the Institut fur Bautechnik, Berlin (IfB) and follows similar procedures to the BBA but with some significant differences both in procedures and the design method described in the certification.

The material properties that are assessed by the IfB are virtually the same as those assessed by the BBA in that they deal with material strength, durability, robustness etc. but these are related to a different design approach for the internal stability calculations. The reinforcement design strength is related in the certificate to the short term strength of the material by factors which are tabulated in the document. These factors can only be determined as a result of extensive long term sustained load creep tests to predict long term strength, as the relationship between short and long term characteristics of polymer reinforcing materials is highly product dependent. The design method described in the certificate is specific to the reinforcing material and the reinforcing material properties assessed.

The IfB monitoring of the products to ensure compliance with the specifications in the certificate is carried out by random sampling and testing by an independent testing house. The details of this random independent testing are specific to the requirements of the IfB.

The method described in the IfB certificate, IfB (1990), was specified for a railway structure at Karlsruhe, Germany which formed a major part of an intricate traffic management scheme.

Project details

This project involved the support of local and intercity rail traffic during the replacement of three old railway bridges which had been constructed in the early 1900's. It was essential that five of the six existing tracks that passed over the bridges should be available and operational at all stages in the project and therefore a systematic construction and demolition sequence was required.

The first stage was to construct a 45° embankment as close as possible to the existing bridges to carry a single new track. Once this had been completed the bridge adjacent to the embankment could be dismantled whilst still retaining the requisite five tracks. A second embankment was then constructed with an 84° face which could carry a further two tracks and enable the second bridge to be demolished. The very steep face of this embankment was dictated by the close proximity of the embankment shoulder to the second bridge.

With three tracks now on the new temporary embankment and the third existing bridge a manageable distance away the new final embankment complete with shorter span bridges could then be completed and the third bridge demolished.

FMPA in Stuttgart were invited to design the reinforced soil structures in accordance with the IfB approval certificate, even though these were temporary structures, because of the critical nature of the loading, i.e. rail traffic. Whilst the normal factor of safety stated in the IfB certificate is 1.75 this was increased to 3 because of the very high expected level of vibration from high speed trains travelling very close to the crest of the embankment.

Design

The design method described in the IfB certificate again looks at external and internal stability but in this case the criteria are based on the appropriate German DIN standards. In this approach the specified value for the internal friction angle for the soils is the residual, constant volume, value ϕ_r.

a) External stability

The external pressures on the reinforced soil block are calculated using the Coulomb equation with the δ value equal to $2/3\phi$, Figure 5. This enables the design to be specific to the actual slope angle of the back face of the reinforced soil block rather than requiring all slopes between 70° and 90° to be designed as if they were vertical. To remain within the application area of the Coulomb equation the slope angle of the back face must not, however, fall below 70°.

The external stability checks of sliding and bearing capacity are carried out in accordance with the German DIN standards 1054 and 4017. The minimum factor of safety against sliding is 1.5 and the minimum factor of safety for bearing capacity is 2. The calculation for bearing is carried out using the foundation soil properties and taking account of the inclination of the resultant applied force in the Terzaghi equations.

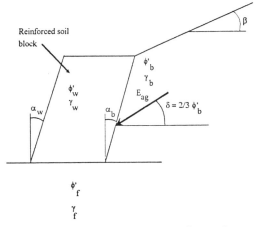

Figure 5

b) Internal stability

Internal stability calculations take the form of a two part wedge analysis through the reinforced soil block, Figure 6.

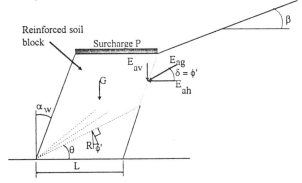

Figure 6

A series of two part wedges was examined with the lower part of the wedge originating at the structure face and passing through the block, and the upper part of the wedge passing up the back face of the reinforced soil block. Where the line of this wedge cuts the back face of the reinforced soil block the active pressure above that point is added to the disturbing forces acting on the wedge. In this case the value of δ is taken to be equal to ϕ.

Reinforcement must be provided to resist the disturbing forces on each wedge with the resistance of the reinforcement being calculated as the design strength given in the IfB certificate. In this case the loading from the rail traffic was taken as a uniformly distributed surcharge of 54 kN/m^2 with a horizontal load of 25 kN/m at track level. The resultant geogrid layouts are shown in figure 7.

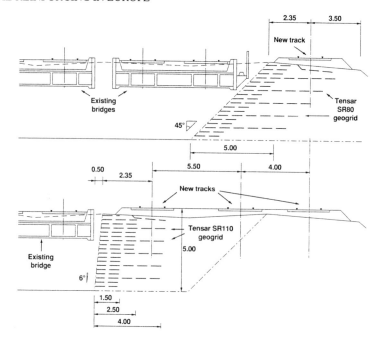

Figure 7

Construction

The 45° embankment slopes were reinforced with 5m long horizontal layers of SR80 at 0.8 m spacing with a wrap-around face detail, which is unusual for such a relatively shallow face angle. However, with the vibration forces expected and the cohesionless fill right up to the face the IfB certificate required such a detail. Short intermediate layers of reinforcement were also used to ensure a good face line and additional face stability.

The construction of the 84° was made more difficult by the restricted nature of the site. The new 45° embankment carrying traffic on one side, a bridge carrying traffic on the opposite side and bridge abutments on the other two sides meant that all the materials had to be moved in relatively small quantities. The existing bridge was used to support a climbing shutter which was lifted as the construction proceeded.

The geogrid layout indicated by the design was SR110 geogrids at 0.6 m spacing at the base and 0.4 m spacing towards the top of the wall. Intermediate geogrid layers were also used to ensure face stability and line.

The performance of the 84° wall was monitored closely both during construction and during trafficking. Initially targets were bonded to the face of the wall immediately after the shutter had been stripped so that the wall face could be monitored during the construction of the new bridge. A second set of measurements were taken by installing steel rods and measuring them geodetically during trafficking. The results of this monitoring of horizontal deformation showed that the maximum movement registered by monitoring the targets was 5.42 mm, at mid-height of the wall. Surveying the rods showed that further deformations during trafficking were insignificant, Figures 8 and 9. No maintenance of the track was required even though the wall was abutted directly against a reinforced concrete bridge abutment and the trains were passing over at a speed up to 120 km/hr, Figure 10.

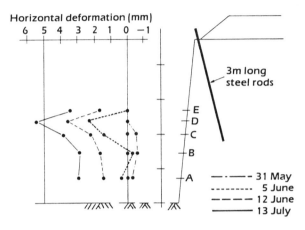

Figure 8

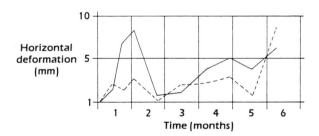

Figure 9

Figure 10

GEOCELL MATTRESS UNDER A MOTORWAY

Project details

The A74 trunk road in Scotland has been steadily upgraded to motorway standard and this has inevitably involved construction of embankments over difficult foundation soils. One particularly difficult area was at the northern end where the motorway was required to pass over large areas of wasteland, some of which was previously quarried.

A section of approximately 850 m long passed through the Greenoakhill sand and gravel quarry, which is still in operation, where the embankment was required to pass over some of the worked out areas. Some of these areas had been filled with quarry wastes, some had been used as silt lagoons and some had been filled with domestic and commercial waste.

This very variable support condition led the designers Strathclyde Regional Council, Department of Roads, to select a solution which enabled the embankments to be constructed without major excavation. The soft underlying soils had an undrained shear strength, c_u, generally of the order of 20 kN/m^2.

Design

Geocell mattresses, 1m deep, have been designed into many schemes around the world and the design approach that has been developed has produced very serviceable and predictable structures. The design method is documented by Bush et al. (1990), Jenner et al. (1988) and a number of papers have been written on specific projects.

In this case the design was based on the ability of the geocell mattress to provide a stiff, plate-like, support layer at the base of the embankment thus

100

spreading and distributing the embankment loads onto the variable foundation soils. This stiff rough base enables the full bearing capacity of the foundation soils to be mobilised, whilst also minimising differential settlement and lateral spread.

The design indicated a geocell to be constructed using SR80 geogrids generally in a "chevron" pattern although in the area of an underpass a "diamond" pattern was adopted. The geocell mattress was formed using a base grid of SS2.

In any design it is important to have confidence in the soil parameters and to ensure that the construction processes do not destroy any good properties that the soils may have. Using the geocell mattress does give the additional benefit of providing a working platform with all the construction plant travelling on top of the geocell mattress and not directly on the soft soil.

Construction

The embankment height over the geocell mattress on this project was generally 4 m with the chevron pattern of cells over the majority of the area, Figure 11. However, where the geocell mattress was required to pass beneath the piled concrete box underpass, the side slope down to the base of the underpass was inclined at 1 in 4 and so the stiffer diamond pattern was adopted, Figure 12. The horizontal section of filled geocell beneath the underpass was also able to give support to the piling rigs installing the steel piles.

The performance of the embankment to date has been as expected with the geocell providing the base stiffness. The materials used for the cell construction do have BBA and IfB approval certification which covers not only the strength but also the durability which is very important in this type of application where waste materials may be encountered.

Figure 11

Figure 12

REINFORCED UNPAVED ACCESS ROAD

Project details

In 1984/85 Torness Power Station on the east coast of Scotland was required to be linked into the national grid system at the intersection point at Smeaton.

The most simple route was for the overhead cables to run adjacent to the main road and rail links but this was unacceptable for environmental reasons and an alternative route was chosen through the Lammeruir Hills.

An access road was required to both enable the initial construction to take place and to provide an access road for maintenance work in the future. This route required the road to traverse long open peat bogs in places with peat thickness varying from 0.5 m to 6 m. In order to try to maintain the continuity of biological life the planning authorities required the road to be constructed without major excavation. Planning requirements also dictated that maximum use should be made of locally won road making materials and that imported materials should be kept to a minimum.

Design

The constraints applied to the project by the planning authorities meant that the road should effectively be floated on top of the peat and that the construction thickness should be the minimum possible whilst remaining serviceable. The low availability of good quality road making materials was also a reason for minimising the granular layer thickness.

The road was required to support the aggregate delivery vehicles during the construction period and these vehicles were required to traffic the road over its full length. Hence some sections of the road had virtually all of the construction materials passing over them.

Geogrids were selected to reinforce the granular layers because their interlock mechanism with the fill stiffens the granular layers and enables a reduced thickness of aggregate to provide the desired performance. The interlocking of the aggregate into the grid apertures prevented the punching of particles into the peat subgrade and also restrained the lateral movements of the aggregate thus preventing pumping.

Construction

A total of 95,000 square metres of geogrid was used in this project. The grid was rolled out onto the existing ground surface without any disturbance of the vegetation, Figure 13. The aggregate was tipped from the delivery vehicles and then spread using a small tracked vehicle with a 3-in-1 bucket which enabled the aggregate to be cascaded onto the grid, Figure 14. A towed vibrating roller then provided the required compaction.

Figure 13

Figure 14

Where the peat was deepest and the traffic intensity was highest SS2 was used and in other areas S1 was installed. The construction depths varied from 450 mm to 700 mm and, although the aggregates were poor by normal highway standards, a very serviceable and durable road was produced .

At times during construction the road was required to carry in excess of 3000 tonnes of aggregate per day for several months and this was endured with minimal maintenance.

On completion of its use as a haul road the road surface was topped off with quarry scalpings and it continues to be used as a service road.

CONCLUSION

Soil reinforcing materials can be used effectively and economically to produce sound engineering solutions to a wide range of geotechnical and civil engineering problems. The technical documents that engineers require to be able to design these structures with confidence have been, and continue to be, developed so that the full benefits of reinforced soil can be utilised.

REFERENCES

BBA, 1988, *Tensar polymer grids for reinforced soil walls.* Roads and Bridges Agrement Certificate No 88/43, British Board of Agrement.

Bush, D.I., Jenner, C.G & Bassett, R.H., 1989, *The design and construction of geocell foundation mattresses supporting embankments over soft ground.* Geotextiles and Geomembranes, Volume 9, No. 1, 83-98.

DOT, 1987, *Reinforced and anchored earth retaining walls and bridge abutments for embankments.* Technical Memorandum BE 3/78 (Revised 1987), Department of Transport.

IfB, 1990, *Zulassungsnummer Z-20.1_102. Bewehrte Bodenkorper mit Tensar-Geogitternm aus HDPE Typ SR2, SR55, SR80 und SR110.* Institut für Bautechnik.

Jenner, C.G., Bush, D.I. & Bassett, R.H., 1988, *The use of slip line fields to assess improvement in bearing capacity of soft ground given by a cellular foundation mattress.* Theory and Practice of Earth Reinforcement, Balkeema, 209-214.

A reinforced soil solution for the M25

Q. LEIPER and C.T.F. CAPPS, Tarmac Construction Limited,
United Kingdom

SYNOPSIS
  Reinforced soil constructions can offer many advantages over
concrete retaining walls. An example is presented where a reinforced
soil alternative is offered and accepted on an M25 widening contract.
The selection and design of the chosen method is described.

INTRODUCTION
  Motorway widening is increasingly being carried out in the United
Kingdom by constructing additional lanes within the existing motorway
boundaries. Tarmac Construction were the successful tenderer for the
M25 widening contract between Junctions 15 and 16 (M4 to M40
Section) on the west side of London, Figure 1. The Engineer for the
contract was Sir William Halcrow and Partners.

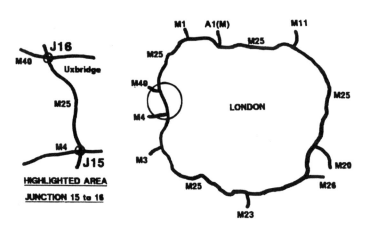

Figure 1 Site Location

The practice of soil reinforcing in Europe. Thomas Telford, London, 1995

The contract commenced in early 1993 and was programmed for completion in early 1994. The paper describes the options considered and the design process for an alternative solution to the contract proposed concrete cantilever retaining wall on deep spread footings.

DESIGN CONSIDERATIONS

The widening contract involved cutting into pre-existing noise bunds, constructed from recompacted London Clay, in places mixed with Terrace Gravels. Figure 2 shows a typical section which indicates the extra 3.65 m of carriageway required.

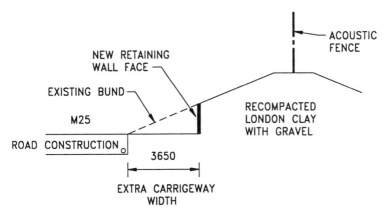

Figure 2 Typical section of noise bund

The acoustic fence, on top of the bund provided constructors with a potential problem. If the construction method necessitated its removal, then a temporary fence, to the same O.D. Level would be required on the back slope of the bund. The presence of this fence imposed both programming and cost constraints on alternative construction options.

The toe level of the designed concrete retaining walls were up to 3 m below the existing carriageway level and as such would frequently penetrate dense water bearing gravels which were present over much of the site. In order to maintain the fence line and deal with groundwater the temporary works for concrete wall construction included sheet piling, support measures and dewatering. It was important that any alternative design addressed these problems. A typical example is shown in Plate 1, on the southbound carriageway, which was built to the Engineer's design.

It was important to obtain an alternative design which satisfied the Engineers philosophy, since he was to adopt the design, and therefore any PI risk, whilst also satisfying the Contractors requirements for a cost effective solution. A series of discussions between contractor and engineer ensued to resolve the design method and parameters to be adopted.

ALTERNATIVE SOLUTIONS

At tender, Tarmac Construction had considered a number of options and these were re-examined once the contract was awarded. Due to the fast track nature of motorway widening contracts, and the need to commence the works immediately, it was only feasible to put forward an alternative for the retaining walls on the northbound carriageway.

A number of specialist suppliers were invited to submit alternative designs to Tarmac for consideration. These options are shown in Figure 3, together with comments on their suitability as an alternative.

Soil nailing, by fired nails was at that time the subject of much discussion in the geotechnical press. It is not the purpose of this paper to review the current state of the art of soil nails, fired or otherwise, however although design methods are little changed since 1992 it is evident that soil nailing is becoming more acceptable in practice. Note that the imminent publication of BS 8006, Strengthened/Reinforced Soils and other Fills and the recent publication of HA68/94 provides designers with guidelines which, in 1992, were not available.

It was considered there was insufficient time for an alternative design proposing the use of fired soil nails to be put forward and therefore this option was not pursued.

Reinforced soil therefore provided the only viable alternative, due in part to new definitions issued by the Department of Transport in HA43/91 in late 1991 which states the following:

"Technical approval procedures shall be followed for strengthened embankments when the angle of the slope face to the horizontal is 70 degrees or greater and the design retained height is greater than 1.5 m. Where the angle of the slope face to the horizontal is 45 degrees or less, geotechnical certification will be required. For strengthened embankments between these limits, the advice of the Overseeing Department should be sought".

The Overseeing Department advised that for this contract geotechnical certification was required for the reinforced slopes. The factor of safety for external stability, agreed with the Engineer, was 1.3, which compared with a factor of safety of 1.5 for structures.

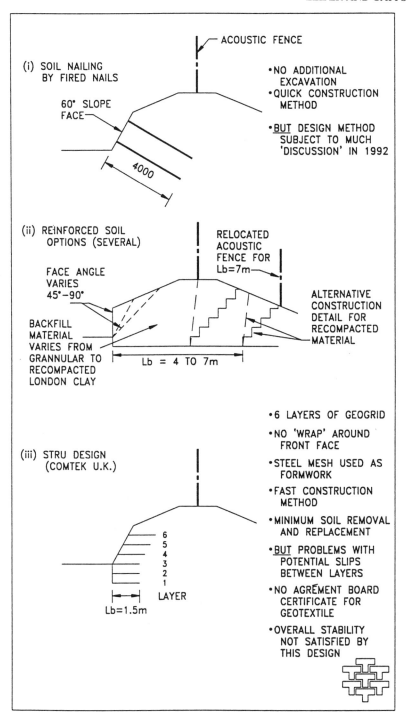

Figure 3 Design options

This effectively reduced either the depth of excavation or the width of excavation for reinforced slopes and therefore made them a viable option compared to concrete retaining walls (Figure 4).

It can be seen from Figure 3 that the Stru design, Rüegger et al. (1988), marketed by Comtec UK offered the most attractive solution to Tarmac as the shorter reinforcement lengths proposed considerably reduced depth and volume of temporary works excavations.

In order to validate this design, Tarmac Construction commissioned a design check using the two part wedge theory developed by Dr J. Love and Dr G Milligan of Geotechnical Consulting Group and University of Oxford respectively. This check resulted in a number of modifications to the Stru design, but was still subsequently rejected by the Engineer.

The two part wedge theory had been used as the design basis for HA68/94, which at that time was in draft form and not yet approved by the Department of Transport. In this respect, the design for the M25 was ahead of its time, in advance of any properly validated design method for use on UK roads.

PARAMETER SELECTION

The selection of appropriate soil parameters was a vital part of the design. The design life for slopes is 60 years, and therefore long term parameters were appropriate. Much has already been published on the London Clay, therefore there was rapid agreement between Tarmac and the Engineer on c' and ϕ' values. Laboratory tests in the site investigation for the contract on recompacted gravelly London Clay in the bunds reported c' values in the range of 5 to 17 kN/m². These results, which would lead to radically reduced geogrid lengths in a reinforced slope design, were treated with some caution by the Engineer, who was concerned about potential variability along the scheme, some 3.8 km of retained slope. To satisfy these concerns and to avoid any delays to the design, c' values applicable to softened London Clay were adopted for these recompacted materials as indicated in Table 1.

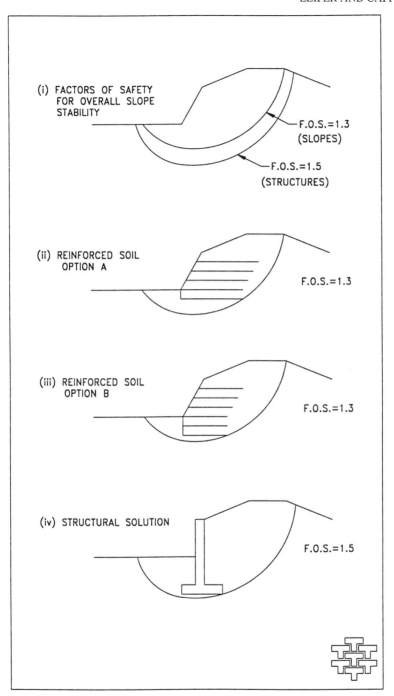

Figure 4 Effect of Factor of Safety on Design

Table 1 Design values adopted

Soil	c'	ϕ'
Recompacted gravelly London Clay	1.5	21.5
Terrace Gravels	0	35
London Clay	1.5	21.5

Considerable discussion also took place on the appropriate porewater pressures to adopt in the design. The effect of different Ru values on geogrid lengths for a typical section of reinforced London Clay is given in Figure 5.

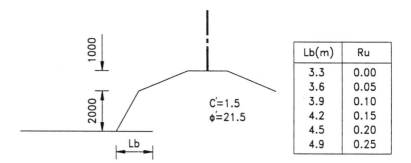

Lb(m)	Ru
3.3	0.00
3.6	0.05
3.9	0.10
4.2	0.15
4.5	0.20
4.9	0.25

Figure 5 Effect of Ru value on geogrid length

The Ru value had a dramatic effect on the reinforcement lengths required. Initial calculations were carried out using the Engineer's value of 0.15 globally throughout the reinforced and insitu embankment. It was felt that this was too onerous a condition for the reinforced section and, following expert advice (Ingold, Jewell, Love, 1993), an Ru closer to zero was put to the Engineer but this was not accepted. An Ru of 0.15 was therefore adopted for design.

DESIGN PROCESS.

  The Stru design comprised flat layers of geofabric with no wrap around at the front face. Face stability during construction was provided using a simple but ingenious formwork, of steel mesh, enabling compaction plant to pass close to the top of the batter as indicated in Plates 2 and 3.

A vegetation geotextile, enclosing 300 mm of topsoil was constructed within the steel mesh. In the long term, both the steel mesh and vegetation fabric will disintegrate leaving the root growth to maintain face stability between the reinforcing layers.

As described above, the Stru design did not comply with current United Kingdom practice. Firstly the resistance to sliding on the base layer was insufficient; secondly potential slip planes between reinforcement layers were not catered for in the design and thirdly, the proposed geofabric did not have an Agrément Board Certificate.

To overcome these problems a revised design utilising a wrap around at the back of the reinforced section was developed by Tarmac Construction Engineering Services and checked by Geotechnical Consulting Group. This alternative caused concern about possible displacement at the face, up to 50 mm as assessed by Geotechnical Consulting Group, and was therefore not accepted by the Engineer. This design is shown in Figure 6.

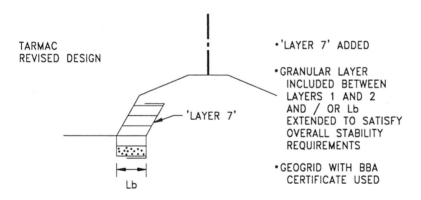

Figure 6 Tarmac layer '7' design

After further discussions and much correspondence with the Engineer the final design method was agreed. It proved to be an interesting mix of available design methods tailored to suit this particular design problem.

The key elements of the design were:

External Stability - The External stability was checked using a circular slope stability analysis, Bishop (1955). This analysis determined the depth and length of geogrid layer 1. For 5 of the 6 cuttings on the site, layer 1 was 0.5 m below road finished level. For each section was analysed for two conditions:

• Permanent condition, with road construction in place.

• Temporary condition, with 0.5 m of road construction removed (for example, during maintenance or reconstruction).

For these conditions factors of safety of 1.3 and 1.1 respectively were adopted.

Internal Stability - Internal stability of the reinforced block was checked by carrying out a Janbu non-circular analysis between each layer of geogrid, Janbu (1957). This check ensured that there was a suitable factor of safety (1.3) against slips either through the backfill material (soil/soil) or along the soil geogrid boundary. The maximum reinforcement force required in the slope, T_{max} was determined using the Scanslope programme, Jewell & Leshchinsky (1991). This programme, like Jewell's charts, can only handle embankments with horizontal crests. An equivalent height H' as shown in Figure 7 was therefore adopted for design.

Sliding - The geogrid length to be required to prevent sliding was calculated using Jewell (1990, 1991).

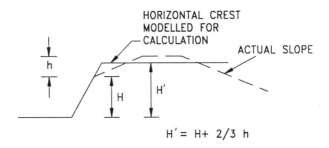

$$H' = H + 2/3\ h$$

Figure 7 Equivalent slope height H' for design

On this basis the design of the reinforced soil slopes went ahead, with further checks using the two part wedge analysis being carried out on Tarmac's behalf by Geotechnical Consulting Group.

On completion of the design of each section of reinforced soil the Engineer rapidly checked and approved the design enabling construction to start on site. A typical section showing the final design layout is shown in Figure 8.

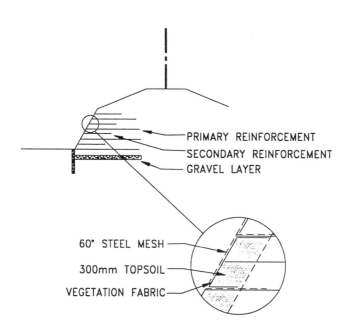

Figure 8 Typical Design Layout

CONSTRUCTION

Construction of the northbound reinforced slopes was successfully completed in a 10 week period compared to the 7 months required to construct the concrete retaining walls on the southbound carriageway, Plate 4. The steel formwork used to construct the facing detail enabled the slopes to be cut and shaped around sign gantry locations, emergency access steps and other special features.

Plate 1 *(Above)*

Reinforced
Concrete Retaining
Wall Under
Construction

Plate 2

Compaction of Fill
at 'Layer 1'

Plate 3

Construction Detail

Plate 4

Reinforced Slope with 60 Degree Front Face Under Construction

Construction of the reinforced slopes demonstrated a number of savings over the concrete wall design, namely:

1   No temporary work ground support or groundwater control required.

2   Re-use of excavated material (London Clay).

3   Fast rate of construction.

4   Dramatic reduction in material import (concrete/steel) and consequently lorry movements.

5   Increased traffic safety due to 3 and 4.

6   Safer worksite for operatives due to 1, 3 and 4

7   A reduced environmental impact provided by a grassed slope as opposed to a vertical concrete wall.

The reinforced soil solution also offered a cost effective alternative with savings to both the contractor and client.

CONCLUSIONS

1   Despite the lack of design regulations, Engineer and Contractor worked together to resolve a satisfactory design method.

2   The new definition of geotechnical certification enabled an alternative solution to become viable.

3   The reinforced soil solution provided an environmentally friendly solution.

4   Both motorway traffic and site safety risks were reduced.

5   Considerable programme and cost advantages can be made using soil reinforcement techniques.

ACKNOWLEDGEMENTS

This paper is published by permission of the Highways Agency. The views expressed are those of the authors and should not be attributed to either the Highways Agency or Tarmac Construction.

The authors are grateful for the contribution and support of their colleagues in the preparation of this paper.

REFERENCES

Bishop, A.W., 1955, *The use of the Slip Circle in the Stability Analysis of Earth Slopes*. Geotechnique Col.5 No.1 pp 7-17.

British Standards Institution, 1994, *Draft BS8006 Strengthened/Reinforced soils and other fills*. BSI London.

Department of Transport, 1991, *Highways, Safety and Traffic*, DOT.

Department of Transport, 1991, *Geotechnical considerations and techniques for widening highway earthworks*. Departmental Advice Note HA43/91, DOT.

Department of Transport, 1994, *Design Manual for Roads and Bridges, Volume 4 Geotechnics and Drainage, Section 1.* Earthworks Part 4, DOT.

Department of Transport, 1994, *Design methods for the reinforcement of highway slopes by reinforced soil and soil nailing techniques*. Advice Note HA68/94, DOT.

Ingold, T.S., 1993, *Private communication.*

Ingold, T.S., 1993, *Report to Tarmac Construction.*

Janbu, N., 1957, *Earth Pressures and Bearing Capacity Calculations by Generalized Procedures of Slices.* Proc. 4th International Conference Soil Mech. Fdn. Engng. Vol 2 pp 207-212.

Jewell, R.A., 1990, *Revised design charts for steep reinforced soil slopes.* Proc. Reinforced Embankments Theory and Practice, Cambridge, Thomas Telford 1-30.

Jewell, R.A., 1991, *Application of revised design charts for steep reinforced slopes*. Geotextiles and Geomembranes Vol 10, No 3, 203-233.

Jewell, R.A. & Leshchinsky, D., 1991, *Geosynthetic reinforced earth structures*, ASCE, 115 (10) pp 1459 - 1478.

Jewell, R.A., 1993, *Private communication.*

Jewell, R.A., 1993, *Design review of the reinforced soil slopes for widening of the M25 motorway between junctions 15 and 16.* Report to Tarmac Construction.

Love, J.P., 1993, *Private communication*

Love, J.P., 1993, *Design Report to Tarmac Construction.*

Ruegger, R., Eugster, M. & Steiner, P., 1988, *Statische modellversuche an geotextilbewehrten verkleidungskonstruktionen.* Beitrag an der K-Geo 88 in Hamburg.

Reinforced modular block walls in the United Kingdom

S. P. CORBET and R. G. FREAKE
G. Maunsell & Partners

SYNOPSIS
The use of modular precast concrete block walls with reinforced soil backfill is a relatively new form of construction in the UK. Design principles have been developed in north America based on conventional design principles for reinforced soil slopes modified to make use of the strength of the facing blocks. This paper presents a brief overview of some walls which have been or are about to be built in the UK and details of an alternative soil reinforcement system which can show significant savings in backfill costs when retaining oversteep cutting slopes.

INTRODUCTION
The use of precast modular block construction for gravity retaining structures is becoming more established in the UK. The use of geosynthetic and other reinforcement to increase the ability of these structures to retain greater heights is still relatively new to the UK and Europe. A design method to exploit the technology has been developed in North America by Bathurst et al. (1994) during the last ten years. Reinforced modular block walls have been used in the UK since the late eighties, but general acceptance of the system has been slow and patchy.

GENERAL PRINCIPLES
The external stability of modular block walls is analyzed using normal methods of analysis for gravity walls. In unreinforced walls the weight of the dry laid blocks and the foundations are the only mass supporting the retained fill. When the retained soil is reinforced the weight of the reinforced block also assists in supporting the retained fill and in resisting forward sliding. The blocks used in modular walls are manufactured from high strength concrete and are available in a many configurations. All of the blocks have keys which provide a mechanical interlock with courses above and below any particular layer of blocks. At present there are three block systems available in the UK; Porcupine, Revetlok and Keystone.

Table 1: Modular Block walling systems available in the United Kingdom

Block	Manufacturer/ Distributor	Principal Dimensions WxDxH (mm) W (kg)	Form
Porcupine	MMG Civil Engineering Systems Ltd	250x350x150 25	
Revetlok	Marshalls Mono Ltd	275x375x150 31	
Keystone	Forticrete Ltd	Standard 457x533x200 47 Compac 457x304x200 38 Caps 457x266x100 22	

The maximum height to which any system can retain soil is a function of the properties of the retained soil, the face angle of the wall, the geometry of the site and any superimposed loadings. Figure 1a shows a typical unreinforced modular gravity wall. Typical maximum heights for walls with a face inclined at an angle of greater than 70° to the horizontal are of the order of 2.0 m to 2.5 m., exceptionally retained heights of 3.0 m may be possible given good soil conditions.

To be able to construct walls which retain greater heights it will be necessary to increase the mass of the wall and to increase the width of the base. The additional mass can be provided as either an additional row or rows of blocks, by backfilling with mass concrete, Figure 1b shows the mass concrete backfill, or by reinforcing the backfill soils with a geosynthetic reinforcement, Figure 1c shows the soil reinforcement.

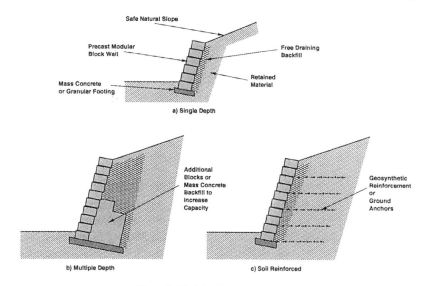

Figure 1 - Modular Block Retaining Wall Systems

Retaining walls adjacent to the superstore development for Tesco in Exeter, Figure 2, were constructed using mass concrete backfill to give additional mass for stability and to prevent sliding.

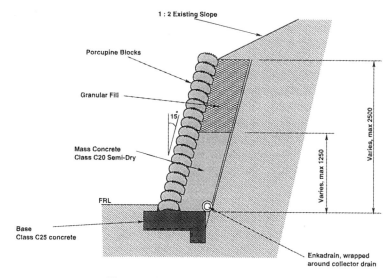

Figure 2 - Section of Multiple Depth Retaining Wall
(Tesco Superstore, Exevale, Exeter)

CASE STUDIES

All the precast concrete block walling systems listed in Table 1 can and have been used successfully in conjunction with geosynthetic reinforcement.

Overall stability is provided by the reinforced soil block acting as a gravity structure. The oversteep soil face is retained by the modular blocks which also aid the stability by virtue of their mass. The mechanical interlock between the blocks also serves to anchor the reinforcement. Extensive testing in North America has been carried out to measure the efficiency of the various block interlocks and their ability to anchor reinforcements.

The case studies presented show some of the methods which can be used to reinforce the backfill soils to enhance stability using geotextiles, geogrids and lightweight soil anchors.

Case Study 1:   Mercedes Benz Wall, Dovercourt Bypass

A short length of the A120 Dovercourt Bypass, Essex, was constrained by an existing sea flood defence wall and the Mercedes Benz new car preparation plant.

At this point the new road was to be constructed on an embankment which was to be 2.4m above the existing ground level. There was insufficient room between the obstructions to allow conventional side slopes to be constructed. Conventional retaining walls were examined, but as the foundation soils were weak and variable, loose Made Ground, wide base slabs were needed for stability and sliding resistance.

A wrap around reinforced soil slope was considered but as there was a significant risk that a geogrid facing would be damaged by vandalism it was decided that a wall with a hard facing was necessary. A modular block wall using Porcupine blocks would not be stable on the weak foundations. To spread the foundation loads and to provide the required sliding resistance the backfill was reinforced with Fortrac 35 PVC covered geogrid.

To allow for any future development in front of and close to the wall the base of the wall was set 1.0m below ground level giving a design height of 3.4m. The wall includes two 90° outside corners which were formed using insitu concrete shaped to match the courses of the blocks. The Fortrac geogrid was anchored between the courses being held by the block interlock spines.

Scheme	A120 Dovercourt Bypass
Designer	G. Maunsell & Partners
Client	Essex County Council
Value	Contract: £7.8 million Element: £45,000
Constructed	1990
Wall System	Blocks: Porcupine Reinforcement: Fortrac 35
Dimensions	Retained Height: 2.4 m (design 3.4m) Length 150 m
Purpose	Minimise landtake adjacent Mercedes Benz new car preparation facility and to avoid the flood wall.
Ground Conditions	Variable - loose/soft Made Ground (ashes,bricks,clay)
Design Methodology	Hand analysis - two part wedge, limit state.
Reason for Choice	Flexibility on variable foundation soils Confined space for construction Speed of construction.

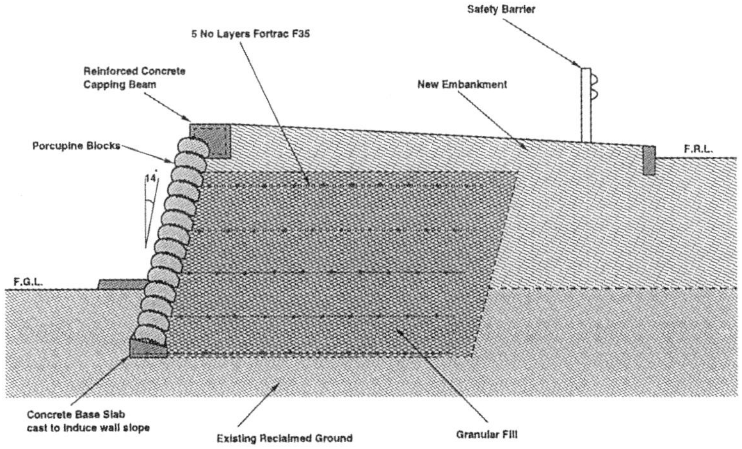

Figure 3 - Section of Reinforced Soil Retaining Wall
(Dovercourt Bypass : Mercedes Benz Wall)

Case Study 2:   *Limmo Site, Bow Creek, Docklands*

In the heart of London's Docklands lies the confluence of Bow Creek and the River Thames. Tidal flood defences extend along both sides of the creek upstream from the confluence. A 40 m length of gabions formed part of the flood defence system on the east bank of the creek.

Instability and a low bearing capacity of the soft soils in the foundations of the gabion wall, allowed the gabion wall to collapse. Once the gabions had collapsed the earth flood defence bank also began to fail endangering the integrity of the flood defence system in the area. Total collapse could allow a very large area of low lying residential and industrial land to be flooded if a surge tide were to occur. Repairs to the flood defences were needed to maintain the integrity of the defences.

A variety of systems were considered for the repairs. Based on both cost and aesthetics, a segmental reinforced block wall was selected by the Client, Thames Region of the National Rivers Authority. The design chosen uses Marshalls Revetlok block system, selected by the client for its aesthetic appearance. The use of the Revetlock system required a geosynthetic reinforcement to reinforce the backfill. A geotextile has been specified as the shape of the blocks is such that geogrids would not develop a high enough anchorage force to transfer the reinforcing forces into the block facings.

To ensure that the new reinforced modular block wall would be stable the soft foundation soils are to be strengthened using vibro-replacement stone columns. The stone columns will have a nominal diameter of 600 mm and will be capped with a 500 mm thick geotextile wrapped granular mattress to distribute loads between the wall and the stone columns.

Scheme	London Tidal Defences	
Designer	Balfour Maunsell Ltd	
Client	National Rivers Authority, Thames Region	
Value	Contract:	£125,000
	Element:	£125,000
Constructed	Commencing May 1995	
Wall System	Blocks:	Revetlok
	Reinforcement:	Stabilenka 150/45
Dimensions	Retained Height:	3.3 m
	Length:	42 m
Purpose	Retain and protect face of tidal flood embankment	
Ground Conditions	4 m of Made Ground over 3 m of very soft Alluvial Clay over Alluvial Sand and Gravel	
Design Methodology	Design Manual for Segmental Retaining Walls (National Concrete Masonry Association (1993))	
Reason for Choice	Aesthetic Appearance	
	Ease of Construction in Tidal Environment	
	Cost	

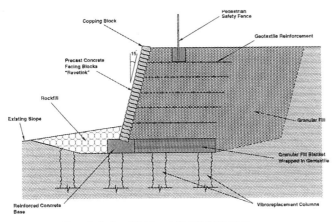

Figure 4 - Section of Reinforced Block Wall (Revetlok)
(Bow Creek Limmo Site)

127

Case Study 3:   *Retaining Walls - Catterick Garrison*

At Catterick Garrison, North Yorkshire, facilities have been extensively upgraded to accommodate troops returning from Nato duties in the former Federal Republic of West Germany.

Ballast Nedam were appointed under a Design and Build Contract which included a number of new buildings and external works.

Following discussions between Ballast Nedam and Forticrete (manufacturers of the Keystone Block), Netlon were instructed to supply construction drawings and Tensar soil reinforcing grids for two separate reinforced soil walls faced with Keystone blocks.

The first wall, from which the Section and Photograph have been taken, was to be tiered with vertical faces and included 45° internal corners.

The second wall which was straight and 70 m long, was to be stepped back at 25 mm per course to give a face inclination of 8 in 1.

Keystone was chosen because of its natural stone appearance and easy installation. The simplicity of the Keystone/Tensar geogrid reinforcement system meant that specialised labour and large construction plant were not required. Accurate positioning of successive courses of block is accomplished by two fibre glass dowels which were simply slotted into preformed locating holes.

To ensure good interaction and drainage close to the face, drainage stone was placed behind and within the facing blocks. A carrier drain was positioned at the base of the wall.

Originally it had been intended to construct the walls with gabions. Preliminary analysis indicated that overall costs would be similar. The aesthetic merits of the Keystone block accompanied by simplicity of construction ensured that the Tensar/Keystone system was preferred.

Scheme	Catterick Garrison Upgrading, North Yorkshire
Designer	Netlon Ltd
Client (Contractor)	M.O.D. (Ballast Needam - Design & Build

Value	Contract:	Not Stated
	Element:	Not Stated

Constructed	1994

Wall System	Blocks:	Keystone
	Reinforcement:	Tensar SR55

Dimensions	Retained Height:	4.4 m
	Length:	Various

Purpose	To maximise the space available for development

Ground Conditions	Not reported

Design Methodology	Design Manual for Segmental Retaining Walls (National Concrete Masonry Association (1993))

Reason for Choice	Aesthetic Appearance
	Simplicity of Construction

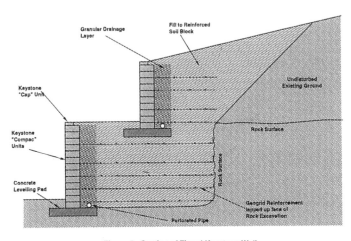

Figure 5 - Section of Tiered Keystone Wall
(Catterick Garrison, North Yorkshire)

129

Case Study 4:   *Porcupine - Platipus Wall Trials*

The project was designed to investigate the feasibility of using Platipus soil anchors to reinforce Porcupine walling blocks and to develop a design method for the system.

The initial stages of the project were centred around the development of design for the system. The wall was initially modelled using a stability program STABL5 (1992) which allows the user to model the soils and the anchors as ties. At this stage the effects of the Porcupine blocks were modelled as a mass and the Platipus anchors were assumed to generate load over their full length. These calculations were the basis for the first layout of anchors to be tested.

The trial consisted of the construction of an 8 m length of Porcupine block wall with Platipus anchors. Standard Platipus anchors were used and specially modified Porcupine blocks were manufactured to allow an anchor plate to be located between the splines.

The first trial wall was loaded with a surcharge of 60 kPa. Platipus anchors were installed at 1.0m centres horizontally and 0.6m centres vertically. Measured horizontal wall displacements of up to 20 mm were recorded.

For the second trial wall the anchor connections were modified to allow anchors to be released during the trial thus increasing the anchor spacing. A serviceability failure, defined as 1% strain, was observed when the applied surcharge was 35 kPa and anchor spacing were 0.75 m horizontally and 1.05 m vertically. The surcharge intensity was reduced to 15 kPa, the anchor spacing increased and surcharge reapplied. The maximum anchor spacing tested was 3m horizontally and 1.05 m vertically and a maximum surcharge of 42 kPa was applied to this configuration of anchors. The wall did not suffer a total collapse and the maximum horizontal movement measured was approximately 60 mm.

The data gathered from the field trials was used as a basis for the development of a series of preliminary design charts using an analytical method based upon the 'Design Manual for Segmental Retaining Walls', U.S. National Concrete Masonry Association (1993).

Scheme	Analysis and Field Trials of a Porcupine Block Retaining Wall Reinforced with Platipus Anchors
Designer	G. Maunsell & Partners
Client	MMG Civil Engineering Systems Ltd/Platipus Anchors
Value	Contract: £15,000 Element: £15,000
Constructed	1994
Wall System	Blocks: Porcupine: Standard and Specially modified Reinforcement: Platipus Anchors 68-DBA
Dimensions	Retained Height: 2.5 m Length 8 m
Purpose	Investigate performance of wall constructed in cut using soil anchors as reinforcement
Ground Conditions	Dense sand and gravel
Design Methodology	Blocks ignored and ground anchors treated as Ties
Reason for Choice	Development project.

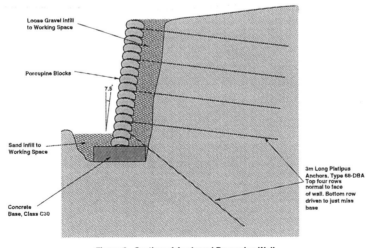

Figure 6 - Section of Anchored Porcupine Wall
(Trial Porcupine/Platipus Wall)

ADVANTAGES OF REINFORCED MODULAR BLOCK WALLS

Reinforced modular block walls offer a number of potential advantages over other retaining wall systems.

1   *Ease and speed of construction*
- Simple to construct
- Requires minimal plant
- Requires no specialist skilled labour
- Units easy to handle

2   *Engineering*
- Reinforced soil construction gives lower bearing pressures on underlying strata than traditional gravity construction, allowing construction on poorer ground
- Blocks are relatively tolerant of differential movements by comparison with many other systems

3   *Durability*
- Precast concrete facing only exposed element
- Reinforcement protected from light and vandalism by facing
- Prefabricated materials have controlled and established properties
- Life of metallic components in anchors predictable in most circumstances
- Possibility of developing synthetic anchors or soil nails to improve durability

4   *Maintenance*
- No maintenance is required.

5   *Flexibility*
- Small unit size allows adaptation to various geometries including:-
  - plan and vertical curves
  - stepped foundations
  - corners
  - tie-ins with other systems

6   *Economics*
Although system costs are comparable with other retaining wall systems the low plant requirements and ease of element handling have positive cost implications for small or inaccessible sites.

7   *Aesthetics*
- A variety of finishes is available from the different systems
- Broken faces giving a more natural stone effect can be achieved
- Blocks can be coloured to give specific effects

CONCLUSIONS

The use of modular concrete block walls would seem to offer many advantages to both clients and contractors. Design engineers need to be aware that whilst the standard design tools are needed, to analyze the systems it is essential that laboratory tests are carried out to check the anchorage pull out strength of the geosynthetic from the facing blocks. This is an important parameter in the design when the anchorage is purely frictional.

ACKNOWLEDGEMENTS

The author would like to express their thanks to the following for permission to publish details of the projects included in this paper:

Essex County Council Highways Department : Dovercourt Bypass

National Rivers Authority, Thames Region : Bow Creek Wall

Netlon Ltd., MOD : Catterick Garrison Wall.

MMG Civil Engineering Ltd., and Platipus Soil Anchors Ltd. :
Porcupine/ Platipus wall trial.

REFERENCES

Bathurst, R. & Simac, M.R., 1994, *Geosynthetic Reinforced Segmental Retaining Wall Structures in North America*. Fifth International Conference on Geotextiles, Geomembranes and Related Products, Keynote Lectures, Singapore, 23pp

National Concrete Masonry Association, 1993, *Design Manual for Segmental Retaining Walls*.

Maunsell Systems Centre, 1994, *STABL5 Version 5.2 General Stability Program*, developed from the source codes written by Perdue University, Indiana USA,

Discussion on Session 1

C.R. LAWSON, Terram Limited, United Kingdom - Discussion Reporter

Mr Corbet, Chairman of the morning session, opened the discussion.

Dr Barley, Keller Colcrete, observed that most of the papers dealt with the use of geosynthetics as the tensile elements. Consequently, he had three questions for the speakers. Firstly, is there a problem with geotextiles when they are placed in contact with concrete, such as at the face of a concrete faced reinforced soil wall? Secondly, have there been any known failures concerning the corrosion of steel strips and whether these have been galvanised or not? Thirdly, what is the approach adopted in BS 8006 to the protection of steel in reinforced soil?

Mr Myles, Soil Nailing, responded to Dr Barley's first question regarding the durability of geotextiles in conjunction with concrete. Speaking on behalf of the BSI Committee on geotextile testing, he stated that the problem of curing concrete had been specifically directed towards the alkaline catalysed hydrolysis of polyester materials. Several years ago, when the BSI Committee came to review the problem of pH levels associated with precast concrete, tests showed that is was very difficult to obtain pH values greater than 8. The reason for this is that in Northern Europe and the United Kingdom there is an acidic atmosphere which carbonises the surface of curing concrete very quickly thus reducing pH. In this case, cast concrete is highly unlikely to be a problem for polyester. Mr Myles noted that there may be a problem if wet spraying concrete directly onto exposed polyester, but this is completely different to the environment of cast concrete panels and modular blocks.

In response to Dr Barley's second and third questions Dr Jones, University of Newcastle, stated that there have been reinforced soil failures using steel both from corrosion and from the construction process. The corrosion failures have not been publicised, however, it was not considered that these were of a significant proportion when one considers the number of these types of walls constructed. Examples of some construction failures were published in *Geotechnique*, Volume XLIV, No. 3. Steel is accepted as a tensile element in BS 8006 as well as other metals. BS 8006 accepts both galvanised and ungalvanised steel. The level of galvanising required in BS 8006 is higher than in France and Hong Kong for example.

Mr Hall, E. C. Civil Engineering, stated that he had constructed both polymeric and metallic reinforced structures and walls with both articulated and full-height facing panels. His view was that full-height panels are difficult to prop during construction. In his experience the articulated panels were far easier to install and more economical. He observed that the use of polymeric or metallic reinforcement would be dictated by the market place. He also made the point that as we move into the era of design-build-finance-operate we are moving away from reinforced soil as a proprietary material, and consequently, what the contractor really wants is the best deal providing value for money and conformance with specification.

In response to Mr Hall, Dr Jones, University of Newcastle, stated that the true economics surrounding full-height panels versus articulated panels revolve around the total cost and quality of the structure. He countered that it is not more difficult for the contractor to build full-height panelled walls and emphasised the point that a more robust structure would result with full-height panels. As an example, he stated that practice in Australia enabled the construction of full-height panel bridge abutments in a single day.

Dr Dikran, Tenax UK, stated that Mr Capps, during his presentation, mentioned that the facing of the reinforced soil slopes on his contract on the M25 were composed of mild steel mesh. Mild steel is known to oxidise within a period of 10 years and when this happens it corrodes as well. Dr Dikran could well envisage that in 20 years time the mild steel facing would be well corroded and there could be some health and safety concerns. He asked Mr Capps to explain what kind of approvals were undertaken and how this facing was designed to the design life expected for motorway widening structures.

In his reply to Dr Dikran, Mr Capps, Tarmac, stated that the Comtec UK system was used for the reinforced soil slopes on his contract. He was not aware of the approvals Comtec went through. He emphasised that the steel mesh facing is temporary works within the slope and it forms no structural entity. He agreed that in time the mesh would disappear but this would not be deleterious to the structure.

Mr Newman, Comtec UK, reinforced Mr Capps' statements. He went on to state that inside the mesh facing is a geotextile which is required to remain in place on a permanent basis and so retain the soil surface. The Highways Agency carried out a safety audit on the system and its installation and this comprised the approval procedure.

Mr Booth, MMG, in drawing attention to the Comtec reinforced slope system noted that the slope face consisted of a vegetation geotextile enclosing 300 mm of top soil. This was then enclosed within a mild steel mesh facing. He considered that, in time, both the mesh and the surface geotextile would disintegrate. Thus, in the long term the stability of the face would be solely dependent on the root growth of the surface vegetation. In his opinion this could not always be relied upon. He went on to state that in the MMG slope system a geogrid was used as a wrap-around at the face to maintain long term face stability. He observed that on some of the M25 sections using the Comtec system no geogrid wrap-around was used. He considered that this would appear to be an under design.

In reply to Mr Booth, Mr Newman, Comtec UK, stated that the surface geotextile currently used in the Comtec system is manufactured from polyester and thus it will only degrade slowly over a long period of time at the soil surface. Its performance is similar in terms of life expectancy to the geogrid wrap-around referred to by Mr Booth.

Mr Booth, MMG, concluded that given the failure of the vegetation on the section of the M25 between the M4 and M40 due to the nature of the grass mixture, the long term performance of the face geotextile is very important. This aspect is brought more highly into focus when one considers that the Highways Agency's view is that these reinforced soil slopes should be maintenance free. In Mr Booth's view the Highways Agency's approach was a mistake inasmuch as maintenance should form part of any vegetated reinforced soil slope.

Mr Booth, MMG, asked Mr Jenner, Netlon, what was the cost implication of the geocell mattress system shown in his presentation compared to an alternative polyester geotextile basal reinforcement material. He contended that both types of materials would provide the same function so why did the engineers opt for a geocell system?

In response to Mr Booth, Mr Jenner, Netlon, explained that the reasons why Strathclyde Regional Council decided on the geocell mattress system at the M74 should be for them to answer. However, from Mr Jenner's viewpoint, the geocell mattress had a track record which SRC found very helpful and it provided a plate-like structure to reduce differential settlements. Mr Jenner noted that the cost of the geocell mattress system is not extreme and construction can be carried out fairly quickly at around the rate of 300 m^2 to 500 m^2 per day.

Dr Jones, University of Newcastle, commented that modular block walls are very popular but one word of warning should be heeded. Modular facing blocks are stiff elements and the wall is constructed by building upwards. If the wall is very high the backfill will settle relative to the facing and this imposes greater stresses on the reinforcement attached between the rigid blocks. This increase in stress may be enough to fail the reinforcement. Considerable care needs to be exercised with high modular block walls. One way around this potential problem is to utilise step walls where the total wall height is great.

Dr Barley, Keller Colcrete, observed that recently there has been some use of timber crib walls in the UK. His concern centred on the life time of the timber in these walls. In addition, from a local stability viewpoint, the timber crib wall does not appear to have any shear capacity.

In response to Dr Barley, Mr Price, Phi Group, stated that his company's timber crib system had just achieved BBA certification which has confirmed its durability in excess of 120 years. He emphasised that the timber used and the way it is treated is far in excess of any treatment level requirements expected in the BSI standard for European softwoods. From the viewpoint of stability, these timber crib walls are designed as a gravity retaining wall. Special attention is paid to the granular infill. A detailed specification is used for this material that is designed to give high granular interlock and integrity between the timber cribs and the structure itself.

Mr Price, Freyssisol, made the point that when dealing with reinforced soil walls one of the details that needs to be considered is the loads to be carried by the reinforcement at the connection to the wall face. He noted that this load can be as high as 75% to 80% of the total reinforcement load. He observed that for modular block walls, although they are approximately vertical, there appears to be no calculation of the required reinforcement strengths at the connection point with the modular blocks. He asked Messrs Corbet and Freak if they had given any consideration to this for the structures detailed in their presentation.

Mr Corbet, Maunsell & Partners, responding to Mr Price, stated that when these modular block wall systems are designed some load reduction at the point of reinforcement connection with the modular blocks is assumed. The justification for this is based on the work carried out by Bathurst in North America. Different patented block systems have different connections between the blocks and reinforcement. Some develop the connection loads by friction and some by end bearing. Load levels at the connections are between 60% and 80% of the total reinforcement force.

Mr Price, Freyssisol, then asked Mr Mannsbart, Polyfelt, what types of safety factors were used for the French reinforced soil walls presented in his paper - was it a partial factor or global factor of safety approach?

In response to Mr Price, Mr Mannsbart, Polyfelt, stated that the design of the French reinforced soil walls was performed using an LCPC computer program. This computer program makes it possible to account for both deformations and forces simultaneously. The design was carried out using a slip circle analysis with the reinforcement layers included. Partial factors of safety were applied to the reinforcements according to the French recommendations. The total partial factor of safety for the reinforcements was 5.5 because of the type of polyester reinforcement used. The computer program also calculates a global factor of safety which was higher than 1.4 in this case.

Mr Tuxford, Euro Erosion Engineering, asked Mr Mannsbart, Polyfelt, for details concerning the vegetation geotextile used in the face of some of the reinforced slopes shown in his presentation. Could Mr Mannsbart advise the extension properties of this geotextile? Mr Tuxford noted that reinforcing materials generally have relatively low extensions.

Mr Mannsbart, Polyfelt, replying to Mr Tuxford, stated that for nonwovens the tensile characteristics are different when in the soil than in isolation. When in-soil testing is used tensile strengths can approach double those of in-isolation strength testing. However, Mr Mannsbart did agree with Mr Tuxford that where the loads are high it is better to use woven geotextiles or geogrids.

Mr Tuxford, Euro Erosion Engineering, asked Mr Jenner, Netlon, about one of the reinforced slopes in his presentation where a geogrid in combination with a nonwoven geotextile had been used in a reinforcing application. He wanted to know how this affected the relationship between geogrid/fill interlock from a bond development viewpoint.

In response to Mr Tuxford, Mr Jenner, Netlon, stated that the particular slope in question had the nonwoven geotextile wrapped around the face of the fill only, and it did not extend into the fill. Therefore the nonwoven geotextile had no effect on geogrid/soil bond within the fill.

Mr Corbet, Chairman, closed the session and thanked all presenters for their presentations and discussers for the ensuing lively debate.

An approach to high reinforced soil structures

G. SEMBENELLI and P. SEMBENELLI,
Piero Sembenelli Consultant, Italy

SYNOPSIS
The behaviour of high reinforced soil structures (HRSS) is quite complex and is not yet fully modelled today. A design approach which combines the theoretical tools available with the experience on several HRSS is presented. All design steps are discussed with comments based upon measurements on full scale structures and test embankments.

INTRODUCTION
Reinforced soil structures (RSS) consist of 2 parts; the facing and the reinforced soil comprising reinforcement and fill. In Italy, a large number of reinforced soil structures has been built with technologies which allow construction of 60° to 70° steep slopes with a fully grassed face. Usually steel wire meshes are used as formwork. The wire mesh essentially provides local support to the fill material during construction. Several patented system are currently used in Italy. Grassed facings blend very well with the environment and are very often used in the Italian Alps. The paper mainly deals with high reinforced soil structures (HRSS).
The complex behaviour of RSS and the lack of models allowing their accurate numerical analysis lead to the adoption of an approach which combines computations, tests and field controls, rather than relying solely on theoretical procedures. This paper approach is illustrated and the results of its application are recounted. The basic steps usually followed when designing HRSS are:

- determination of the foundation profile and features and assessment of ground water pressures and flow lines

- determination of chemical and mechanical characteristics of construction materials and possibly test embankments

- determination of the total force required for the equilibrium and the length of individual reinforcement

- thorough drafting of the structure with extensive detailing

- close monitoring of the structure from construction

FOUNDATION PROFILE

The determination of foundation and groundwater profiles is of utmost importance for assessing overall behaviour of a HRSS. Although this issue is sometimes overlooked, it must be pointed out that the long term behaviour of a RSS strongly depends on its foundation. Clearly, the water table profile can be modified by a HRSS built at the toe of a natural slope. Usually ground water is thoroughly studied and piezometer monitored, all water springs are carefully located and gauged. Controls include chemical analyses of groundwater. Steep slopes apply high load levels and sharp stress gradients to the foundation. Any weak area may become over-stressed. It therefore becomes imperative to perform investigations at a spacing which is much closer than otherwise necessary.

MATERIAL PROPERTIES

The long term behaviour of reinforced soil is strongly influenced by the chemical compatibility between construction materials and neighbouring components. Chemical compatibility is very important in potentially aggressive environments, such as waste disposal sites, but care must also be exercised in natural environments, where organic acids, high calcium or gypsum contents may adversely interact with the geosynthetics. Chemical or thermal analyses of components, such as soil, groundwater, and polymers, are usually carried out to detect any adverse condition.

An accurate determination of the overall mechanical properties of reinforced soil is not yet possible since it requires models, which are not yet available. In the practice, the properties of reinforced soil are still derived by mixing the results of conventional soil mechanics tests on fill materials and *in-isolation* tests on reinforcement. The in-isolation properties of geosynthetics are of limited significance for HRSS and therefore substantial engineering judgment must be applied.

Tests are being developed to determine the in-soil properties of geosynthetics. Such tests are usually derived from soil mechanics tests, modified to include reinforcement, however, it is difficult to reproduce field conditions in the laboratory. Scaling of reinforced soil and geosynthetics is one additional problem which limits a straightforward application of laboratory tests results.

These shortcomings may be overcome by the use test embankments, a practice widespread for dams but not HRSS. Test embankments allow full scale optimisation of construction procedures as well as checks on construction induced strains, locked in stresses and construction induced damage of the reinforcement.

Tensile creep tests must be carried out to assess creep properties of geosynthetics. Due to the potentially long test time, such data are usually provided by the manufacturer. The maximum allowable geosynthetic force is controlled by geosynthetic type and polymer characteristics. Probably creep tests can better model relatively stiff reinforcements, like geogrids and woven geotextiles, rather than weak nonwoven geotextiles.

EXAMPLES OF TEST EMBANKMENTS

The test embankment, shown in Figure 1, was 1.9 m high, some 10 m long and 3 m wide, with a total volume of 300 m³ . The fill material was spread in 0.25 m thick lifts and compacted with 6 passes of a 1.75 m wide, smooth drum vibratory roller with a 4500 kg drum mass. The roller was set on low frequency and high amplitude to provide a centrifugal force of about 143 kN. During compaction the roller moved parallel to the slope. All construction details exactly duplicated the prototype. A total of 3 layers of reinforcement was placed, at 0.5, 1.0 and 1.5 m from the base. On the top of the last reinforcement 0.4 m of compacted fill were added. The maximum fill height on the lower reinforcement was hence 1.4 m. The centre portion of the embankment was reinforced with geogrids and geotextiles in the outer zones. The prime objectives were to check construction induced strains in the geogrids and the survivability of the geotextiles.

The HDPE geogrid was Tenax TT401 with a 200 mm wide strip tensile strength of 80.7 kN/m, per ASTM D-4595, with failure at around at 15% strain. The geotextile was a Landolt needlepunched PET continuous filament nonwoven with a mass per unit area of 350 g/m² . The average machine direction strength was 44 kN/m at 49% strain and 18 kN/m at 56% strain in the cross-machine direction. Tests were to SN 640 550 (1983) on 100 mm wide by 200 mm long strips.

Figure 1   Test embankment for Champagne HRSS. Heavy compaction is applied on the whole reinforced area, starting from the facing edge

The fill material was rock chippings and fines produced by a tunnel boring machine, combined with some alluvium. The material was angular, well graded, slightly silty sand and gravel. The maximum particle size was $D_{max} \approx 40$ mm, but coarser particles, up to 200 mm, were tolerated. Fines were non plastic. The maximum dry unit weight obtained with Modified AASHTO Energy (2650 kJ/m3) was 22.8 kN/m³ . Triaxial compression tests, carried out on 100 mm diameter samples of the fraction finer than 20 mm at a dry unit weight of 21 kN/m³ and under an effective confining pressure of 500 kPa, was 43 °. The friction angle at 20% axial strain was 38 °. Dry unit weights, determined on the surface of the compacted lifts, varied between 21.4 and 22.1 kN/m³ , corresponding to 94 to 97 % of AASHTO modified optimum dry unit weight. The bulk modulus, determined from 300 mm diameter plate load tests in the vertical stress range 150 to 250 kPa, varied between 50 and 100 MPa.

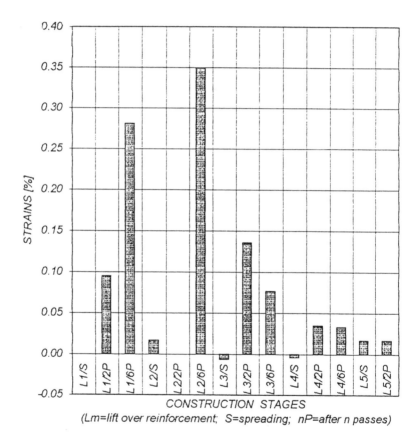

(Lm=lift over reinforcement; S=spreading; nP=after n passes)

Figure 2 Strains accumulated during compaction of each of the 5 lifts, placed above the instrumented geogrid at a test embankment for Champagne HRSS. Each lift was 0.25 m thick. Strains were measured by a strain gauge located 1 m away from the facing

One geogrid was instrumented with CEA-06-062-UW-120 strain gauges, manufactured by Measurement Group of USA, located 1, 2 and 3 m from the facing, along the axis of the geogrid roll. Strain gauges were placed in the middle of the ribs. Average geogrid strains have been correlated to local strains, measured by strain gauges in the centre point of individual ribs, with a calibration carried out on a geogrid specimen, instrumented with the same strain gauges and tested, in-isolation, to ASTM D-4595. The calibration was then used to determine actual elongations of the geogrid as well as its actual load-elongation curve, from the strain gauges readings.

While constructing the embankment, readings were taken at each lift, after spreading of the lift, after 2 passes and after 6 passes of the roller. The weight of the first lift, just after spreading, produced a substantial change in the strain gauge readings. This was related to removal of the wrinkles and hence such strains were not relevant. Further readings showed that strains were increasing at each of the above stages.

The elongations measured by the strain gauge which was nearest to the slope are shown in Figure 2. The accumulated strains during compaction were in the order of 0.27%, for the first lift, and 0.35%, for the second. The additional lifts produced no or negative strains in the geogrid. The total measured strain was about 0.74 %. The corresponding locked in force after compaction of the first 3 lifts was about 7.5 kN/m, as shown in Figure 3. The strain gauge located 2 m away from the slope showed a similar trend, with total measured strains in the order of 0.4%.

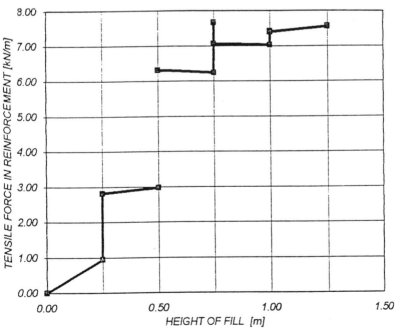

Figure 3   Construction tensile force developed in geogrid 1 m from edge

After loading, the trial fill was dismantled and two geotextile samples, 0.9 and 1.4 m deep, were carefully recovered. They were tested to determine the loss of strength due to mechanical damage. The distribution and type of damage were thoroughly recorded. Several samples were taken in the most damaged zones and tested. A set of tensile strength tests on both standard size and wide width specimens were carried out on damaged and undamaged samples. The number of single damages were recorded for each specimen. The results, shown in Figure 4, demonstrated a strong relationship between loss of strength and the type and number of damages, according to Koerner et al. (1990) and Paulson (1990). The average decay of tensile strength of the geotextile was about 50%. However, it must be pointed out that the damaged portion of the geotextile was less than 20% and that damage was randomly distributed, as shown in Figure 5. The actual average survivability factor of safety, FS_S was hence set at 1.1.

Strain gauges application and calibration took three to four days. Construction of the test embankment and recovering the reinforcement samples took about 8 hours. A crew of 3 workers, 1 engineer supervisor and 2 machines operators were mobilised for the test embankment.

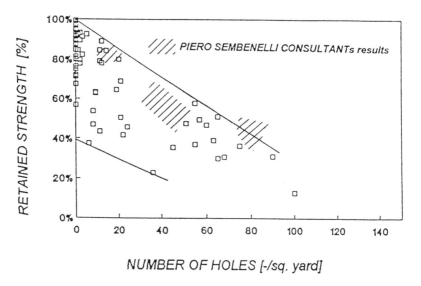

Figure 4 Results of survivability tensile tests on nonwoven geotextiles recovered from a test embankment. Results from other published works (Paulson, 1990) are given for comparison

Figure 5   Geotextile sheet recovered from a test embankment after compaction

In a different test embankment, built with the same materials and procedures, a geotextile was instrumented with eleven 60 mm long, PL-60/120 strain gauges, manufactured by TML of Japan, formed by a filament protected by two polyester films. As shown in Figure 6, only the ends of each strain gauge were bonded to the geotextile, using silicon glue, to allow the free rearrangement of the geotextile filaments during loading. Laboratory tensile tests were carried out on, instrumented strips of geotextile, 50 and 200 mm wide, to check the set up and for calibration. Although the polyester alloy proved a little too stiff with respect to the geotextile, the gauge gave a linear response up to strains of 1.5%. Then the bonds broke. A calibration to compensate for pressure effects was carried out before placing the instrumented geotextiles, loading each strain gauge with several concrete cubes, up to 20 kPa.

After placing the instrumented geotextiles, readings were taken upon spreading each lift and after 2 and 6 passes of the roller. About 1.25 m, 25 kPa of vertical pressure, of reinforced soil fill was then added. In parallel with this operation, horizontal displacements of the facing were measured by surveying. The strains mainly developed as a consequence of spreading the first lift and during compaction of the first metre of fill. After 6 roller passes, any additional rolling had little effect on the strains. At 1 m from the face, total construction strains were in the order of 0.4 to 0.8%. Only half of them was due to compaction. Although the strain gauges were bonded in a non standard manner, the strains measured were in good agreement with those measured in nearby sections by long base extensometers.

Surprisingly, construction strains measured in the geotextiles were lower than those measured in the geogrids. This may be due to the lower stiffness of geotextiles *eg* during compaction a larger portion of soil strength is mobilised when a geotextile is inserted as reinforcement and, as a consequence, a lower fraction of the driving forces is taken up by the reinforcements.

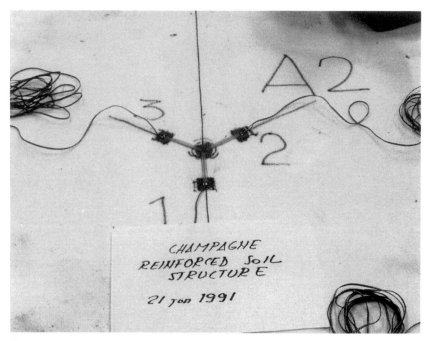

Fig. 6 - Strain gauges applied on a nonwoven geotextile reinforcement for test embankment installation

FORCE AND LENGTH REQUIREMENTS OF REINFORCEMENTS

The total horizontal forces required for the equilibrium as well as the length of the reinforcements are usually determined with computations based on limit equilibrium. Several rules have been developed, for computing the tensile force on each reinforcement. This requires additional assumptions regarding the distribution of the total horizontal force over the reinforced height. The FHWA Manual (1989) provides a complete set of suggestions.

It is considered that until soil-reinforcement interaction and stress-strain curves are more closely modelled, simplified methods, which do not take into account interslice forces, are probably more reliable. At least for high structures, the effect of reinforcement should be taken into account only as a resisting force, neglecting the geometrical component which reduces the driving force. The simplified Janbu Method is particularly helpful, since it can render explicit the total horizontal component of driving and resisting forces and compute the horizontal tensile force required for equilibrium. The use of a horizontal component instead of the tangential one, to simulate the overall stabilising force required, is better to model condition of incipient movement.

When dealing with stepped faced structures, which are made with several reinforced soil blocks, the horizontal force requirements must be computed for the single block as well as for all the combinations of blocks, assumed as unreinforced and homogeneous. The total horizontal force required for each block or for each combination of blocks is then distributed over the corresponding height. For heights greater than 6 to 8 m, usually half of the total horizontal force is assumed to be taken by the lowest third of the block. The required horizontal force at each reinforcement level can hence be taken from the envelope of all distributions.

The reinforcement must be long enough to carry all the tensile stresses applied to the soil, in the top portion of the HRSS, and to redistribute the shear stresses in the lower portion. Using limit equilibrium methods, the length of reinforcement is selected so that it reaches beyond the critical slip surface. Physically, it means that the length of reinforcement depends on the fill and backfill characteristics rather than on those of the reinforcement. Very often overall stability governs the length of lower reinforcement.

The above criteria were used to compute the total horizontal force at different stages of construction of the test embankment described above, along a slip surface passing through the strain gauges alignment. During compaction, it was assumed that the effect of the roller could be modelled as a static load equivalent to the drum weight, while the vibration only had the effect of reducing the angle of friction to its residual value, say approximately $34°$. This was also assumed to produce incipient sliding, eg FS = 1. The static condition after compaction was modelled assuming the roller weight was no longer active and the friction angle of the material was back to its peak level of $43°$.

The horizontal component of the required tensile force, from the simplified Janbu method with a factor of safety unity, were $T_f = 15$ kN/m, during compaction, and $T_f = 4$ kN/m, for static post-compaction conditions. From the test embankment results, the total force locked in the geogrids, after compaction, was estimated to be about 20 kN/m. Such force is of the same order of magnitude as the force computed for during compaction conditions, but much higher than that computed for post compaction conditions. As a consequence, a substantial fill height can be added before the force in the reinforcement may start increasing again. This is equivalent to a kind of overconsolidation. The height up to which the overconsolidation effects can be felt, in a geogrid reinforced soil built with the adopted construction procedure, can be roughly estimated as equivalent to 10 to 14 m of fill.

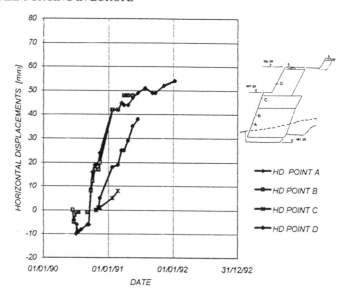

Figure 7   Horizontal displacements measured at Champagne HRSS embankment between June 1990 and January 1992

Figure 8   Main section at Champagne Embankment. The horizontal displacements shown in Figure 7 were measured on the central section of the arch shaped portion. The reinforcement was geogrids in the arch zone and geotextiles above

If the total horizontal force locked in the reinforcement by compaction is greater than that required for equilibrium, some stress redistribution and inward movement should be expected, if the reinforcement is relatively stiff and elastic. Figure 7 shows inward movements actually measured on the lowest two plates at Champagne HRSS which was 23 m high, with a 60 to 70° steep facing, Sembenelli et al. (1994). The reinforcement behind the lowest plates were geogrids, while the reinforcements behind the upper part of the structure were geotextiles. The monitored section is in the centre of the niche shown in Figure 8.

Figure 7 shows that in any case the complete redistribution of stresses requires substantial time after construction. During this time, soil consolidation, stress transfer from soil to reinforcement, stress redistribution and possibly reinforcement creep take place. In a section some 8 m high, reinforced with geotextiles and built with the same procedure described above, average construction strains over a 3 m wide band near the facing were in the order of 0.18% and the additional, long term, thee years, strains were in the order of 0.3%. The hyperbolic shape of the delayed strain-time curves suggest that this process could be described with relationships similar to those used consolidation.

The force requirements computed with limit equilibrium methods are those necessary to ensure equilibrium at the latest stage of this pseudo-consolidation process. In spite of this, the use of equilibrium criteria alone is still not enough for properly defining both the behaviour and the factor of safety of HRSS. Strain compatibility and actual in-soil behaviour of reinforcement should be taken into account. This appears particularly true when dealing with creep assessment, for which the actual force applied on each reinforcement should be known.

DRAFTING AND DETAILING

Although the number, location and length of reinforcing layers are the key items in the design of HRSS, it is not the only issue. This is particularly true when dealing with long, stepped or complex structures, for which considerable engineering judgment must be applied. Good practice requires that construction drawings cover not only the overall geometry and the reinforcement distribution, but also the layout and details of the drainage systems, for both surface and ground waters, placements details of each reinforcement layer and connections with concrete structures. Figure 9 illustrates a typical layout of the surface drainage developed for a structure now being built in the Italian Alps. The lower quarter of such HRSS is shown in Figure 10.

A set of construction drawings is usually devoted to defining the location in plan of all the reinforcement layers. This kind of detailing not only leads to an optimised use of the reinforcement, but also prevents improper overlapping, especially where the facing is not straight but curved, as illustrated in Figure 11. Special care is usually paid for the transitions or connections with adjacent structures or valley sides.

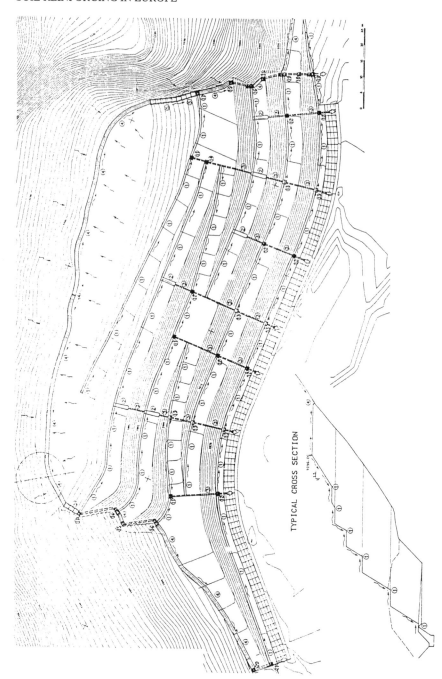

Figure 9   Layout and surface drainage provisions at Verrand HRSS embankment. The structure, currently under construction in the Italian Alps, will be 37 m high of which 27 m are reinforced.

Figure 10 Verrand HRSS embankment during construction in January 1995. The picture shows the lower bank of Figure 8, looking N-NW, which is about a quarter of the final height

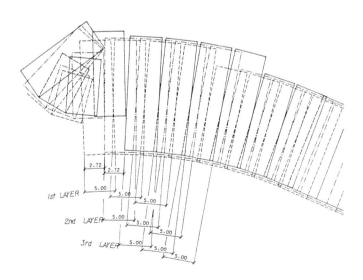

Figure 11 Typical detail of a construction drawing of a HRSS. Location and size of each reinforcement sheet are specified

MONITORING

Monitoring of HRSS is of fundamental importance and should be prescribed for all structures exceeding a height of 8 m. A proper monitoring system should allow measurements to be taken at the earliest construction phase. The most simple, and most direct, measurements which can be made are of displacements and strains. Out of the several tools currently available for measuring displacements and average strains, distance measurements by topographic surveying and long base extensometers are the most suitable. Most job sites can provide reliable installation and measurements. Although inclinometers have been used in connection with RSS, they only allow accurate measurements once construction is complete. This is not desirable. The use of instrumented reinforcement can be very valuable. To date it is not very accurate and is not a suitable practice for routine jobs. As part of routine monitoring activities, burying reinforcement samples, to be unearthed after 5, 10, 20 and 40 years, is strongly recommended for assessment of durability. Samples should be buried at convenient places in the embankment, with the same procedure used during construction of the reinforced fill.

REFERENCES

Christopher, B.R., Gill, S.A., Giroud J.P., Juran I., Mitchell, J.K. & Dunnicliff J., 1989, *Design and construction guidelines for reinforced Soil structures*. Federal Highway Administration, Report No. FHWA-RD-89-043, McLean, VA.

Jewell, R.A., 1990, *Strength and deformation in reinforced soil design*. Proc. IV Int. Conf. on Geotextiles, Geomembranes and Related Products, Vol. 3.

Koerner G.R. & Koerner, R.M., 1990, *The installation survivability of geotextiles and geogrids*. Proc. IV Int. Conf. on Geotextiles, Geomembranes and Related Products, Vol. 2.

Leshchinsky D. & Boedecker, R.H., 1989, *Geosynthetic reinforced earth structures*. ASCE, Jrn. of Geotechnical Eng., Vol. 115, No. 10.

Leshchinsky D., 1994, *RESLOPE: supplemental notes*. Uni. of Delaware.

Paulson, J.N., 1990, *Summary and evaluation of construction related damage to geotextiles in reinforcing applications*. Proc. IV Int. Conf. on Geotextiles, Geomembranes and Related Products, Vol. 2.

Sembenelli, G. & Sembenelli, P., 1994, *Experiences with high reinforced soil slopes*. Proc. V Int. Conf. on Geotextiles, Geomembranes and Related Products, Vol. 1.

Steep reinforced slopes

P. RECALCATI and P. RIMOLDI, Tenax SpA, Italy

ABSTRACT
Reinforced soil is a composite material in which the engineering properties of soil, which is strong in compression and weak in tension, are greatly enhanced by the addition of a small volume of reinforcement which is strong in tension. Commonly the reinforcement is in the form of a geogrid. Geogrids are two dimensional synthetic products with high tensile strength and apertures which allow interlocking with the soil. Their main applications are to stabilization of soft soil and reinforcement of steep slopes. This paper illustrates some of the available solutions for the construction of steep slopes reinforced with geogrids.

INTRODUCTION
Polymer geogrids for soil reinforcement were developed in the United Kingdom and Japan at the end of the seventies and have since been used worldwide with it not being uncommon to find reinforced slopes in excess of 20 m high. Geogrid reinforced slopes are now more commonly used for permanent works where design lives may be between 50 and 120 years. Consequently geogrids may be subject to almost constant load for times up to 10^6 hours. Different types of geogrids are available and these may be classified as i) extruded, hot formed, uniaxially and biaxially drawn, in PP or HDPE; ii) extruded, cold punched, uniaxially and biaxially drawn, in PP or HDPE; iii) woven PET yarns, arranged in bundles, covered with PVC or other types of sheathing; iv) PET strips sheathed in LDPE and thermally bonded at the intersections.

MAIN APPLICATIONS OF STEEP REINFORCED SLOPES
There are many applications for steep reinforced slopes, such as:

♦ Reinstatement of landslides in natural slopes or cuttings

♦ Construction of storage facilities such as solid or liquid containments

♦ Construction of steep fill slopes such as noise bunds and embankments

♦ Widening of roads or other filled areas by a steep slope extension

REQUIRED REINFORCEMENT CHARACTERISTICS

Frictional behaviour

When a horizontal tensile load is applied to a geogrid with regular apertures the resulting tangential stress resisting pullout, comprises two components. The first is related to the frictional shear stress, developed between the geogrid and soil, while the second is related to the passive resistance the soil mobilizes against the transverse bars of the geogrid. By direct shear tests it is possible to define the coefficient of interaction

$$f_{ds} = \tan\delta / \tan\phi'$$

where

δ is the friction angle of the soil-geogrid interface
ϕ' is the friction angle of the soil

Typical values for the coefficient of geogrid interaction, f_{ds}, are given as 0.8 to 1.0, Picarelli et al. (1993). The value of the available force at a point along a reinforcement depends on the properties of the reinforcement and the bond stress mobilized there. Bond stress is important in preventing direct sliding along a reinforcement or pullout of the reinforcement. The magnitude of bond stress can be expressed as:

$$\tau_b = \sigma_n' \, f_{po} \, \tan\phi'$$

where

f_{po} is the factor of pullout factor
σ_n' is the normal stress

Typical values of f_{po} for geogrids are 0.8 to 1.05 and the maximum pullout resistance that can be developed is $T_b = 2\,L\,B\,\tau_b$, where L and B are the length and width of the reinforcement in the anchorage zone.

Tensile strength

GRI Test Method GG1 suggests that tensile strength be measured on a single representative rib unit and then factored up to calculate the tensile strength per unit width, T_{grid}, such that $T_{grid} = T_{rib} n_{rib}$ where n_{rib} is the number of ribs per unit length and T_{rib} is the tensile strength of a single rib. Alternatively ISO 10319, for wide width tensile testing requires use of a geogrid specimen approximately 200 mm wide and containing at least one row of nodes, excluding those nodes held in the jaws. The tensile strength is then given as $T_{grid} = c \cdot T_{wide\ width}$, where $T_{wide\ width}$ is the tensile strength of the sample and c is defined as N_m/N_s in which N_m is the number of tensile elements per metre width of product and N_s is the number of tensile elements within the test specimen.

Creep behaviour

The long term mechanical properties of a geogrid depend on its creep behaviour. Creep behaviour depends on temperature, load, time, loading conditions, polymer and the structure of the product. Using the results of creep tests, performed for at least 10,000 hours at temperatures of typically 10, 20, and 40 °C, combined with time-temperature superposition it is possible to extrapolate, Montanelli & Rimoldi (1993), the load, T_{creep}, which produces a maximum strain 10% over 120 years. The creep behaviour exhibited by HDPE geogrids depends upon the precise characteristics of the polymer while the behaviour of PET geogrids depend upon the structure of the product, The value of T_{creep} for both types of geogrid is about 40% of the short term ultimate tensile strength. When T_{creep} has been determined, the Long Term Design Strength is simply LTDS = T_{creep}. If it is not possible to carry out the creep test required to determine T_{creep} then the LTDS may be calculated from the short term tensile strength by applying a factor of safety to allow for the effects of creep. In this case the LTDS is T_{grid}/FS_{creep} where FS_{creep} is a function of the importance of the work, the expected life and the kind of reinforcement. For important projects FS_{creep} ranges between 5 and 10.

Junction strength

Junction strength can be determined using GRI Test Method GG2 applied to a tee-shape specimen. Since geogrids are designed on the basis of their LTDS a rational requirement is that the junction strength, F_j, should be at least equal to the LTDS multiplied by a factor of safety, FS_j, such that $F_j > LTDS \cdot FS_j$. Montanelli & Rimoldi (1994) have reported junction strength of various types of geogrid.

Installation damage

Geogrids may be damaged during installation with this damage causing a reduction in the tensile strength of the reinforcement. The operational strength may be calculated by the application of a factor of safety, FS_{damage}, defined as the ratio of the original, undamaged, strength to the exhumed, damaged, strength eg $FS_{damage} = T_{grid}/T_{exhumed}$. Wright & Greenwood (1994) present the results of damage tests performed at TRL following the procedures set out by Watts & Brady (1990).

Chemical and biological resistance

To determine the design strength of a reinforcement it may be necessary to allow for the effects of chemical or biological attack occurring during the design life of the reinforcement. Appropriate factors of safety, $FS_{chemical}$ and $FS_{biological}$, may be determined by comparing the short term tensile strength of the reinforcement before and after exposure to a chemically or biologically aggressive environment. Once approved, Euro Standards TC189/WG5/N125 Chemical Resistance and TC189/WG5/N126 Biological Resistance will provide test procedures.

Determination of the design strength

If creep testing had been carried out, the allowable long term strength, T_{allow}, is given as :

$$T_{allow} = T_{creep}/(FS_{damage} \cdot FS_{chemical} \cdot FS_{biological})$$

If creep testing has not been carried out, and provided $F_j > (T_{grid}/FS_{creep}) \cdot FS_j$, the allowable long term strength, T_{allow}, is given as :

$$T_{allow} = T_{grid}/(FS_{damage} \cdot FS_{chemical} \cdot FS_{biological} \cdot FS_{creep})$$

If not

$$T_{allow} = T_{grid}/(FS_{damage} \cdot FS_{chemical} \cdot FS_{biological} \cdot FS_{creep} \cdot FS_{junction})$$

The design strength T_{des} is finally found by applying a further factor of safety, FS_{design}, typically in the range 1.25 to 1.50, depending upon the difficulty and importance of the project, to give :

$$T_{des} = T_{allow}/FS_{design}$$

DESIGN CRITERIA

For a dry cohesionless soil the limiting slope angle, β_{lim}, to which an unreinforced slope may be safely built, cannot exceed friction angle of the soil, *eg* $\beta_{lim} \leq \phi'$. For slopes steeper than β_{lim} it is necessary to provide some additional forces to maintain equilibrium, *eg* a gross force T provided by soil reinforcement. T may be expressed as $T = \frac{1}{2} k \gamma H^2$ where H is the height of the slope, γ is the unit weight of the soil and k is an equivalent earth pressure coefficient depending on the angle of the slope β, the soil strength parameters c' and ϕ' as well as the pore pressure coefficient $r_u = u/z$. For a vertical face the coefficient k equals the coefficient of active earth pressure k_a and when β is between ϕ' and 90°, k has a value between zero and k_a.

The additional forces required to provide equilibrium for a steep slope, with an adequate margin of safety against any potential failure mechanism, can be determined by a limit equilibrium analysis. Possible failure mechanisms are described by many authors including Leshchinsky & Perry (1988), Mangiavacchi et al.(1987) and Jewell (1991). Detailed design methods are also supplied by manufacturers such Exxon (1992), Tensar (1986) and Tenax (1995). The design problem can be set as follows: once the geometry of the slope is defined, the surcharge load fixed, the geotechnical characteristics of the soil known and the design resistance T_{des} of the grids set, it is necessary to find the number, the vertical position and the length of the reinforcing layers required to provide the equilibrium for every possible failure mechanism.

CONSTRUCTION METHODS AND SYSTEMS

Wrap around

To date, the construction method most widely used in Europe is the *wrap around* technique, which involves wrapping the geogrid around the face of the slope to protect it from progressive erosion. The technique may be used with or without formwork but formwork is necessary if a smooth face is required. An illustration of climbing formwork is given in Figure 1. Alternatively a temporary timber formwork may be employed, Figure 2, or, if the face is stepped, the face formwork to the current lift may be secured by steel pins driven into the previous lift, Figure 3.

Proprietary systems

Few proprietary systems based specifically on geogrid reinforcement are patented in one or more countries in Europe. The following are three examples.

Tenax Rivel - a vegetated retaining wall system which uses sacrificial steel mesh formwork which aids construction of slopes up to 80° and allows a very uniform faced geometry to be achieved, Figure 4. Rates of construction are high so the overall cost is relatively low.

Due to the use of biomats, which provide a medium for preventing erosion and supporting plant growth, the slope is readily vegetated. Vegetation is enhanced by hydroseeding the face upon completion of the structural component. at the end of the construction of the reinforced soil structure. Construction involves cutting the geogrids to the required length and bending the steel facing mesh to the required angle. These sacrificial facing mesh units are aligned at the face of the slope, overlapped by about 50 mm, and jointed by steel wires. A biomat is placed on the back face of the formwork and stabilising hooks are fixed to the formwork every 500 mm, Figure 4. The reinforcing geogrid is placed and anchored by means of U-shape staples whence soil is placed and compacted to typically 300 mm thick layers. This process is repeated until the required slope height is achieved, Figure 5. Typical construction rates are 30 to 50 m² of face per day using a team of four people and plant comprising a truck, an excavator, a roller and a small compactor.

Mecamur - a retaining wall system characterized by a patented steel mesh face module which is connected to HDPE geogrids, Figure 6. These steel modules can be plugged together to obtain any geometry, Figure 7. Since no geogrid is wrapped around the face, long term stability is provided by the root mass, formed by the vegetation planted over the face, once the steel facing modules have corroded. Additionally a geomat, and sometimes a biomat, is placed at the face to provide long term erosion protection and local stability. This system is economic since it does not require cranage because the components may be manhandled.

157

Terra Bloc - employs a face block in the form of a soil filled triangular prism with a face vegetated by turves, Figure 8. The base and the triangular sides of the prism are formed of steel mesh, while a geotextile is folded all around the block, with exclusion of the face side. A biaxial PP geogrid is wrapped around the prism so that the geogrid creates a loop which may be used for lifting. The block is around 500 mm high and 600 mm across the base with a length ranging between 2 and 4 m. Once the foundation of the slope is well compacted the block is lifted by the loop with a crane, or excavator, and placed. After placing the block, the loop is folded toward the outside face of the slope, over the vegetated face of the block, Figure 9. Then about 250 mm of soil is placed and compacted behind the block. The loop is then opened and the geogrid is placed over the compacted soil for a maximum length of about 2.5 m. This process is repeated until the desired height is obtained. An advantage of this system is that it provides an instantly vegetated face.

REFERENCES

Jewell, R.A., 1991, *Application of revised design charts for steep reinforced slopes*. Geotextiles and Geomembranes, Vol. 10, No. 3.

Leshchinsky, D. & Perry, E.B., 1988, *On the design of geosynthetic reinforced walls*. Geotextile and Geomembranes, Vol. 8, No. 4.

Mangiavacchi, R., Nova, R. & Pellegrini, G., 1987, *Analisi di stabilita' dei muri in terra rinforzata*. Rivista Italiana di Geotecnica, Anno XX, n.3

Montanelli, F. & Rimoldi, P., 1993, *Creep and accelerated creep testing for geogrids*. Proc. Geosynthetics '93.

Montanelli, F. & Rimoldi, P., 1994, *The development of junction strength tests for geosynthetics*. Proc. 5th International Conference on Geotextiles, Geomembranes and Related Products.

Picarelli, L., Cazzuffi, D., Ricciuti, A. & Rimoldi, P., 1993, *Laboratory investigations of the shear strength of geogrid reinforced soils*. Proc. ASTM Symp. on Geosynthetics Soil Reinforcement Testing Procedures.

Watts, G.R.A. & Brady, K.C., 1990, *Site damage trials on geotextiles*. Proc. 4th International Conference on Geotextiles, Geomembranes and Related Products.

Wright, W.C.A. & Greenwood, J.H., 1994, *Interlaboratory trials on installation damage in geotextiles and comparison with site trials*. ERA Technology, Report 93-0915.

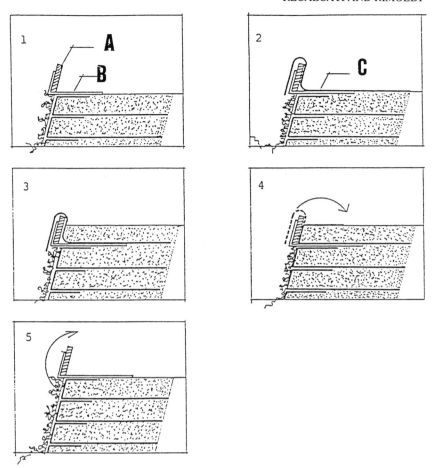

Figure 1 Wrap around with movable formwork: A) timber table;
B) scaffolding tube; C) geogrid.

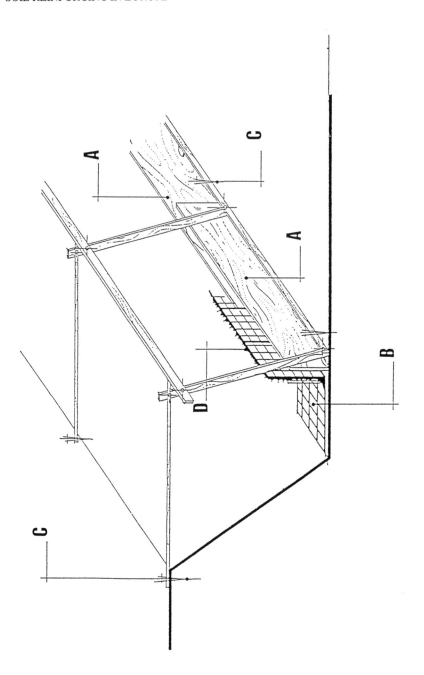

Figure 2   Wrap around with a timber structure: A) temporary table;
B) geogrid; C) staple; D) turf.

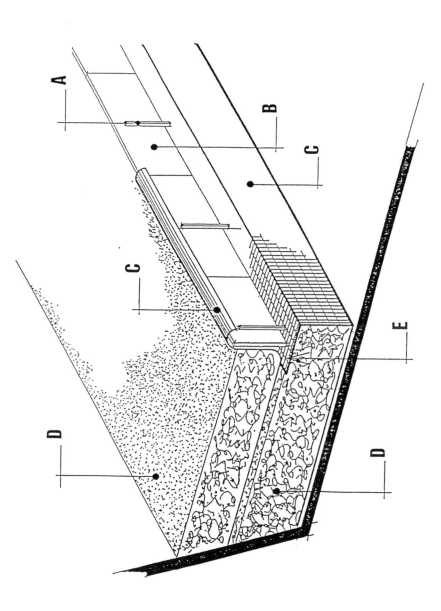

Figure 3 Wrap around with timber tables and steel pins: A) steel pin;
B) wooden table; C) geogrid; D) compacted soil; F) staple.

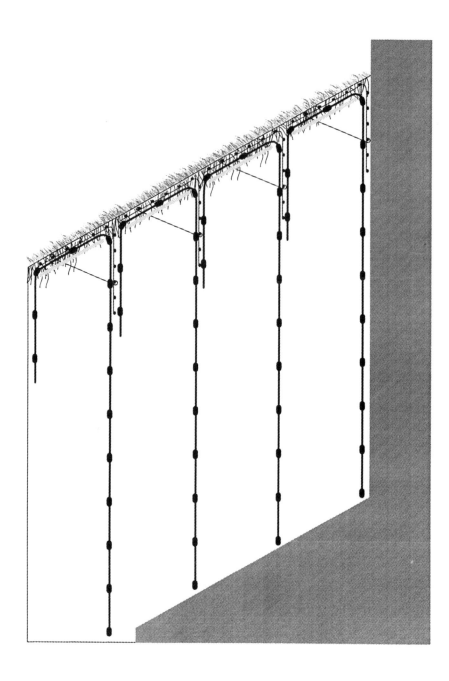

Figure 4 Rivel system

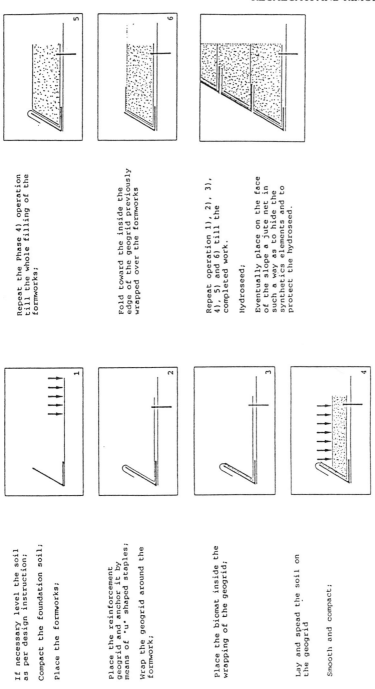

Repeat the Phase 4) operation till the whole filling of the formworks;

Fold toward the inside the edge of the geogrid previously wrapped over the formworks

Repeat operation 1), 2), 3), 4), 5) and 6) till the completed work.

Hydroseed;

Eventually place on the face of the slope a jute net in such a way as to hide the synthetics elements and to protect the hydroseed.

If necessary level the soil as per design instruction;

Compact the foundation soil;

Place the formworks;

Place the reinforcement geogrid and anchor it by means of "u" shaped staples;

Wrap the geogrid around the formwork;

Place the biomat inside the wrapping of the geogrid;

Lay and spead the soil on the geogrid

Smooth and compact;

Figure 5 Rivel construction procedure

163

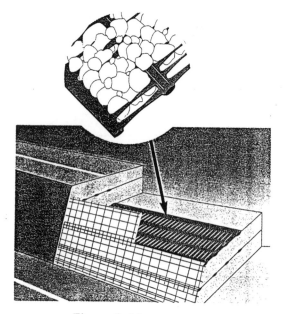

Figure 6 Mecamur system

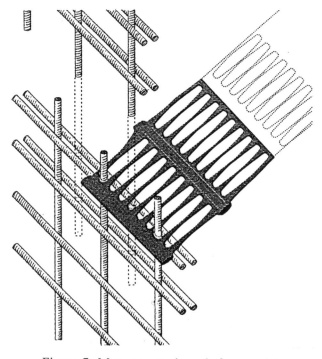

Figure 7 Mecamur steel mesh face modules

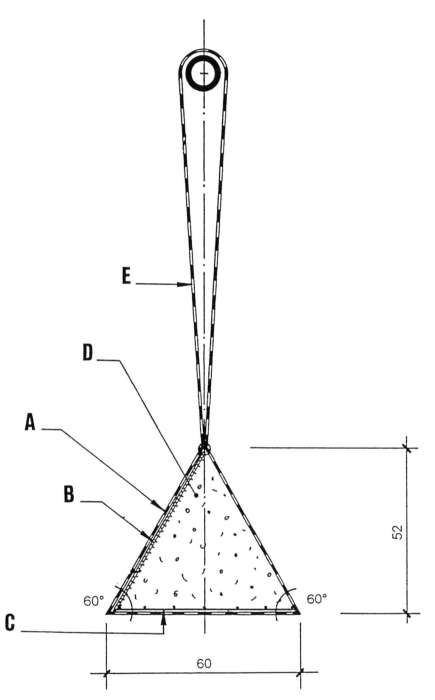

Figure 8 Terra Bloc system face block: A) biaxial geogrid; B) turf; C) steel mesh; D) soil; E) loop.

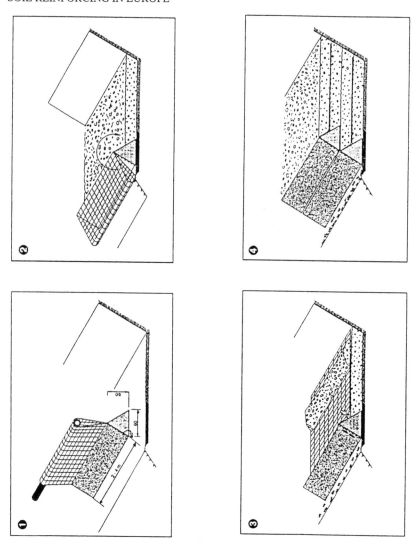

Figure 9 Terra Bloc construction procedure

Dormant sub-surface reinforced soil structures

P. R. RANKILOR, Consulting Engineer, United Kingdom

SYNOPSIS

There is a generic group of geosynthetic reinforced soil structures which may be termed *dormant*. These structures are built beneath the surface of the ground, to perform some task at a future date, in the event of foreseen changes of circumstances. Examples include the use of geogrids over areas of potential mine shaft collapse; geotextiles beneath presently stable embankments, and sub-surface reinforced soil walls to prevent structural movement in the event of lateral ground movements.

INTRODUCTION

The design and specification of geosynthetic reinforced soil structures is now common place. The majority are above the ground and fall into the apparent classification of reinforced soil walls. However, some have not been designed using the usual criteria, but were designed to be inactive at the time of construction, pending a change in the physical circumstances of their location. Suggesting this classification and bringing it to the attention of design engineers, may encourage the design of more structures and the generation of new ideas. The following are four examples of dormant sub-surface reinforced soil structures.

STRUCTURES OVER MINE SHAFTS

There are parts of the United Kingdom where coal mining has taken place in the past and subsequent development has covered all traces of mine shafts at the surface. Around the top of most mine shafts there would be large quantities of fill. Shafts were invariably boarded up near the top, often at the rockhead level, and covered over with ash and fill.

This situation is potentially unstable since the timbers tend to rot with time and shaft collapse may ensue. There is a further danger that many shafts were unrecorded and the exact position of most of those which were recorded is not certain. Geophysical techniques are unreliable in locating shafts and drilling from the surface is a hit-and-miss operation which is time consuming and expensive. Consequently, locating all known shafts in a given vicinity does not preclude the presence of other unrecorded shafts. Therefore, direct shaft location is not a final solution.

One approach to this problem is to not locate each shaft, but to design a suitably strong geogrid cover which is placed just beneath the surface of the ground, over the whole potential collapse area. Fortunately, there are some simple design criteria that can be applied. It is normally expected that, when collapse occurs, it will do so at the level of bedrock beneath the superficial soils and fills, not below. The collapse is generally considered to form a cone of 25° to 35° at the time of initial settlement, later expanding outwards to 45°.

As shown in Figure 1, a reinforcing synthetic is laid over the area to intercept all potential collapses. Its main design criteria include the allowance for sufficient anchorage and strength to prevent excessive sag in the event of collapse. The design objective is that if persons are over the shaft at the time of collapse, their lives will be saved. They must be lowered the minimum distance practical, must not be damaged by sliding soil and must be able to climb out of the supported collapse cone.

There are other examples of this kind of use, where geosynthetics are used to intercept catastrophic collapse of the surface from crown-hole development over areas of abandoned shallow room-and-pillar mine workings. It is believed that this technique was pioneered in Scotland and now a number of roadway structures have been built in the United Kingdom using this dormant geosynthetic method.

In order to meet the criterion of grip, a geogrid will always be superior to a textile where a thin soil cover is mandatory. Also, grids can be interlocked easily. Finally, they are ideal to permit the penetration of roots from vegetation and to permit free drainage of a natural kind to take place.

STRUCTURES ADJACENT TO MINE SHAFTS

During the design of the groundworks for a major motorway in the north of England, it was noticed that the carriageway was to pass close to the edge of a major mine shaft from an abandoned colliery. Although the mine shaft had been sealed off by the then National Coal Board, it had suffered internal collapse and the structure was in danger of failing at rockhead. As can be seen in Figure 2, the potential collapse threatened the stability of the new motorway.

The proximity of these two structures created some interesting considerations. For example, the first option was to move the centre-line of the motorway. Anyone familiar with the lengthy processes involved in selecting and obtaining a route knows that adjustment is an impractical option unless all else fails, because of the inevitable time and cost implications.

Alternatively, the second conventional option was to finance the stabilisation of the shaft either under contract, or by purchasing the shaft from the Coal Board. This was not practical owing to the mix of professional responsibilities and long term liabilities that would result. Just placing a drilling rig over a collapsing shaft is a dangerous operation.

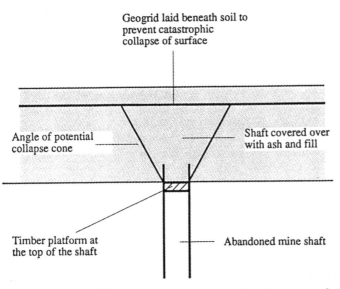

Geogrid laid beneath soil to
prevent catastrophic
collapse of surface

Angle of potential
collapse cone

Shaft covered over
with ash and fill

Timber platform at
the top of the shaft

Abandoned mine shaft

Fig.1. Dormant geogrid layer to intercept potential collapse cone from
deteriorating mineshaft.

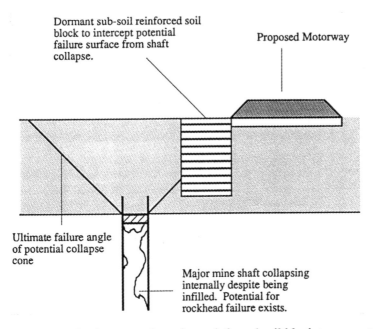

Dormant sub-soil reinforced soil
block to intercept potential
failure surface from shaft
collapse.

Proposed Motorway

Ultimate failure angle
of potential collapse
cone

Major mine shaft collapsing
internally despite being
infilled. Potential for
rockhead failure exists.

Fig.2. The use of a dormant sub-surface reinforced soil block to prevent
lateral movement and damage to a highway at some unspecified time
in the future.

169

In this context, it is interesting to consider, as was proposed, the possibility of constructing a sub-surface retaining wall, designed to intercept the potential failure surface from the shaft in the event of a collapse. This is shown in Figure 2.

There are two design options available. Firstly, to construct the retaining wall in such a way that it acts as a final retaining wall in the event of shaft failure and, secondly, to construct it to hold the road, but to need additional work in the event of shaft failure. Since the wall would hopefully, never be utilised, the second, less expensive option was the obvious choice. In essence the wall would be built at minimum cost, with no facing elements and without imposed stress. Consideration would be given to choosing materials with the best lifetime expectancy and to choosing clean well drained granular fill to provide the most inert environment possible under the given circumstances. There would, no doubt, be settlement of the road, but not catastrophic failure. Thus, safety of vehicles would be ensured and reinstatement costs minimised.

STRUCTURES ON SLOPES ADJACENT TO OTHER PROPERTY

There are frequent situations when civil engineering structures must be built on sloping ground and where the foundation conditions are potentially unstable. Sometimes, structures are uncomfortably close to adjacent land ownership boundaries where other pre-existing structures are threatened. Under these circumstances, it is possible to use sub-surface dormant reinforced soil blocks to form a keyed-in foundation block to ensure future stability. One example is shown in Figure 3.

In this case, multiple problems existed. A sloping rockhead surface was covered by glacial deposits, leading to potential instability at the rockhead interface. Part way down the slope, a canal had been constructed and, although presently disused, its refurbishment and re-use was being considered by the owners. Above this canal was a steeply sloping site which had been over-tipped with undifferentiated fill for some time. The fill had become unstable and the site was slumping downwards, already beginning to disturb the canal below.

The solution adopted was, as shown in Figure 3, to sheet pile and excavate a deep foundation zone into the soft mudrocks below, to form a keyed-in foundation. This was built as a multi-layer polyester woven geotextile reinforced soil construction, with geotextile wrap-round at the edges of the buried block. The design and amount of compaction of the imported granular fill was very important in this case, since the object of this basal block was to have maximum rigidity to minimise movement.

Above the dormant structure, was constructed a series of conventional reinforced soil banks, with sloping faces, wrap-round textile and soil over-cover. Although polyester was used for the majority of the structural elements, in the very top few metres, it was considered uneconomic to use it, so a heavy grade of polypropylene woven textile was used to form the upper layers.

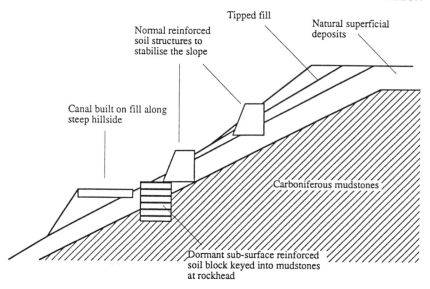

Fig.3. Dormant sub-surface reinforced soil block to prevent possible future damage to a canal on a steep hillside from movement along the interface between superficial materials and rockhead.

Geojute was used as a final cover to prevent surface rain wash erosion. This site has behaved satisfactorily for several years. The dormant base structure gives confidence that it will do so into the future.

DORMANT GEOTEXTILES BENEATH EMBANKMENTS

It is not common, but bound to happen from time to time, that an embankment is to be constructed on land which is sufficiently strong to support it, but not strong enough to provide it with an adequate safety factor. The preliminary design of such an embankment may show, for example, that the initial factor of safety against rotational slip failure is 1.1, increasing with time to 1.2 as pore pressure decreases. It may also be a requirement of the design that the factor of safety should be 1.3.

If a factor of safety of 1.3 has been specified and must be provided. The one option is to change the geometry of the structure by, for example, reducing its height, slope angle or fill density for example. Changing the geometry is not a proper solution if the structure was originally designed to perform a given function requiring the original shape and level. Fill density can rarely be varied substantially without generating high costs, for example by using expanded polystyrene.

Possibly the optimum solution is to use a dormant geotextile reinforcing layer at the base of the embankment. This is designed to add its tensile strength to the restoring moment elements of the calculation against slip circle failure. At the time of construction, the textile will be minimally strained (if at all) and will thus not be stressed, since the embankment will be constructed at a safety factor of 1.1. The textile is designed to have the appropriate ultimate tensile strength and design strain strength at a life period equivalent to that of the main structure. It will not require a particularly strong textile to provide a ten percent increase in moment around the failure circle. Allowance for deterioration of strength with time is still speculative, but trebling the current calculated strength should suffice and should still be quite economical. No re-adjustment of structure geometry is needed and no delay in construction. The dormant textile may never be used, but in the event of conditions deteriorating such that the in-soil strengths become stressed to their limits, then the textile will be there to add its own structural contribution and increase the safety factor at that time.

ACKNOWLEDGEMENT

The Author wishes to thank UCO Technical Fabrics NV for their support in the preparation of this paper.

Basal reinforced embankment practice in the United Kingdom

C. R. LAWSON, Terram Limited, United Kingdom

SYNOPSIS

Three basal reinforced embankment techniques have been in use in the United Kingdom for over 15 years. Basal reinforcement is used to provide additional embankment stability, to provide additional embankment stability and prevent settlement, and to prevent embankment collapse due to the formation of a void in the foundation. The paper reviews these three basal reinforcement techniques and highlights the reinforcement requirements in terms of the applied load regimes over time. The methods currently used to determine the basal reinforcement load regimes are also examined.

INTRODUCTION

In the United Kingdom, basal reinforcement is used in the construction of embankments in three situations, Figure 1:

- To provide additional stability for embankments constructed on soft and very soft foundation soils, Figure 1a;

- to provide additional stability and prevent the settlement of embankments on soft and very soft foundation soils when used in conjunction with a piled foundation treatment, Figure 1b;

- to prevent collapse and limit vertical movement of the embankment surface following the formation of a void in the foundation, Figure 1c.

Where basal reinforcement is used to provide additional stability only, Figure 1a, its role is to maintain equilibrium until consolidation can occur in the soft foundation soil. The foundation soil strengthens with time during consolidation and finally supports the embankment loading without need for the reinforcement. Reinforcement of an embankment on soft soil reduces construction material quantities, reduces land acquisition and reduces construction time.

Where the basal reinforcement is used to provide stability and prevent differential settlements and localised movements, Figures 1b & 1c, its role is to intercept and interrupt the localised shear deformations which can occur in the embankment due to the presence of a piled foundation, Figure 1b, or a void in the foundation, Figure 1c. These two applications are closely related, the first involves a local increase in vertical stress, due to the supporting piles,

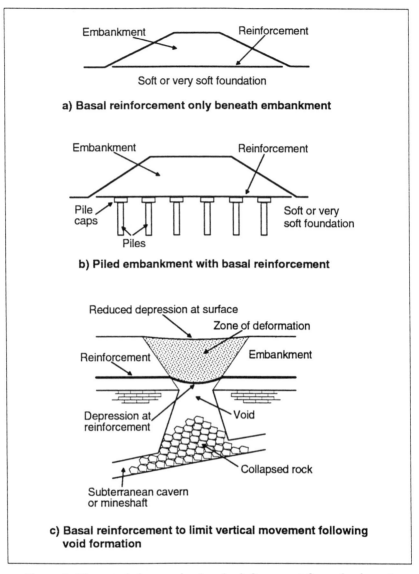

a) Basal reinforcement only beneath embankment

b) Piled embankment with basal reinforcement

c) Basal reinforcement to limit vertical movement following void formation

Figure 1 Three techniques using basal reinforcement for embankment construction

while the second involves a local loss of vertical stress, due to foundation subsidence. In both cases the reinforcement is acting to prevent the propagation of local shear deformation from the loading discontinuity through the soil above. Equally important is the fact that as the system starts to deform the reinforcement acts also as a membrane in tension, physically supporting normal stresses. In the case of the reinforced piled foundation the reinforcement is required to restrain localised shear deformations for the full life of the structure. However, in the case of the foundation void the reinforcement is required to restrain localised shear deformations only over the period of time the void exists.

The limit state (or limit mode) approach has proved an effective technique for determining basal reinforcement requirements. There are two limit states - ultimate and serviceability. Ultimate limit states apply to those conditions that result in structural collapse while serviceability limit states apply to those conditions where deformations result in a loss of serviceability. For each of the limit states assessed, tensile loads and strains are determined for the reinforcement to ensure that each of the limit states are not exceeded. For basal reinforced embankments an additional level of complexity exists inasmuch as the load regimes applied to the reinforcement are not constant with time.

LOAD REGIMES APPLIED TO THE REINFORCEMENT

Figure 2 shows diagrammatically the time-related load regimes applied to the reinforcement for the three basal reinforced embankment cases. For basal reinforced embankments on soft foundation soil, Figure 2a, the load applied to the reinforcement rises to a maximum value, T_r, at the end of embankment construction and then decreases with time as the foundation soil consolidates and gains in shear strength. At some point in time the foundation soil has adequate shear strength to fully support the embankment and the reinforcement is no longer required. Depending on the rate of gain in foundation shear strength the required design life of the reinforcement can be significantly less than the design life of the embankment.

For basal reinforced piled embankments, Figure 2b, the load applied to the reinforcement rises to a maximum value, T_r, at some point after completion of embankment construction when consolidation of the foundation soil between the pile caps has occurred. After this point in time there may be some small increase in reinforcement strain which results in a small reduction in tensile load but, effectively, the load applied to the reinforcement remains constant with time over the remaining design life of the embankment. Thus, the required design life of the reinforcement is equal to the design life of the embankment.

For basal reinforced embankments spanning voids, Figure 2c, no load is applied to the reinforcement until a void formation event occurs at some point in time after embankment construction. When this occurs the load applied to the reinforcement rises to a maximum value, T_r. After this there may be some small increase in reinforcement strain which results in a small reduction in tensile load but, effectively, the load applied to the reinforcement remains constant with time over the remaining design life of the embankment if no corrective maintenance is carried out on the void. If corrective maintenance is carried out on the void then the load applied to the reinforcement returns to zero. The required design life of the reinforcement is equal to the design life

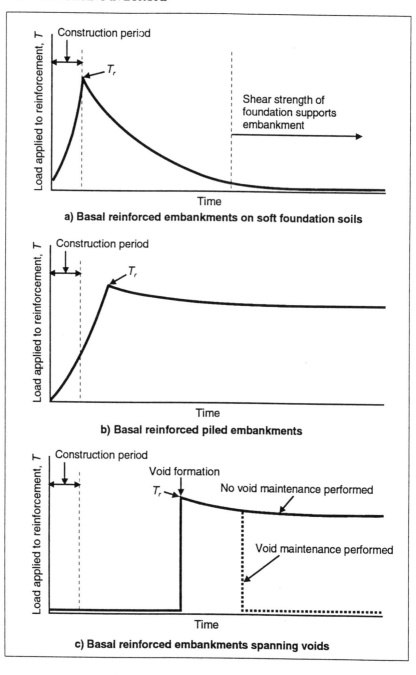

Figure 2 Time-related reinforcement load regimes in basal reinforced embankments

of the embankment even though the reinforcement may, or may not, carry loads during this time.

Fundamental to all basal reinforced embankments is the assessment of the maximum applied reinforcement load, T_r, as well as the time over which the applied loads *can* occur[1]. For basal reinforced embankments constructed on soft foundation soil the magnitude of T_r and the time over which loads are applied to the reinforcement are a function solely of geometry and soil characteristics. For basal reinforced piled embankments the magnitude of T_r and the time over which loads are applied to the reinforcement are a function of geometry, soil characteristics *and reinforcement characteristics*. For basal reinforced embankments spanning potential voids the magnitude of T_r and the time over which loads are applied to the reinforcement are a function of geometry, soil characteristics, reinforcement characteristics *and planned maintenance strategies*. Table 1 shows those factors affecting the maximum applied reinforcement load and those affecting the time over which the load is applied.

Table 1 Influence of various factors on applied reinforcement loads

	Maximum applied reinforcement load, T_r	Time of applied loads
1. Embankments on soft foundations		
(a) Geometry	✓	✓
(b) Soil characteristics	✓	✓
2. Piled embankments		
(a) Geometry	✓	
(b) Soil characteristics	✓	
(c) Reinforcement characteristics	✓	
3. Embankments spanning voids		
(a) Geometry	✓	
(b) Soil characteristics	✓	
(c) Reinforcement characteristics	✓	
(d) Maintenance strategies		✓

Current practice in the United Kingdom concentrates on the determination of the maximum applied reinforcement load, T_r. The time period over which the loads are applied to the reinforcement are chosen in a conservative manner based on anticipated future events. For simplicity, the applied loads are normally considered to be constant with time. This naturally builds a level

---

[1] For prudence, the maximum *possible* time period should be assumed because future events may be difficult to predict.

of conservatism into the choice of the reinforcement. In many instances the additional cost associated with a complex analysis to determine the changes in applied reinforcement loads with time may not be justified from the viewpoint of reinforcement cost savings.

USE OF BASAL REINFORCEMENT TO PROVIDE ADDITIONAL STABILITY

The use of basal reinforcement in the construction of embankments over soft foundation soils provides additional stability to the embankment prior to foundation consolidation. This additional stability enables the embankment to be constructed quicker, enables steeper side slopes to be utilised and reduces embankment fill quantities. As discussed already, it is important to note that the basal reinforcement is required only until the foundation has consolidated and can fully support the embankment loading. Thus, the time period over which the reinforcement is required is relatively short compared to the design life of the embankment.

In the United Kingdom, two variants, in addition to the conventional basal reinforcement technique have been used to provide additional short term stability. The two variants along with the conventional basal reinforcement technique are shown in Figure 3.

Vertical drains are used in combination with basal reinforcement to enable the foundation soil to consolidate more quickly, Figure 3b. This has benefits from the viewpoint of shorter construction periods, but also from the viewpoint of being able to utilise higher percentage loads in the reinforcement[2]. The planning of the construction sequence is important to ensure the vertical drains are installed prior to reinforcement placement (if possible) in order to prevent extensive damage to the reinforcement.

Stone-filled mattresses have also been used for basal reinforcement, Figure 3c. Claimed benefits, in addition to tensile resistance, are cited as reduction in differential settlements and a more even distribution of stress on the soft foundation, Bush et al. (1989). At this stage there is some disagreement in the literature concerning the additional benefits of stone-filled mattresses beyond tensile resistance. Consequently, it would appear prudent to design stone-filled mattresses on the basis of tensile resistance only (in an identical manner to conventional basal reinforcement on soft soils) and neglect any of the additional quoted benefits until such time as they have been proven and quantified.

The ultimate limit states pertaining to basal reinforced embankments on soft foundations are shown in Figure 4. Three of these govern the load applied to the reinforcement - rotational stability, Figure 4b; lateral sliding, Figure 4c;

---

[2] If the reinforcement is required for a shorter period of time then higher percentage load levels can be carried by the reinforcement.

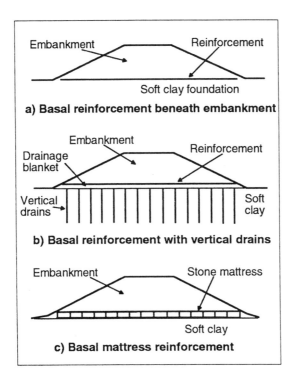

Figure 3 Three variations of basal reinforcement to provide short term
stability

and foundation extrusion, Figure 4d. Each limit state needs to be assessed to
ensure both the reinforcement and the adjacent soil can support the applied
loads. In addition, the serviceability limit states also need to be assessed, of
which there are two - excessive strain in the reinforcement, Figure 5a, and
foundation settlement, Figure 5b. Both of these limit states also affect the
loads applied to the reinforcement.

Over the last 15 years a considerable amount of work has been carried out
on developing analysis techniques to assess the ultimate limit states of basal
reinforced embankments, and consequently, the applied reinforcement loads.
Currently, four types of analysis techniques are used - plasticity solutions,
analytical solutions, limit equilibrium methods and continuum methods.

Plasticity solutions:

Solutions based on plasticity analyses have been proposed for basal
reinforced embankments on soft foundation soil, Jewell (1988), Houlsby &

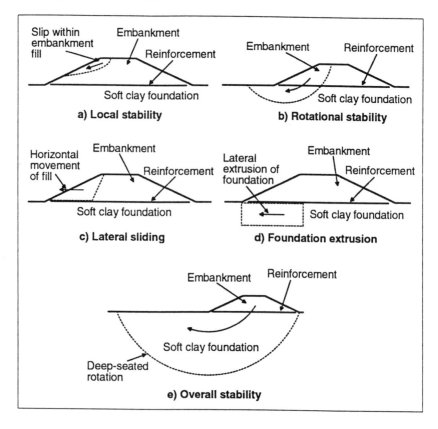

Figure 4   Ultimate limit states for basal reinforced embankments on soft
foundations (After BS 8006 : 1994)

Jewell (1988). Two sets of solutions have been published; for a foundation of limited depth and constant shear strength, and for a deep foundation with shear strength increasing linearly with depth. The solutions enable the unreinforced, partially reinforced and fully reinforced cases to be determined. Plasticity solutions provide a simple approach for the initial proportioning of basal reinforced embankments and are useful for preliminary designs.

Analytical solutions:

More recently, direct analytical solutions (based on plasticity solutions) have been developed for preliminary design purposes, Jewell (1995). The solutions cover the two cases of shallow foundation with constant shear strength and deep foundation with shear strength increasing linearly with depth. The solutions enable a preliminary assessment to be made of the required

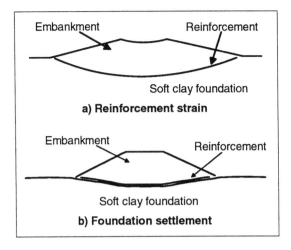

Figure 5 Serviceability limit states for basal reinforced embankments on
soft foundations (After BS 8006 : 1994)

embankment geometry, the maximum applied load in the reinforcement and
the required reinforcement stiffness.

Limit equilibrium methods:

Limit equilibrium methods have proved effective for the design of basal
reinforced embankments on soft foundation soils, and were the earliest
methods used e.g. Haliburton *et al.* (1977). Methods based on both moment
and force equilibrium have been used.

Limit equilibrium methods based on slip circles are currently easy to
perform because of the proliferation of computer software. However, slip
circle analyses have a number of limitations when applied to basal reinforced
embankments and these must be recognised and taken into account during
design.

1. The conventional slip circle approach cannot automatically take into
   account the deformations arising as a result of including reinforcement.
   These deformations affect the choice of reinforcement, the magnitude of
   the shear strength in the foundation and the interface shear strength.

2. For soft foundations of shallow depth the use of conventional slip circle
   analyses may underestimate the reinforcement requirements for stability. In
   this instance the use of translational wedges may give more appropriate
   results.

3. Conventional slip circle analysis assumes full positive bond between the reinforcement and the adjacent soils. This may not be the case with some reinforcements.

Continuum methods:

Continuum methods such as the finite element and finite difference methods have also been used to model basal reinforced embankments. These methods have normally been applied where the scale of the project warrants, where the engineering characteristics of the soils are complex, and/or where accurate settlement determinations are required. Limit equilibrium methods and plasticity solutions cannot take into account the effects of embankment settlement on the required properties of the reinforcement, Figure 5b, nor on the performance of the embankment as a whole. Continuum methods are the only techniques which readily lend themselves to these situations. For realistic results from continuum methods both the correct soil and interface models and close attention to the appropriate soil parameters are essential.

The methods available to assess the serviceability limit states of basal reinforced embankments on soft foundations are much less prevalent than those used to assess the ultimate limit states. The reason for this is that any approach in detail is necessarily complex and, in general, requires sophisticated analytical procedures, e.g. continuum methods. Consequently, serviceability limits have been applied based on either empirical values, which have been observed to work in practice (for reinforcement strain), or by neglecting the presence of the reinforcement (for foundation settlement).

For reinforcement strain, an appropriate limit of a maximum of 5% for short term strain has been proposed based on general practice, BS 8006 : 1994. However, it should be noted that recommending fixed strain levels of this magnitude may not take into account strain compatibility with the adjacent soil during loading. Lower reinforcement strain levels may be warranted where foundation soils are deformation-sensitive.

For the assessment of foundation settlement, simple consolidation theory may be used with the deflected shape of the reinforcement subsequently approximated. Alternatively, more sophisticated analyses using continuum methods may be adopted. Continuum methods are the only technique that can model foundation settlement with the inclusion of reinforcement.

Two examples of basal reinforced embankments constructed over soft foundation soils are shown in Figure 6. The embankment section shown in Figure 6a was constructed over a brown fibrous peat foundation. The planned construction involved surcharging the embankment by 0.6 m for 1 year, and then remove the surcharge and construct the pavement layers. To ensure adequate stability a 200 kN/m woven polyester geotextile was used as the basal reinforcement. It was considered that this reinforcement fulfilled the strength and the time of load application requirements.

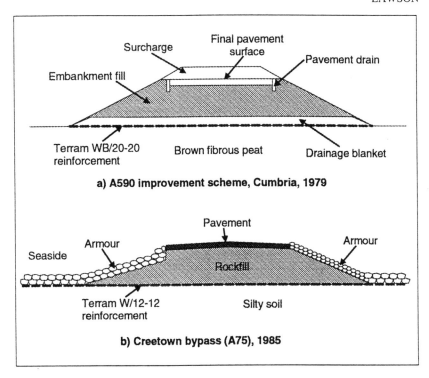

Figure 6 Two examples of basal reinforced embankments over soft
foundation soils in the United Kingdom

The embankment shown in Figure 6b was constructed over silty estuarine
deposits. To provide adequate stability in raising the embankment in a single
lift basal reinforcement was adopted. Because it was considered that
consolidation would occur quickly the reinforcement used was a woven
polypropylene geotextile with a tensile strength of 120 kN/m.

USE OF BASAL REINFORCEMENT IN CONJUNCTION WITH PILES TO PROVIDE ADDITIONAL STABILITY AND PREVENT SETTLEMENT

While basal reinforcement alone provides additional stability to
embankments constructed on soft foundation soils it does not affect the
consolidation characteristics of the soft foundation soil. In instances where
both embankment stability and settlement control is required basal
reinforcement has been combined with foundation piling. Conventional piled
embankments, without basal reinforcement, utilised large diameter pile caps
and raking piles along the embankment extremities to ensure the maximum
embankment loading was transferred directly onto the piles. With the addition
of basal reinforcement, small diameter pile caps can be utilised and no raking
piles are required, Figure 1b.

Because of their ability to enhance embankment stability and control settlement basal reinforced piled embankments have found use in those situations where new embankment construction abuts stable, with regard to settlement, structures. In the United Kingdom this technique has been utilised in two situations:

- To prevent differential settlement between new embankment construction over soft foundation soils and an existing embankment where settlement has ceased, and

- to prevent differential settlement between new embankment construction over soft foundation soils and a bridge structure with a piled foundation.

The ultimate limit states pertaining to basal reinforced piled embankments are shown in Figure 7. Those directly related to the assessment of the maximum load applied to the basal reinforcement are shown in Figures 7c & 7d where the reinforcement is required to transfer the vertical embankment loading onto the pile caps and counteract the outward thrust of the embankment. In the direction along the length of the embankment the maximum load applied to the reinforcement is due to the transference of the vertical embankment loading only.

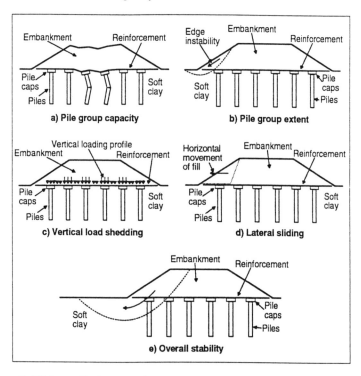

Figure 7 Ultimate limit states for basal reinforced piled embankments (After BS 8006 : 1994)

Across the width of the embankment the maximum load applied to the reinforcement is due to the combination of transference of the vertical embankment loading and resistance to the horizontal outward thrust. Fundamental to the assessment of maximum load applied to the reinforcement is the determination of the load attributable to the transference of the vertical embankment loading. The presence of relatively rigid piles in the soft foundation gives rise to a complex vertical stress distribution at the base of the embankment due to soil arching between adjacent pile caps. This is further complicated by the three-dimensional nature of the problem as well as the presence of the compressible soft foundation soil between the pile caps. To date, analytical methods are most commonly used to determine the load applied to the reinforcement due to the vertical embankment loading. Continuum methods, while offering considerable potential are only just being investigated, e.g. Jones *et al.* (1990).

Analytical methods:

To determine the vertical stress acting at the base of the embankment between the pile caps by analytical methods a number of simplifying assumptions have to be made in order to reduce the problem to manageable proportions. Firstly, it is normally assumed that the foundation soil between the pile caps does not support any vertical embankment loading. Thus, all of the vertical embankment loading not supported directly by the pile caps is supported solely by the reinforcement. This enables a conservative estimate of the load applied to the reinforcement and removes the effect of changes in applied reinforcement load due to foundation soil consolidation.

Secondly, a soil arching model has to be used to determine what proportion of the vertical embankment loading acts between the pile caps. The most commonly proposed models are based on projecting subsurface conduits, John (1987), Jones *et al.* (1990) or suspended hemispherical vaults, Hewlett & Randolph (1988). BS 8006 : 1994 utilises the former model which results in ratios of vertical stress applied between the pile caps to average vertical stress at the base of the embankment (p'_f / σ'_v) as shown in Figure 8. The average vertical stress at the base of the embankment, σ'_v, being the sum of the embankment weight plus surcharge loading.

Thirdly, the applied vertical embankment loading is assumed to deflect the reinforcement thus generating tensile loads. To simplify the mathematics BS 8006 : 1994 assumes a parabolic deflection of the reinforcement with the load in the reinforcement determined as follows:

$$T_{rp} = \frac{s(s-a)f_f\,p'_f}{2a}\sqrt{1+\frac{1}{6\varepsilon}} \tag{1}$$

where,

T_{rp} is the tensile load in the reinforcement due to vertical embankment loading, per unit width

s is the spacing between piles

a is the size of the pile caps

f_f is a partial factor applied to the loads = 1.3

p'_f is the average vertical stress acting on the reinforcement between pile caps

ε is the strain in the reinforcement

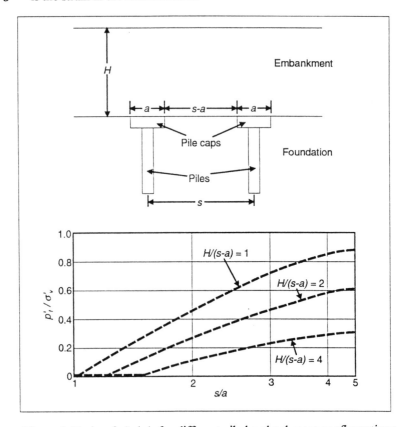

Figure 8 Ratio of p'_f/σ'_v for different piled embankment configurations
(After BS 8006 : 1994)

The maximum applied reinforcement load, T_r, will be T_{rp} along the length of the embankment, and T_{rp} plus the horizontal outward embankment thrust across the width of the embankment.

Continuum methods:

As stated previously, continuum methods are only just beginning to be used for basal reinforced piled embankments. The major reason for this is that versions of continuum methods have only recently become readily available with the required modelling sophistication. Reinforced piled embankments present a complex three-dimensional problem. While simplification to a two-dimensional plane strain problem makes the analysis easier, it may well underestimate the vertical stresses acting between the pile caps, and thus the load applied to the reinforcement. In addition, considerable strain is likely to occur in the system and thus a large strain continuum analysis would appear warranted.

The serviceability limit states pertaining to basal reinforced piled embankments are shown in Figure 9. Both have an effect on the load applied to the reinforcement. Excessive reinforcement strain, Figure 9a, affects the load carried in the reinforcement, Equation 1, as well as the surface condition of shallow piled embankments. Foundation settlement, Figure 9b, also affects the load carried in the reinforcement by applying greater strains. Continuum methods are the only techniques available to carry out a serviceability limit analysis of basal reinforced piled embankments.

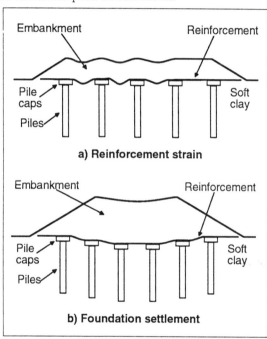

Figure 9 Serviceability limit states for basal reinforced piled embankments
(After BS 8006 : 1994)

Two examples of basal reinforced piled embankments are shown in Figure 10. Figure 10a shows a section through basal reinforced piled embankments which were utilised to prevent differential settlements between new embankment construction and an existing railway embankment which had been in place for 100 years, Jones *et al.*(1990). Construction time constraints prevented other techniques from being used and thus the basal reinforced piled embankment technique was adopted. The reinforcement was crosslaid across the tops of the pile caps with the stronger reinforcement placed in the direction across the width of the embankment.

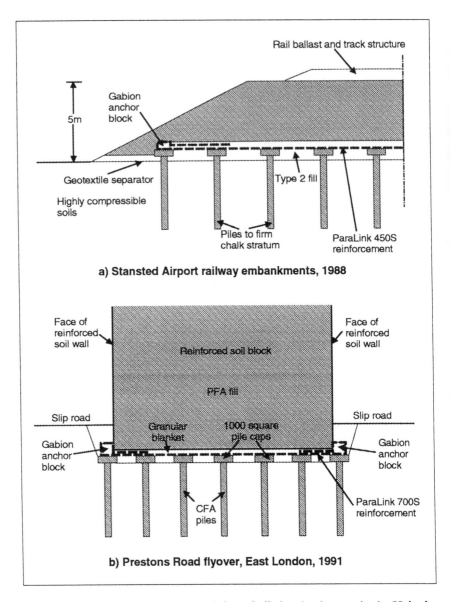

a) Stansted Airport railway embankments, 1988

b) Prestons Road flyover, East London, 1991

Figure 10 Two examples of basal reinforced piled embankments in the United Kingdom

Figure 10b shows a section through a basal reinforced piled foundation which was utilised to prevent differential settlements between new abutment construction and a flyover bridge with piled foundations in East London. The foundation conditions consisted of compressible alluvial soil overlying London Clay. The site was highly congested, both above and below ground level, which imposed the solution adopted - a double reinforced soil wall abutment founded on a basal reinforced piled platform.

USE OF BASAL REINFORCEMENT TO CONTROL VERTICAL MOVEMENT FOLLOWING FORMATION OF A FOUNDATION VOID

Voids can form in the foundation beneath structures due to a variety of reasons either natural or man-made. Natural processes which cause void formation are the subterranean erosion of soil deposits in karsitic areas or the leaching in salt deposits. Man-made processes which cause void formation are normally underground mining.

The consequences of void formation and the resulting subsidence beneath a structure range from a total loss of structural integrity (e.g. when a building collapses) to a mild serviceability loss (e.g. when a mild depression forms in a highway pavement). Specific foundation treatments are required to ensure subsidence remains within predefined design tolerances. Three categories of foundation treatment exist:

- 'active' measures, e.g. foundation grouting of all known void occurrences;

- 'intermediate' measures, e.g. the use of foundation rafts;

- 'passive' measures, e.g. do nothing until subsidence occurs and then apply a maintenance treatment to the distressed structure.

The use of reinforcement falls into the intermediate category where the reinforcement is installed at the base of the embankment or pavement structure. The reinforcement *works to restrict* (but not fully prevent) the vertical displacement of the surface of the structure when subsidence occurs. Basal reinforcement is particularly relevant for flexible structures, e.g. embankment fills and pavements, which can undergo some degree of differential deformation while still maintaining integrity.

The typical load regime applied to the reinforcement is as shown in Figure 2c. The reinforcement loading is zero until an "event" occurs (i.e. a void forms beneath the embankment) at some point in time. The reinforcement is required to support the fill and maintain the structure in a serviceable condition for a period of time thereafter. The approach to be adopted towards corrective maintenance following void formation in the future is fundamental to the design of the reinforcement. If it is planned not to carry out corrective maintenance following void formation then the reinforcement has to support and maintain the fill in a serviceable condition over the remaining design life of the structure. However, if it is planned to perform corrective maintenance at some point following void formation then the reinforcement is only required to support the fill for the intervening period of time. For high cost structures, e.g. motorway and railway embankments, it is common practice to fill any voids which may occur, while for lower cost structures, e.g. small embankments and pavements, the cost of void filling is not normally justified. Because of its profound effect on reinforcement properties the philosophy regarding subsequent treatment of voids should be resolved *prior to any design being undertaken.*

Like basal reinforced piled embankments, the use of reinforcement to support fills over voids constitutes a complex interaction problem. While the ultimate limit state deals with the rupture of the reinforcement, in reality the serviceability limit state governing maximum allowable deformation at the surface of the embankment dominates reinforcement selection. Both analytical and continuum methods have been used to assess the serviceability limit.

Analytical methods:

Two analytical models have been developed to determine the required reinforcement characteristics at the base of fill spanning a void, Giroud *et al.* (1990), BS 8006 : 1994. The model proposed by Giroud *et al.* (1990) pertains to situations where the serviceability conditions at the surface of the fill are not relevant, and as such, is of little use for transport related structures. The BS 8006 model is dependent on maintaining required serviceability conditions at the surface of the fill and is particularly relevant to transport related structures, Figure 11.

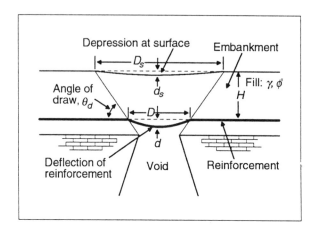

Figure 11 Analytical model describing the use of reinforcement to span a foundation void (After BS 8006 : 1994)

To simplify the analytical models a number of assumptions have to be made, namely:

- The assumption that the foundation beneath the reinforcement is rigid.

- Either the acceptance of full arching in the supported fill or its neglect.

- The assumed shape of the deformed reinforcement conforms to a simplified geometry.

- The reinforcement deforms only within the void area and the strain within this area is uniform.

- The interaction of the reinforcement with the supported soil during deformation is neglected.

The model used in BS 8006, Figure 11, assumes that no arching occurs within the supported fill. This may be considered an ultimate case because the worst loading condition occurs when the fill is in a state of full collapse and has to be fully supported by the reinforcement. In this state, a strain-controlled system is generated whereby the maximum allowable differential deformation at the surface of the fill, d_s/D_s in Figure 11, is controlled by the maximum allowable strain in the reinforcement, ε_{max}, at the base of the fill. For plane strain conditions, i.e. a long void, the BS 8006 model yields the following relationship:

$$\varepsilon_{max} = \frac{8\left[\dfrac{d_s}{D_s}\right]^2 \left[D+\dfrac{2H}{\tan\theta_d}\right]^4}{3D^4} \tag{2}$$

where the variables are as shown in Figure 11.

The tension in the deflected reinforcement spanning the void is determined as follows (assuming a parabolic deflection):

$$T_r = 0.5\lambda f_f (\gamma H + w_s) D \sqrt{1+\frac{1}{6\varepsilon}} \tag{3}$$

where,

T_r is the maximum tension in the reinforcement, per unit width

λ is a load shedding factor, for plane strain conditions $\lambda=1.0$

f_f is a partial factor applied to the loads = 1.3

γ is the unit weight of the fill

H is the height of the fill

w_s is the surcharge acting on top of the fill

D is the distance across the void

ε is the strain in the deflected reinforcement

Clearly, to meet the surface differential deformation requirements ε in Equation 3 should be less than or equal to ε_{max} in Equation 2.

Continuum methods:

Continuum methods have been applied to the analysis of reinforced fills spanning voids, e.g. Lawson *et al.* (1994). The advantage of continuum methods is that they can accurately predict soil behaviour and model complex geometries without the need to predetermine the failure mode. For the case of reinforcement spanning a void physical instability and large strains occur. Consequently, the continuum method must be able to model this behaviour. This is best achieved by using the finite difference method. Continuum methods enable an analysis of the major factors that affect basal reinforcement spanning a void, namely:

- Void span - the larger the void the higher the applied reinforcement loads and the greater the required reinforcement stiffness;

- Fill height to void span ratio - the larger this ratio the more soil arching occurs resulting in a limiting applied reinforcement load;

- Fill cohesion - small amounts of cohesion increases arching and reduces the loads applied to the reinforcement;

- Reinforcement stiffness - the greater the reinforcement stiffness the lower the differential deformation at the surface of the fill layer;

- Foundation type - the type of foundation beneath the reinforcement influences the magnitude of the differential deformation at the surface of the fill layer.

Two examples of basal reinforced embankments spanning potential voids are shown in Figure 12. Figure 12a shows the use of basal reinforcement inserted beneath the subbase layer of pavements in estates in Cornwall. For centuries Cornwall has been the location of extensive underground tin extraction; the vast majority of tunnels being narrow in size, near to the surface and uncharted. Subsidence due to the collapse of these tunnels has become a major problem with housing, roads and water services. One solution adopted for roads is to utilise basal reinforcement such that in the event of subsidence beneath the pavement the reinforcement will support the pavement and maintain trafficability. Current practice is to install the reinforcement prior to placement of the subbase layer and extend the reinforcement beneath the footpath areas in order to generate adequate bond at the edges of the pavement.

Figure 12b shows the use of basal reinforcement for the construction of highway embankments over subsidence prone areas in Ripon, North Yorkshire, Lawson *et al.* (1994). The area has long been affected by surface instability due to sinkhole development emanating from dissolution of the underlying gypsum strata. Vast subterranean caves up to 200 m long and 25m high are considered to be in existence. The largest of hundreds of surface sinkholes around Ripon is 80 m diameter and 30 m deep. To ensure the future stability of the completed bypass embankments basal reinforcement was

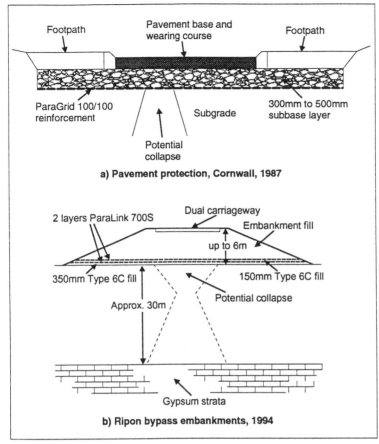

Figure 12 Two examples of basal reinforcement spanning voids in the United Kingdom

incorporated into the construction; the reinforcement being required to span a design void diameter of 10 m.

CONCLUSIONS

The three basal reinforcement techniques presented in this paper have been in use in the United Kingdom for 15 years and as such are not completely new. Because they represent complex foundation interaction problems, refinements in design and analysis have been carried out in parallel with application. Even today it is envisaged that further refinement will occur as more sophisticated analysis methods, e.g. continuum methods, are applied more commonly to these basal reinforcement applications. However, it must be recognised that the increase in analytical sophistication must be offset by significant savings in material cost. It should be also recognised that as the analysis methods become more sophisticated the required material properties become more specific. At some stage further analytical sophistication will not be warranted from the viewpoint of material savings alone.

REFERENCES

BS 8006, 1994, *Strengthened/reinforced soils and other fills.* British Standards Institution, July (final draft).

Bush, D.I., Jenner, C.J. & Bassett, R.H., 1989, *The design and construction of geocell foundation mattresses supporting embankments over soft ground.* Geotextiles & geomembranes, Elsevier, Vol. 9, No. 1, 83-98.

Giroud, J.P., Bonaparte, R., Beech, J.F. & Gross, B.A., 1990, *Design of soil layer - geosynthetic systems overlying voids.* Geotextiles & geomembranes, Elsevier, Vol. 9, 11-50.

Haliburton, T.A., Douglas, P.A. & Fowler, J., 1977, *Feasibility of Pinto Island as a long-term dredged national deposit site.* U.S. Army Waterways Experiment Station, Miscellaneous paper D-77-3.

Hewlett, W.J. & Randolph, M.A., 1988, *Analysis of piled embankments.* Ground Engineering, April, 12-18.

Houlsby, G.T. & Jewell, R.A., 1988, *Analysis of unreinforced and reinforced embankments on soft clays by plasticity analysis.* Proc. VI Int. Conf. on Numerical methods in geomechanics, Innsbruck, Vol. 2, 1443-1448.

Jewell, R.A., 1988, *The mechanics of reinforced embankments on soft soils.* Geotextiles & geomembranes, Elsevier, Vol. 7, No. 4, 237-273.

Jewell, R.A., 1995, *The use of geotextiles for soil reinforcement.* CIRIA, (in press).

John, N.W.M., 1987, *Geotextiles.* Blackie, Glasgow.

Jones, C.J.F.P., Lawson, C.R. & Ayres, D.J., 1990, *Geotextile reinforced piled embankments.* Proc IV Int. Conf. on Geotextiles, geomembranes & related products, The Hague, Vol. 1, 155-160.

Lawson, C.R., Jones, C.J.F.P., Kempton, G.K. & Passaris, E.K.S., 1994, *Advanced analysis of reinforced fills over areas prone to subsidence.* Proc V Int. Conf. on Geotextiles, geomembranes & related products, Singapore, Vol. 1, 311-316.

Calculation of the displacements of a full scale experimental soil nailed wall - French National Research Project Clouterre

P. UNTERREINER, DDE Martinique, F. SCHLOSSER, Terrasol and
B. BENHAMIDA, CERMES-ENPC Noisy-le-Grand, France

SYNOPSIS
    A finite element analysis pertaining to the performance of a full scale experimental soil nailed wall was performed. A detailed description of the determination of the mechanical parameters of the individual components of the nailed wall and their interaction is presented. The simulation of the first five phases of the wall construction has given results which agree very well with the field observations and measurements.

INTRODUCTION

Soil nailing is a recent soil reinforcing technique which consists in placing bars in the in situ soils while excavation goes on by phases. Its spectacular success during the last two decades is due to its technical and economical advantages for constructing in situ earth support systems such as retaining walls, bridge abutments, and steep slopes.

The original idea of reinforcing in situ soils using driven or grouted steel bars started in the early seventies in France with the construction of a first wall in Versailles in, Rabejac & Toudic (1974). Different research and development projects started about the same period in Germany and in the USA. A research project entitled *Bodenvernagelung*, took place from 1975 to 1980 in Germany and studied seven well instrumented full scale soil nailed walls, Gässler (1993). In the USA, a similar research program on sail nailing was conducted by Shen et al., (1981) and a full scale experimental wall was instrumented and monitored.

In France, a National Research Project called Clouterre was conducted from 1986 to 1991 with the objective to understand better the behaviour of soil nailed walls during construction, in service and at failure. The project achieved its objectives by the construction, instrumentation and monitoring of three full scale experimental soil nailed walls which were pushed to failure. These five years of research, studies, and tests on soil nailing resulted in the publication of French Specifications entitled *Soil Nailing Recommendations 1991* (French version, 1991 and English version, 1993). These Recommendations present in details the whole design and construction process, from geotechnical investigation to field quality control.

The design recommended at the present time is based on the classical limit equilibrium method of slices generalized to soil reinforcement with the help of the multicriteria approach, Schlosser (1982). This method allows analysis and checking the stability of a structure but does not enable calculation of displacements.

Research is going on within the frame of a second National Research Project entitled Clouterre II whose principal objective is to develop serviceability limit state design based on displacement calculation methods.

Within the frame of the first National Research Project Clouterre, three full scale experimental soil nailed walls were taken to failure by three different modes. The analyses of these three different modes of failure have been performed using the multicriteria approach, Schlosser et al. (1991, 1992, 1993). The purpose of this paper is to present the calculation of the displacements during construction of the first full scale experimental soil nailed wall using finite element methods.

Very few calculations of the displacements have been performed on these three extensively instrumented full scale walls, Nanda (1988), Chiguer (1989), Saïba (1989). Those calculations were based on very simple assumptions concerning the interaction between the nails and the soil, namely either full adherence or rigid perfectly plastic behaviour. When compared to the measurements, the obtained results can be considered as acceptable for the tensile loads in the nails but disagree too much with displacements for both the facing and the soil.

Modeling of reinforced soil structures is an up to date subject of research. Three dimensional analyses have been performed by Smith (1992) on retaining walls and Chaoui (1992) on nailed slopes. At the present time these analyses are too consuming of computer time to be used on a daily basis for serviceability limit state designs of regular structures. However, both studies confirm that two dimensional calculations are acceptable at least for small deformations, during construction and loading, when the structure is far from failure. As state of the art 2D calculations of reinforced soil structures, one can refer to Salama (1992) who used strain hardening-softening models for both soil and soil-nail interfaces in order to interpret measures obtained on a full scale soil nailed wall. In order to make Class A predictions of a polymeric reinforced model wall, Bathurst et al. (1987) have used Duncan hyperbolic model for the soil. In a recent study, Quaresma et al. (1993), have modeled both soil and soil-geotextile interfaces with an elasto-plastic model to interpret the behavior of geotextile reinforced backfill on a soft ground.

The use of complex constitutive models does not seem to improve really the quality of the calculated displacements. Indeed, the accuracy which can be gained with an increasing number of constitutive parameters is lost by the uncertainties on these parameters which are most of time estimated from in situ tests results.

After a synthetic presentation of the considered soil nailed wall including the geometry, the mechanical properties of the various components, and the relevant measurements during construction, we will detail the assumptions of the calculation with a particular emphasis on the equivalence between the properties of the real 3D structure and the ones of the 2D model. Calculated displacements and tensile loads are compared with the measurements performed during construction.

THE SOIL NAILED WALL

The soil nailed wall was constructed in an experimental backfill, 7 m high, built with special care at the site of CEBTP near Paris. In particular, the homogeneity and density of the backfill were controlled at each phase of its construction on a dense sand foundation. The Fontainebleau sand used was placed and compacted to obtain a relative density of 0.6 and unit weight of γ_{min} = 13.1 kN/m^3 and γ_{max} = 16.9 kN/m^3. The nailed wall was 7 m high, 7.5 m wide and contained between two lateral walls covered with a double polythene layer to ensure plane deformations. The wall was built step by step by alternating 1 m high the excavations with the placing of the nails with horizontal spacing of 1.15 m. The nails are inclined 10° with respect to the horizontal direction and their lengths vary between 6 to 8 m, Figure 1.

The construction has been interrupted for two months between phases five and six. During this interruption which occurred during a cold winter, very significant "creep" displacements were measured. In this article, we will focus on the first five phases which were constructed within a few weeks and thus are free of creep displacements.

The Fontainebleau sand is in a medium to dense state (D_R = 0.6) and has an average unit weight of 16.1 kN/m^3. The linear elastic perfectly plastic behavior model requires five mechanical properties which are : Young's modulus, E, Poisson's coefficient, ν, cohesion, c, internal friction angle, ϕ, and dilatancy angle, ψ.

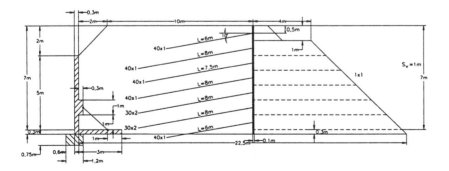

Figure 1 Cross section of the full scale experimental soil nailed wall

The mechanical properties of the backfill and foundation soils were evaluated based on data published on the sand Fontainebleau type, the pressuremeter test results conducted at the site and from triaxial tests results performed at the CERMES, Dupla & Canou (1994).

Numerous correlations have been developed between the Ménard pressuremeter modulus, E_M, and the modulus of deformation, E, to be considered for displacement calculations. It is generally agreed that the ratio E/E_M varies between 2 and 4, depending on the type of soil, the level of deformations which is considered, etc. For the considered structure, 7 m high, we have selected a ratio of 2 for the reference calculations.

Two pressuremeter tests were conducted down to a depth of 5 and 6 m within the backfill which has been excavated and nailed, Plumelle (1987, 1993), Unterreiner (1994), Figure 2. The average pressuremeter modulus over the 7 m height is 10 MPa. For the reference calculation, a value of twice this modulus, i. e. 20 MPa, is taken for the Young's modulus.

Two other pressuremeter tests were carried out down to 6 and 20 m in the foundation soil, Schlosser et al. (1993). The results of those deep pressuremeter tests show the existence of a very hard soil layer ($E_M \gg 50$ MPa and $p_l \gg 5$ MPa) between 7 to 11 m beneath the backfill in which the soil nailed wall was constructed. The mesh of the numerical model, therefore, ends at the top of this hard layer. The average pressuremeter modulus between 0 and 7 m is 35 MPa. Therefore, a value of 70 MPa is taken for the Young's modulus of the foundation soil.

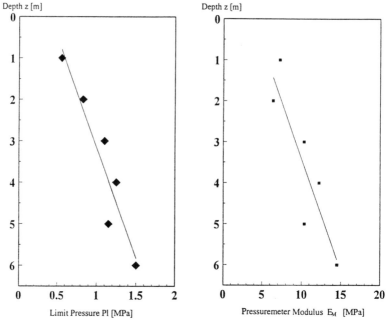

Figure 2 Pressuremeter test profile in the backfill soil - measurements and linear regression

Compression and extension triaxial tests were performed on medium to dense Fontainebleau sand samples, Dupla & Canou (1994), Table 1. The initial tangent modulus of the four compression tests (D_R varies between 0.6 to 0.65) performed with a confining pressure varying from 25 to 100 kPa are comprised between 21 and 59 MPa. For the same range of confining pressure calculated as the mean in situ pressure, we obtain a Ménard pressuremeter modulus varying between 9.5 and 20.7 MPa. The compression triaxial tests yield thus a ratio E/E_M in the range of 2.2 to 2.8 which agree with the choice of a value of 2.

Table 1 Compression triaxial tests results (after Dupla & Canou, 1994)

I_D [--]	σ_c [kPa]	z [m]	E_t [MPa]	E_U [MPa]	ϕ [°]	ψ^* [°]	v [--]	E_M ** [MPa]
0.65	100	10.35	59	153	36.4	22.3	0.37	20.7
0.60	75	7.76	46	121	37	21.2	0.42	17.0
0.65	50	5.18	35	108	39.1	32.6	0.40	13.2
0.60	25	2.59	21	60	40.3	33.2	0.41	9.55

(*) : $\sin \psi = \sqrt{(2/3) \cdot s/(1-s)}$, where s is the slope of the $(\varepsilon_v, \varepsilon_1)$ curve.

(**) : E_M is the average Ménard pressuremeter modulus at a depth such that $\sigma_c = \dfrac{\sigma_v + 2K_0\sigma_v}{3}$ with $K_0 = 1 - \sin \phi$.

Concerning the plastic constitutive parameters of the Fontainebleau sand, an important database is available in the literature. Within the frame of Clouterre, all the calculations performed at ultimate limit state on the soil nailed wall have been done using an internal friction angle, ϕ, of 38° and an apparent cohesion, c, of 3 kPa. This couple of values has given very satisfactory results, Schlosser et al. (1992, 1993, 1994).

The above mentioned triaxial tests carried out at the CERMES, Dupla & Canou (1994), give an angle of friction in compression varying between 36° and 40° depending on the confining pressure. These results agree with the previous choice of (ϕ, c) values which we will use for displacement calculations.

A well graded sand with little fines and a small water content like the considered Fontainebleau sand has an apparent cohesion of a few kPa. The determination of this apparent cohesion is essential because of its influence on the local stability of the soil when it is excavated and left non protected. The evaluation of this cohesion, which is due to capillary forces existing between the grains has been the subject of two important studies.

A mixture of Fontainebleau sand with different contents of silt, varying between 0 and 50%, and with different water contents varying between 6 and 12% has been studied by Petit (1987). The results indicate that when the water content increases the apparent cohesion decreases. For a water content of 10.7% and a clay content of 5%, which correspond to the site conditions of the soil nailed wall, an apparent cohesion of 3 to 4 kPa is obtained and agrees with our previous choice.

Similar results have been published by Gässler (1993) concerning another well graded fine sand. The apparent cohesion was found to depend upon the strain level due to the rearrangement of the grains. For this sand, with an average water content of 5.8%, the cohesion varies between 2 and 6 kPa which agrees with the previous study by Petit (1987).

Besides these two parameters (c and ϕ) which define the Mohr-Coulomb failure envelop, one needs the angle of dilatancy, ψ, which controls the plastic deformations. At the present state of knowledge, this angle can be determined only with laboratory tests and volume measurements. The only data available have been published by Dupla and Canou, (1994) from triaxial tests. In compression, the angle of dilatancy varies between 21° and 33° whereas in extension it is in the range of 10° to 15° with in both cases a confining pressure varying between 25 and 100 kPa. For the calculations, a dilatancy angle of 25° has been chosen which corresponds to the average value of the triaxial tests results obtained for the confining stresses corresponding to the first seven meters of the backfill. For the foundation soil, an angle of dilatancy of 20° has been chosen.

The interaction between the nails and the soil is modeled assuming a linear elastic perfectly plastic behavior. The elastic parameter, k_τ, corresponds to the initial mobilization of the lateral friction while, the plastic parameter q_s, which is independent of the confining pressure like cohesion, corresponds to the unit skin friction. Both k_τ and q_s have been determined from an in situ pull-out test performed at the site before the construction of the soil nailed wall.

MEASUREMENTS DURING CONSTRUCTION

The observations and the measurements performed on the soil nailed wall have been the subject of many Clouterre internal reports and articles, Plumelle (1987, 1993), Recommendations Clouterre (1991). In the following only the essential measurements will be presented.

The interpretation of the measurement results of full scale structures are always subject to discussion because of the hypotheses on the raw data that have to be made. In particular, the deformations measured along the aluminum reinforcements can be transformed to traction efforts only after making assumptions on the cracking of the grout and the plastification of the aluminum. Concerning the experiment, the results obtained by Plumelle (1987) can be considered, in many respects, as the best ones with respect to the present state of knowledge.

Concerning the slope inclinometer measurements, a similar problem is encountered since the measured values correspond to the relative displacements. The initial interpretation of the inclinometer data has been based on the assumption that at the bottom level of each temporary excavation there is no displacement in the soil. Retrospectively, this hypothesis can be considered as a strong one considering the results of the numerical simulations performed so far. All these calculations give small displacements at the toe of the wall but non null. Therefore, all the inclinometer measurements previously published have been re-evaluated by making the hypothesis that the displacements are null only at the toe of the inclinometers. The obtained displacements are slightly more important but remain in the range of the values usually observed on full scale structures. These new values have been chosen as reference ones for all the finite elements calculations performed hereafter.

The construction of the first five metres of the soil nailed wall has been achieved in one month from December 1984 to January 1985. During the interruption that lasted two months, between phase 5 and 7, a significant increase in displacement of about 2.4 mm at the top of the wall occurred due to creep.

The present study focuses on instantaneous deformations exempt of any creep effect. Therefore, only the measurements of the first five phases will be analyzed and compared to the finite element results.

CALCULATION OF DISPLACEMENTS

Due to the one dimensional size of the nails, a soil nailed wall has a three dimensional geometry which can not be modeled straightforward without making assumptions. In particular, one has to pay attention to the fact that cross-sections vary along the wall whereas in geotextile or mesh reinforced earth structures they are all identical. In that latter case, calculations conditions (2D calculations) assuming plane strains are admissible without further assumptions. In the case of soil nailed wall, one has to be more careful before performing 2D calculations which assume plane strain conditions.

The equivalent plate model in which the reinforcing elements are replaced by a plate extended to the full width and breadth of the wall has been used extensively. See for example Al-Hussaini et al. (1978), Chaoui (1992). This model makes a very strong hypothesis concerning the adherence between the soil and the inclusion for the determination of the equivalent modulus and a contradictory one which allows a relative displacement of the soil with respect to the nails in order to estimate the limit lateral friction. The discontinuity of the soil below and above a range of nails is introduced. However, this can be alleviated by introducing continuity conditions within a finite element mesh. An other problem related to this method is the non unicity of calculating the equivalent 2D parameters which have to be used in the plane strain calculations , Chaoui (1992), Unterreiner (1994).

A second approach has been proposed, for example, by Naylor (1978) and Unterreiner (1994). In this approach the nails are placed, conceptually, outside the soil and their interaction is modeled using load transfer functions which transfer the shear stress between the nails and the soil. The soil remains continuous in both directions. The equivalent 2D parameters can then be determined easily by making clear assumptions, for example, on the equality of the total traction in a row of real nails and the modeled ones. The two-dimensional analysis performed hereafter uses the second approach.

MODELLING OF THE DIFFERENT COMPONENTS AND THEIR INTERACTION

Both the foundation and the backfill soils are modeled using a linear elastic perfectly plastic model with a Mohr-Coulomb criterion and a non associated flow rule. Based on the pressuremeter and triaxial tests results, mentioned above, the constitutive parameters used for the finite elements calculations are compiled and presented in Table 2.

The nails consist of hollow aluminum tubes grouted in the sand. Figure 1 summarizes the lengths, diameters and thicknesses regarding each nail row. The behavior of the nails is represented by a linear elastic model for the range of tensions which was measured on the wall during the first five phases of construction. Further and near to failure plasticity would have to be accounted for. Laboratory tests conducted on a nail constructed in the same sand and with same technique as for the full scale structure show a yield stress of 245 MPa for a 40 mm diameter tube and 235 MPa for a 30 mm diameter tube. The elastic limit, measured at 0.2% is 127 MPa and 94 MPa, respectively. The equivalent 2D parameters needed for the calculation have been estimated from the values obtained on the real nails taking into account the horizontal spacing between the nails , Table 3.

Table 2   Data used in the reference calculation for backfill and foundation soils

Backfill soil		
Young's modulus constant with depth $(\langle E_M \rangle_{z=0 \text{ to } 7.3 \text{ m}} = 10 \text{ MPa})$	$E = 2 E_M$	$20 \ 10^3$ kPa
Unit weight	γ	16.1
Poisson coefficient	ν	0.33
Angle of internal friction	ϕ	38°
Angle of dilatancy	ψ	25°
Cohesion	c	3 kPa
Foundation soil		
Young's modulus constant with depth $(\langle E_M \rangle_{z=7.3 \text{ to } 14.3 \text{ m}} = 35 \text{ MPa})$	$E = 2 E_M$	$70 \ 10^3$ kPa
Unit weight	γ	17
Poisson coefficient	ν	0.33
Angle of internal friction	ϕ	38°
Angle of dilatancy	ψ	20°
Cohesion	c	0

Table 3 Summary of the nails parameters

Young's modulus (real nails)	E	$70 \cdot 10^6$ kPa
limit elastic stress (real nails)	σ_e	$110 \cdot 10^6$ kPa
Young's modulus (model nails)	$\tilde{E} = E/S_h$	$61 \cdot 10^6$ kPa
limit elastic stress (model nails)	$\tilde{\sigma}_e = \sigma_e/S_h$	$95.65 \cdot 10^3$ kPa
Model nail section (equal to real nail section in order to have the relationship $\tilde{E}\tilde{S} = ES/S_h$)	$\tilde{S} = S$	varies according to each nail layer

The facing is made of a mesh reinforced shotcrete and its behavior is approximated with a linear elastic model. Young's modulus of the facing is taken equal to $25 \cdot 10^6$ kPa with a unit weight, γ, of 24 kN/m³ and a Poisson coefficient, v, of 0.2.

The constitutive behavior of the soil-nail interface is modeled with a linear elastic perfectly plastic model. Both the elastic coefficient of mobilization, k_τ, and the unit limit lateral friction, q_s, have been estimated from Clouterre correlations. Those correlations are based on the pressuremeter modulus, E_M, for k_τ and on the limit pressuremeter pressure, p_l , for q_s. The estimations thus obtained have been confirmed with the analysis and back calculation of an in situ pull-out test performed before construction using same nail and same technique as for the wall, Table 4.

Table 4 Summary of the soil-nail interaction parameters

normal rigidity of interface	K_n	10^{+8} kPa/m
tangential rigidity of interface $$K_s = K_\tau \frac{\pi D_c}{2S_h}$$	K_s	$5.94 \cdot 10^3$ kPa/m
coefficient of mobilization of lateral friction $K_\tau = 2\langle E_M \rangle/mD_c$, with $\langle E_M \rangle_{z=0\,to\,7.3\,m} = 10MPa$ and m = 4.6	K_τ	$69 \cdot 10^3$ kPa/m
boring diameter (real nails)	D_c	$63 \cdot 10^{-3}$ m
horizontal spacing (real nails)	S_h	1.15 m
cohesion of interface elements $$C_i = \frac{\pi D_c}{2S_h} q_s$$	C_i	9.25 kPa
friction angle of interface elements	ϕ_i	0°
unit skin friction (real nails) $q_s = 0.1 p_l$, with $\langle p_l \rangle_{z=0\,to\,7.3\,m} = 1.07$ MPa	q_s	107.5 kPa

Despite the complexity of the structure studied, a simple mesh using a relatively small number of rectangular 8 nodes elements is used, Figure 3.

The foundation soil elements are about 1 m by 1 m, while the backfill ones are 0.5 m by 1 m. The soil-nail interface elements have 6 nodes.

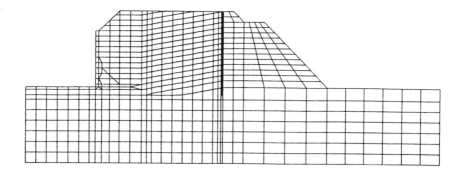

Figure 3 Mesh used in the Finite Element calculations (CESAR-LCPC)

Boundary conditions are located so that they will have negligible effects on the structure. On the bottom boundary, the displacements are zero both laterally and horizontally which correspond to the very dense sandy substratum encountered during the borings, while at the right and the left vertical boundaries, horizontal displacements are maintained equal to zero.

COMPARISON OF CALCULATED AND MEASURED VALUES

A reference calculation was performed using a finite element code (CESAR-LCPC). The set of parameters chosen is presented in Tables 1 to 4. Only the first five phases of construction of the nailed wall have been analyzed. At the contact of the soil with the nail at the facing, different local mechanisms can occur such as the pull-out of the nail out of the shotcrete or the facing may hang during the construction if it slides along the wall. A special combination of different elements was developed within the frame of this study to be used in analyses of soil nailing problems.

In the following lines, special emphasis has been given to the distribution of the tensions in the nails, the lateral movements of the facing, and the deformations within the nailed soil. Comparisons of calculated values with field measurements is presented only for phase 3 and phase 5.

Progressive soil decompression due to the successive excavation phases generate lateral displacements of the soil. These displacements induce tensions in the nails through friction between the soil and nails. At the end of phase 5, when the first five layers of nails are installed, only the four upper ones are subject to tension. In fact, the lowest layer of nails is subject to negligible tensions. It will become loaded only if construction goes on further or if the wall is subject to creep deformations. Figure 4 shows the traction distribution calculated in the nails along with the measurements at phase 5.

Due to the scale adopted in the figure, the calculated curves appeared very different from the measured ones. However, a close comparison of the numerical values give a difference in the range of - 3 kN to + 4 kN. Larger values were found by Nanda (1988), Chiguer (1989), Saiba (1989).

Comparison of displacements measured at the facing and within the nailed soil with calculated ones is shown on Figures 5 and 6. The amplitude of the displacements at the top of the facing is calculated with good precision. However, the incurved shape of the displacements of the bottom of the facing is not obtained. To be able to model this shape, one would have to assume that either the first layer of nails has a lesser pull-out resistance or the top soil is less resistant.

Results obtained within the soil at 4 m from the facing were in good agreement with field observations for phase 3, while for phase 5, the calculated values at 2 m from the facing are the ones which fit best the measurements. It should be noted that over the upper first meter, the inclinometer results do not give the same tendency than in depth due to unavoidable field perturbations.

Displacements at the facing and within the nailed soil are estimated in a range of - 1 mm to + 3 mm for phase 5. The obtained results are good compared to previously published ones, Nanda et al. (1988, 1989).

Initial stresses were calculated by applying gravity forces progressively. This resulted in an initial state of stresses totally different from the geostatic one due to the geometric complexity of the structure. Initially, the soil is plastified in some areas, particularly at the back of the future nailed soil next to the existing concrete retaining wall, beneath the backfill to be nailed, and at the toe of the slope to be excavated, Figure 7a. At the end of phase 5, initially plastified areas remain but new ones appear behind the facing, Figure 7b. Their shape is very similar to a Coulomb wedge. However, the amplitude of the cumulative plastic deformations, in those areas, remains very small around 10^{-2} %. However, locally around the toe of the facing, the plastic deformations of shearing may attain very high values of about 8 %, Figure 8.

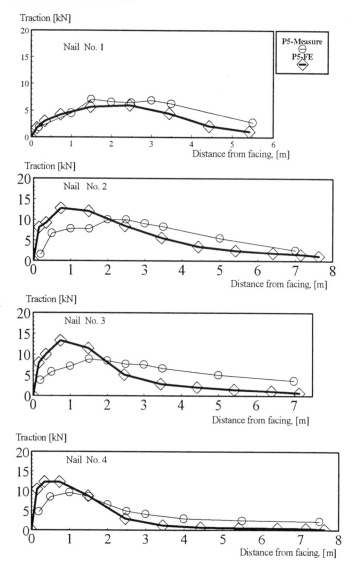

Figure 4 Tensile load distribution in the nails at the end of phase 5

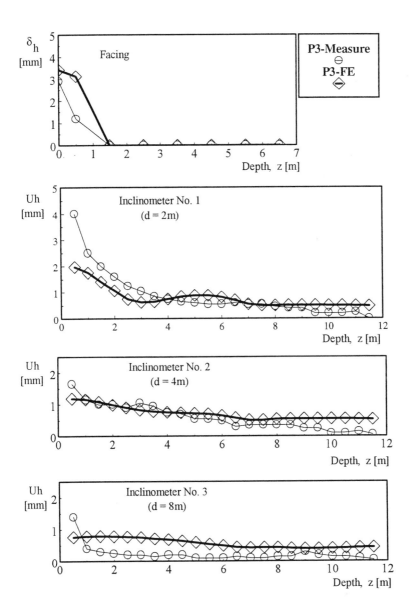

Figure 5 Horizontal displacements at the facing and within the soil at phase 3

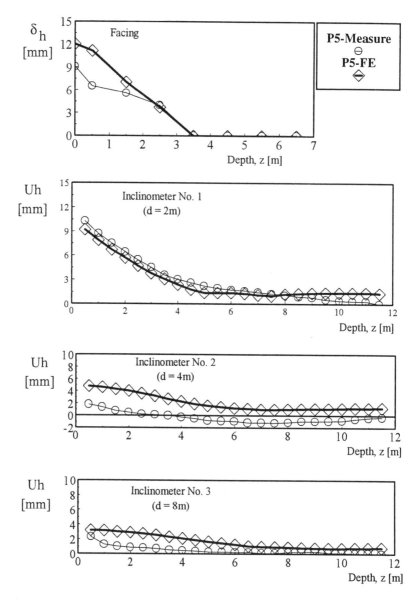

Figure 6 Horizontal displacements at the facing and within the soil at phase 5

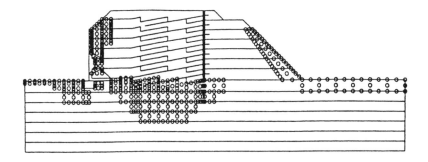

Figure 7a   Plastified areas before construction (phase 0)

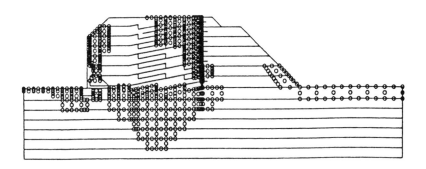

Figure 7b   Plastified areas at end of phase 5

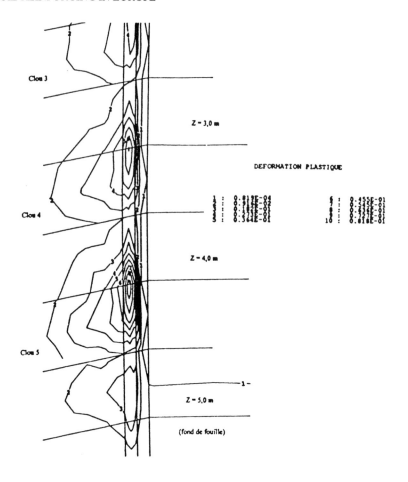

Figure 8   Isovalue curves for the accumulated plastic shear deformations
around the toe of the facing

CONCLUSIONS

The finite element modeling of the construction of the first full scale experimental soil nailed wall of the Clouterre Project using a plane strain analysis gives very good results.   In particular, there is a good agreement between the calculated and the measured values for the tensions in the nails as well as for the displacements of the facing and the soil. This good agreement is due to two factors: firstly a precise formulation of the equivalence between the properties of the real nails and the ones of the 2D model and secondly the choice of constitutive parameters which correspond best to the site conditions, based on a detailed study of existing data and tests.

REFERENCES

Al-Hussaini, M.M. & Johnson, L.D., 1978, *Numerical analysis of a reinforced earth wall.* Proc. Symp. on Earth Reinforcement, ASCE Annual Convention, Pittsburgh, Pennsylvania, USA, pp. 98 - 126.

Bathurst, R. J. & Koerner, R. M., 1987. *Results of Class A Predictions for the RMC Reinforced Soil Wall Trials, The Application of Polymeric Reinforcement in Soil Retaining Structures.* NATO Advanced Study Institutes Series, Kluwer Academic Publishers, pp. 127 - 172.

Chaoui, F., 1992, *Etude tridimensionnelle du comportement des pieux dans les pentes instables.* Thèse de doctorat à l'Ecole Nationale des Ponts et Chaussées, Paris, France

Chiguer, M., 1989, *Contributions à l'étude théorique et expérimentale du renforcement par clouage.* Thèse de doctorat à l'Ecole Nationale des Ponts et Chaussées, Paris, France

Dupla, J. C. & Canou, J., 1994, *Caractérisation mécanique du sable de Fontainebleau à partir d'essais triaxiaux de compression et d'extension.* Rapport Interne Clouterre II, CERMES-ENPC

Gässler, G., 1993, *The first two field tests in the history of soil nailing on nailed walls pushed to failure.* Civil Engineering European Courses, Renforcement des sols: expérimentations en vraie grandeur des années 80, Paris, France, pp. 7 - 34.

Nanda, A., 1988. *Finite Elements Analysis of Nailed Walls.* Rapport interne, CERMES, ENPC.

Naylor, D., 1978, *A Study of reinforced earth walls allowing strip slip.* Proc. Symp. on Earth Reinforcement, ASCE Annual Convention, Pittsburgh, Pennsylvania, USA, pp. 618 - 643.

Petit, G., 1987, *Contribution à l'étude expérimentale du comportement des massifs en sol cloué.* Rapport de Stage de Fin d'Etudes, CERMES-ENPC

Plumelle, C., 1987, *Expérimentation en vraie grandeur d'une paroi clouée.* Revue Française de Géotechnique No. 40, pp. 45 - 50

Plumelle, C., 1993, *Conception, exécution et expérimentation d'un massif en sol cloué en vraie grandeur.* C. R. Symposium International sur le Renforcement des Sols: Expérimentations des années 1980, ENPC, Paris, pp. 35 - 62.

Quaresma, M., Magnan, J. P., & Delmas, P., 1993, *Etude de deux remblais expérimentaux sur argiles molles renforcés à la base par des géotextiles (Site de Guiche, Pyrénées Atlantiques).* Lab. Cent. des Ponts et Chaussées, Paris, Série Géotechnique, No. GT 55, p. 187.

Rabejac, S. and Toudic, P., 1974, *Construction d'un mur de soutènement entre Versailles-Chantiers et Versailles-Matelots.* Revue générale des chemins de fer, 93 ème année, pp. 232 - 237.

Recommandations Clouterre 1991 pour la conception, le calcul, l'exécution et le contrôle des soutènements réalisés par clouage des sols. ENPC, Paris (in French) and FHWA, Washington (in English).

Saiba, O., 1989, *Simulation numérique d'un soutènement en sol cloué: Etude du comportement en phases de construction et application à un ouvrage expérimental.* Thèse de doctorat de l'Université Paris VI, p. 246.
Smith, I.M., 1992, *Some results of computations regarding reinforced soil.* Colloque ENPC, Informatique et Geotechnique, Paris, Presses ENPC, pp.479 - 488.

Salama, M. E., 1992, *Analysis of Soil Nailed Retaining Walls.* Ph.D. Thesis, University of Illinois at Urbana-Champaign.

Schlosser, F., 1982, *Behavior and design of soil nailing.* Proc. Symp. Recent Developments in Ground Improvement Techniques, AIT, Bangkok, pp. 319 - 413.

Schlosser, F. & Unterreiner, P., 1991, *Soil Nailing in France: Research and Practice.* C. R. 70ème Congrès annuel TRB, Washington D.C., pp. 72 - 79.

Schlosser, F., Plumelle, C., Unterreiner, P. & Benoit, J., 1992, *Failure of a full scale experimental soil nailed wall by reducing the nail lengths (French National Project Clouterre.* C. R. Symp. International sur la Pratique en Renforcement des Sols, Fukuoka, Japan.

Schlosser, F., Hoteit N., & Pierce, D., 1993, *Expérimentation en vraie grandeur d'un mur Freyssisol-Websol en sol renforcé.* C. R. Symposium International sur le Renforcement des Sols: Expérimentations des années 1980, ENPC, Paris, pp. 299 - 320.

Schlosser, F., Unterreiner, P. & Plumelle, C., 1993, *Validation des méthodes de calcul de clouage par les expérimentations du Projet National Cl;outerre.* Revue Française de Géotechnique, No. 64.

Schlosser, F., & Unterreiner P., 1994, *Renforcement des sols par inclusion.* Techniques de l'Ingénieur, C245.

Shen, C. K., Bang, S., Romstad, K. M.. Kulchin, L. & De Natale, J. S, 1981, *Field measurement of an earth support system.* ASCE, J. of the Geot. Eng. Div., Vol. 107, No. GT12, pp. 1625 - 1842.

Unterreiner, P., 1994, *Contribution à l'étude et à la modélisation numérique des sols cloués: application au calcul en déformation des ouvrages en soutènement.* Thèse de doctorat à l'Ecole Nationale des Ponts et Chaussées, Paris, France.

Stabilization of a cutting slope along a high-speed railway line using extremely long nails

G. GÄSSLER, FH Munich, Dept. of Civil Engineering, Germany.

SYNOPSIS
During construction work for the high speed railway line Mannheim-Stuttgart (SW-Germany) a cutting slope with a height of 23 m and an inclination of 1:1.75 was stabilized using soil nails. In order to avoid sliding especially on fossil slip surfaces a total of more than 12 000 m of nails were grouted into the soil mass consisting of Keuper Marl. This paper gives results of "pullout" tests on nails and the principles of the stability calculation based on the two-block failure mechanism.

INTRODUCTION
The geotechnical engineer is more and more confronted with the problem of stabilizing long and deep cutting slopes in hilly or mountainous areas with unfavourable geological conditions. There is a variety of different technical measures for selection to establish stable and sufficiently safe cuts. The following case study reports on the stabilization of a 23 m high cutting slope using soil nailing. New and unusual was the length of the mounted nails. However, not only because of that this soil nailing project was different from classical nail wall constructions.

GEOLOGY AND STABILITY PROBLEMS IN STABILIZING THE CUTTING SLOPE
The new high-speed railway line Mannheim-Stuttgart constructed between 1984 and 1991 crosses the Stromberg hills between km 62 and 75. The Stromberg Hills consist entirely of the strata layers of the Keuper, i.e. weak clay silt stone and sand stone.
It is mainly the clay silt stone which causes geotechnical problems. In particular the Bunte Mergel formation tends to slide when being excavated. The reason for this is mostly the reactivation of fossil slip surfaces (geological landslides during the ice age) during the excavation process. Such landslides had been earlier studied by Wichter (1980) in the same formation very close to the Stromberg Hills.
Between km 71.7+40 and km 72.8+60 the Burgbergtunnel crosses the Stromberg Hills. The western part of the tunnel, about 450 m in length, was constructed in open excavation. After completion the required cut, with a batter of 1:1.2, proved to be unsafe. As can be seen in Figure 1, the cut lead to the occurrence of a landslide on fossil slip surfaces. This required stabilization by numerous prestressed ground anchors.

The practice of soil reinforcing in Europe. Thomas Telford, London, 1995

Figure 1   Landslide in the excavation slope of the
                western section of the Burgberg tunnel

The same geological conditions existed in the section in front of the west tunnel portal, where a cutting slope with a height of 23 m and a batter of 1:1.75 was necessary. On the uphill slide the natural slope rises with an inclination of about 6°. During the first excavation stage it was already clear that water seepage and fossil slip surfaces were present. The author dealt with the soil exploration and stability assessment of this section revealed that despite the less severe batter of 1:1.75, as opposed to the one of 1:1.2 which ended in failure, the necessary safety factors of 1.3 or 1.4 as required by DIN 4084 could not be achieved without additional stabilizing measures. As a result various methods of securing safe conditions for the cutting slope were discussed:

(a) Reducing the inclination of the slope
    A reduction of the inclination scale of the slope was soon rejected because of the considerations relating to the increased land take, the additional de-forestation and finally, because of the excavation, transportation and depositing of considerable quantities of soil.

(b) Permanent anchoring
    The prestressed forces of ground anchors mean that they have the immediate effect of stabilizing a cutting slope. As the author has learnt from colleagues responsible for the neighbouring section where the landslide had occurred, prestressed ground anchors proved their effectiveness there during the restoration works. However, for permanent slopes or cuts prestressed anchors should be monitored for at least the first two or three years of service. Additionally the long term problem relating to the corrosion of the steel anchors cannot be ignored.

(c) Bored piles

Stabilization using bored piles would only be possible relative to the static requirements if additional prestressed anchors were placed at the top of the piles. Apart from the reasons mentioned in (b), this solution is less advantageous because bored piles could only be arranged in one or two rows parallel to the slope. In other words, they could not be placed over the slope surface as a whole. This may have lead to the occurrence of local sliding uphill or downhill of the one or two pile rows.

(d) Soil nailing

Soil nailing is a method of reinforcing the ground in-situ and finds applications with retaining structures and slope stabilization, BGS News (1991). Depending on the orientation, soil nails carry tension forces or shear forces or both, tension and shear forces, Gässler (1992). In this case the nails were installed nearly horizontal and supposed to stabilize the slope by carrying tension forces in the main strain direction and by enhancing the shear strength in actual or potential slip surfaces. As opposed to ground anchors, nails are bonded with the soil along their total length using cement mortar grouting. Therefore ugly plates or concrete beams on the surface are not necessary for the nails inserted into flat slopes. Slopes stabilized using nails cannot be recognized after completion, as the upper nail ends are covered by a surface layer of about half a metre thickness, Figure 2. As nails are principally not prestressed and nail forces are always less than anchor forces, no high tension steel is needed, which means less sensitivity to corrosion. Finally, monitoring during service state is not necessary.

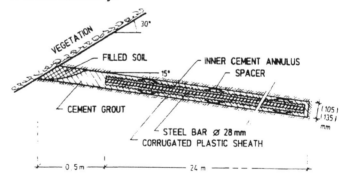

Figure 2   Soil nail reinforcing a flat slope, without plate and nut at the free (greened) surface

Considering the benefits and drawbacks of the different methods, in the given case soil nailing turned out to be the most favoured solution, both technically and economically.

216

DESIGN

A design procedure for the nailing of excavation cuts or steep slopes was first introduced by Gässler and Gudehus (1981), and later in an extended version by Gässler (1987 and 1988). It is based on the kinematic failure mechanism of rigid bodies.

For nailed retaining walls a solid facing consisting of reinforced shotcrete or prefabricated elements is always necessary to bear the lateral earth pressure, which is reduced, however, as a result of the nailing reinforcement and the special procedure of stepwise excavating with temporarily unsupported cuts, Figure 3. The nails, usually consisting of steel bars with rolled threaded ends are connected to the facing using a nut and a nail plate, Gässler (1990).

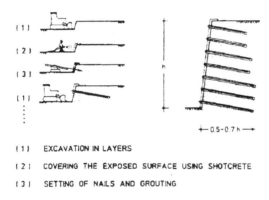

(1)   EXCAVATION IN LAYERS

(2)   COVERING THE EXPOSED SURFACE USING SHOTCRETE

(3)   SETTING OF NAILS AND GROUTING

Figure 3   Construction method for a nailed retaining wall near to the vertical (Gässler, 1990)

However, in the section near the west portal of the Burgberg tunnel the global stability of a rather flat cutting slope was a requisite whereby simple grass seeding on the slope surface was considered to be sufficiently resistant against erosion. This nailing project involving a flat slope without any solid facing was new and required an adapted static solution.

It should be mentioned that so-called injection lances or injection nails have already been used to stabilize slopes, for example in France, in Switzerland and in Germany. These injection nails are installed mostly vertical and perpendicular to potential or existing shear surfaces, fulfilling the function of dowels. In the United Kingdom a special technique was developed to shoot nails into the ground, more or less perpendicular to the ground surface and to the assumed shear surface. This type of nail is also capable of carrying shear. However, because of their small diameter, the bending and shearing forces are relatively small compared to nails acting preferably in tension, Pedley, et al (1990). For this reason the author generally designs soil nailing projects with preference for tension carrying nails. For all that, depending on circumstances, nails orthogonal to the slip surface can be the better solution in some cases, Gässler (1992).

As opposed to a nailed wall near vertical, the axial force of a long nail in a flat slope will have its maximum value at the slip surface decreasing to zero at both ends in limit state. Nevertheless, the calculation method of kinematic failure mechanisms developed for nailed retaining structures, Gässler (1988), remains valid in principle and can be applied.

The inclination of the observed fossil slip surface, about 10° downhill, and the shape of the landslide which occurred in the 1:1.2 inclined cutting slope in the neighbouring section led to the assumption of a two-block failure mechanism. Such a failure mechanism with nearly straight slip lines had taken place in a clay-pit of the same formation about 5 miles away from the Burgberg tunnel and had been intensively studied by Wichter (1980), as already mentioned above. In the case of straight fossil slip lines with reduced shearing resistance, conventional analyses using circular slip surfaces yield factors of safety which overestimate the actual margin of safety against sliding. Therefore, the stability calculation was executed on the basis of the two-bock failure mechanism of Figure 4. This Figure shows the cross-section with the largest height of the slope, 23 m, and the corresponding force polygon to find the required nail forces required to give sufficient stability.

According to Fellenius, the factor of safety η is defined as follows

$$\eta = \frac{\tan \phi}{\tan \phi_d}$$

with ϕ angle of internal friction in the fossil slip surface
   ϕ_d angle of internal friction required for equilibrium in the design state (limit state), whereby the ultimate axial nail forces are taken into account

Following DIN 4084, $\eta = 1.3$ was required. However, it must be admitted that this value was to reached entirely for the low probability case that a fossil slip surface might pass through the foot of the slope in the cross section of greatest height.

The shear parameters of the soil used in the stability calculations are also shown in Figure 4. The values were found from the basis of back-analyses of the landslide mentioned above and the research results by Wichter (1980).

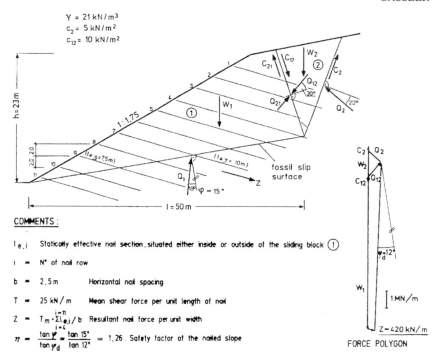

Figure 4   Cross-section of the nailed slope with the assumed two-block failure mechanism and force polygon

For the load case with "fissure water" a relatively small value of $\eta = 1.15$ was accepted, because a system of long drain pipes consisting of perforated PVC-tubes was provided for draining the water within and behind the nail zone. The drain pipes, 80 mm in diameter, were inserted into predrilled boreholes inclined upwards at above $5°$ and were expediently longer than the nails, Figure 5.

The static analyses required an array of 15 m, 20 m and 24 m long nails with horizontal spacings of 2.5 m and vertical spacings of 2.0 m. The total length of all nails was about 12 000 m.

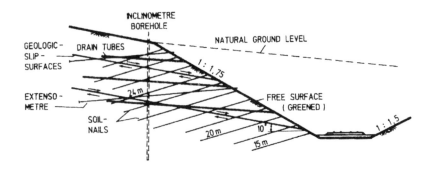

Figure 5   Cross-section of the nailed slope with drainage and instrumentation

PERFORMANCE

Every nail was well protected against corrosion by an outer sheath of plastic (PVC). This sheath of corrugated shape, minimum thickness 1 mm, enclosed an inner cement annulus of nearly 15 mm thickness around the GEWI steel bar of 28 mm diameter as shown in Figure 6. This type of a permanent nail, based on the Bauer system represents the German standard at present, Gässler (1990).

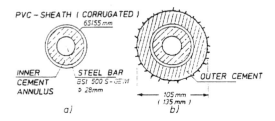

Figure 6   Cross-section of a permanent nail
     a) pre-fabricated in the workshop, ready for transport
     b) inserted into the predrilled borehole and grouted

The permanent nails were prefabricated in a workshop about 30 miles away and transported in their total length to the building site. Figure 6a shows the cross-section of the nail for transport and Figure 6b the cross-section of the nail set into the ground and grouted.

By means of a 18 m long drilling auger, a special development of the contractor Bauer GmbH which could be lengthened to 24 m, the rate of predrilling of the long nails was very high. The drilling machine was

220

placed on a berm, which was excavated stepwise to a depth of 2 m after completion of each row of nails.

Simultaneously the drain pipes, up to 35 m long, were inserted into the predrilled boreholes. The drains which had a steady flow of water, about 10% of all drains, were connected with collecting tubes leading to the lateral drainage of the railway track at the bottom.

Figure 7 shows a view of the nailing works at the bottom the upper part of the western portal of the Burgberg tunnel. The slope to be nailed was nearly 200 m long parallel to the railway track.

Figure 7   View of the cutting slope during the nailing works

PULLOUT TESTS AND FORCE DISTRIBUTION ALONG THE NAILS

A certain number of nails were tested by means of pullout tests to verify the mean shear resistance per unit metre of nail length previously assumed in the stability calculation.

The total length of the test nails was 13.5 m, the grouted length was always 10 m, with the exception of the second special test nail shown in Figure 11, so that the free length was 3.5 m. Representative for the results of more than 20 pullout tests, the measured tensile forces F of two nails are plotted versus the measured total displacement of the nail head in Figure 8.

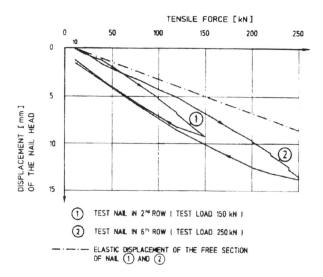

Figure 8   Load displacement curves of two representative nails

The mean shear force required was 15 kN/m in the upper three rows, top layers and weathered rock, and 25 kN/m in all the following rows. As can be seen from this figure the measured values satisfied the required ones. Furthermore, one can deduce from the un-loading curves at zero tensile force that the remaining, plastic displacements of the nails were very small.

Two special test nails not belonging to the regular array of the nails were instrumented with electrical strain gauges placed at regular intervals of 2.0 metres, so that the distribution of the axial forces could be measured along the grouted nail section. Figure 9 shows the set up of a pullout test of an instrumented nail. The solid concrete plate seen on the picture served as an abutment only during the pullout tests.

The force distribution of the first special test nail at different load stages is shown in Figure 10. At low forces the shear stresses between soil and nail are mobilized more at the upper end of the grouted section and the force distribution curves are of approximately parabolic shape. At higher loads, 200 kN, the distribution curves become linear, so that the assumption of a constant mean shear force per unit length $Tm = F/l$ is justified in limit state design, at least in soft or slightly weathered Keuper Marl layers.

Figure 9   Set up of a pullout test of an instrumented nail

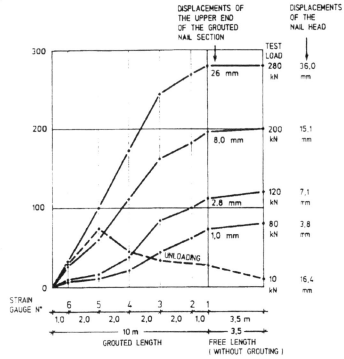

Figure 10   Axial force distribution along the first instrumented
             nail at different load steps during pullout test (soil:
             weathered Keuper Marl)

The result of the second pullout test of a nail with attached strain gauges is shown in Figure 11. This test nail was placed nearer to the bottom of the slope. One can see from the shape of the force distribution curves that the nail was set in non-weathered solid layers of the Keuper Marl, as the curves follow a parabolic shape at low forces, 100 kN to 220 kN, as well as at higher forces, 300 kN to 420kN, whereby the lower last third of the grouted nail section is practically un-mobilized. Nevertheless, the mean shear force, roughly approximated by $Tm = 420/11.5 = 36.5$ kN/m, is on the safe side. It can be seen from comparison of Figure 10 and Figure 11 that the distribution of the axial force along the nail is governed by the stiffness ratio of the steel bar and the surrounding soil.

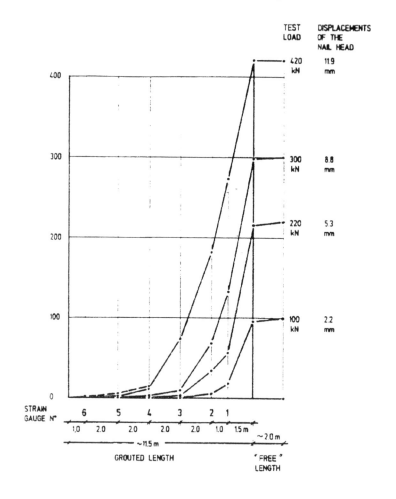

Figure 11   Axial force distribution along the second instrumented nail at different load steps during pullout test (soil: solid Keuper Marl)

Generally, the design engineer has to assume an adequate axial nail force distribution for a soil nail for the limit state. In cases of nails with usual lengths, say up to 5 m - 8 m in dense granular soils, or 7 m - 10 m in clayey soils, a linear shape for the axial force from the earth sided end of nail, to the potential or actual slip surface may be assumed. The mean shear force per unit length, Tm, has to be checked by a certain number of pull-out tests, say, 3 to 5 percent of the total number of installed nails.

The measurement of force and displacement at the upper end of the nail, the nail head, is sufficient for most practical cases. However, the application of strain gauges is useful for research and contributes to a better understanding of the mechanical behaviour of nails in service and in the limit state. For pull-out tests it is recommended that the grouted length of a nail should correspond to that assumed between the potential slip surface and the earth-sided nail end in the stability calculation. Only in a few cases may the assumption of a parabolic shape for the axial nail forces in limit state be necessary. However, one has to be aware of the fact that the distinct shape can only be estimated by the present state of knowledge. Nevertheless, the limit state design method of nailed walls on the basis of kinematic failure mechanisms of rigid bodies remains principally untouched by the assumed distributions of nail forces.

In all pullout tests the calculated values of the mean shear force could be reached or even overstepped, so that the stabilization of the slope using nails was carried out as it had been designed.

MONITORING

Three boreholes for inclinometer measurements and four extensometers were installed to monitor the lateral displacement of the reinforced slope. Shortly after completion slight relaxation movements of less than 1 cm were measured. After two years the displacements at the top of the slope did not exceed 2 cm. Today, there is no more monitoring in service state, however one can state that the slope is in an absolutely stable condition. The completed nailed slope now covered by a green facing is shown in Figure 12.

CONCLUSIONS

The practical execution of this nailing project showed that:
Prefabrication in a workshop, transport to the site and installation of extremely long nails, up to 24 m in one piece, is practicable.
No facing using shotcrete or any other solid material is necessary for flat (e.g., 1: 1.75 inclined) slopes, however, seeding grass requires an adequate season.
Prefabricated nails guarantee permanent protection against corrosion.
Design based on long nails acting in tension can be very expedient in order to stabilize slopes.
Pullout tests of nails are necessary to validate the static assumptions; in this case good test result have confirmed static assumptions of the shear bond between nail and soil as well as quality of execution.

Figure 12   Completed nailed slope covered by a green surface

REFERENCES

BGS News, 1991, *Soil nailing - a solution looking for problems.* Ground Engineering, Jan/Feb, 42-43

Gässler G., 1987, *Vernagelte Geländesprünge - Tragverhalten und Standsicherheit.* PhD Thesis, Institute of Soil Mechanics and Rock Mechanics, University of Karlruhe, FRG, Vol. 108

Gässler G., 1988, *Soil nailing - theoretical basis and practical design.* Theory and Practice of Earth Reinforcement, Balkeema, 232-237

Gässler G., 1990, *In-situ techniques of reinforced soil.* State-of-the-Art Lecture, Int. Reinforced Soil Conf., Glasgow, Scotland, 185-196

Gässler G., 1992, *Report and Discussion of Session 5.* Proc. Int. Geotechnical Symp. on Earth Reinforcement Practice, Fukuoka, Japan, 1992.

Gässler G. & Gudehus, G., 1981, *Soil nailing - Some aspects of a new technique.* Proc. 10th Int. Conf. Soil & Found. Eng., Stockholm, Vol. 3

Pedley M. J., Jewell R.A. & Milligan G.E.W., 1990, *A large scale study of soil reinforcement interaction.* Ground Engin. Part 1-July, Part 2-Sept.

Wichter L., 1980, Festigkeitsuntersuchungen an GroBbohrkernen von Keupermergel und Anwendung auf eine Böschungsrutschung. Inst. of Soil Mech. & Rock Mech., Univ. of Karlsruhe, FRG, Vol. 84.

The joint use of ballistic soil nailing and reinforced soil in Huddersfield

G. J. HALL, E.C. Civil Engineering Limited, United Kingdom

SYNOPSIS

This paper describes the design, supply and construction of retaining structures comprising both ballistic soil nailed slopes and conventional reinforced soil, at the Alfred McAlpine Stadium in Huddersfield during the latter months of 1994.

INTRODUCTION

Late in 1994 Alfred McAlpine Building (Northern Ltd) were nearing completion of their contract to construct the new all seater football stadium for Huddersfield Town Football Club, Figure 1. Indeed the stadium was already in use by the client for league football and rugby fixtures. Part of the earlier works had required excavation into an existing slope to construct the Kilner Bank Stand. The rear of this stand is supported by contiguous bored piling and the temporary works associated with the piling required a bench to be cut into the slope to permit access for the piling rig. The bench then remained cut into the mudstone slope with side slopes at approximately 85° to the horizontal. To create access to the Kilner Stand, the existing slope at low level had been trimmed to a near vertical face. Both slopes were stable in the short term but had begun to weather and work was needed to stabilise the embankment over the long term, especially as a high pressure gas main passed close to the top of the upper slope. British Gas had already expressed concern about the long term stability of the embankment.

SITE GEOLOGY

The site investigation had been carried out in 1992 in order to permit final designs to be formulated for the proposed football stadium. The site had been utilised by a variety of industrial users over the past 150 years and various amounts of made ground overlaid the area, generally in the form of clinker. A large amount of tar was discovered in addition to various dyes. However in the vicinity of the Kilner Bank, ground levels had been lowered beneath the contaminants into weathered mudstones. The mudstone extended down for some 20 m to a thin layer of coal.

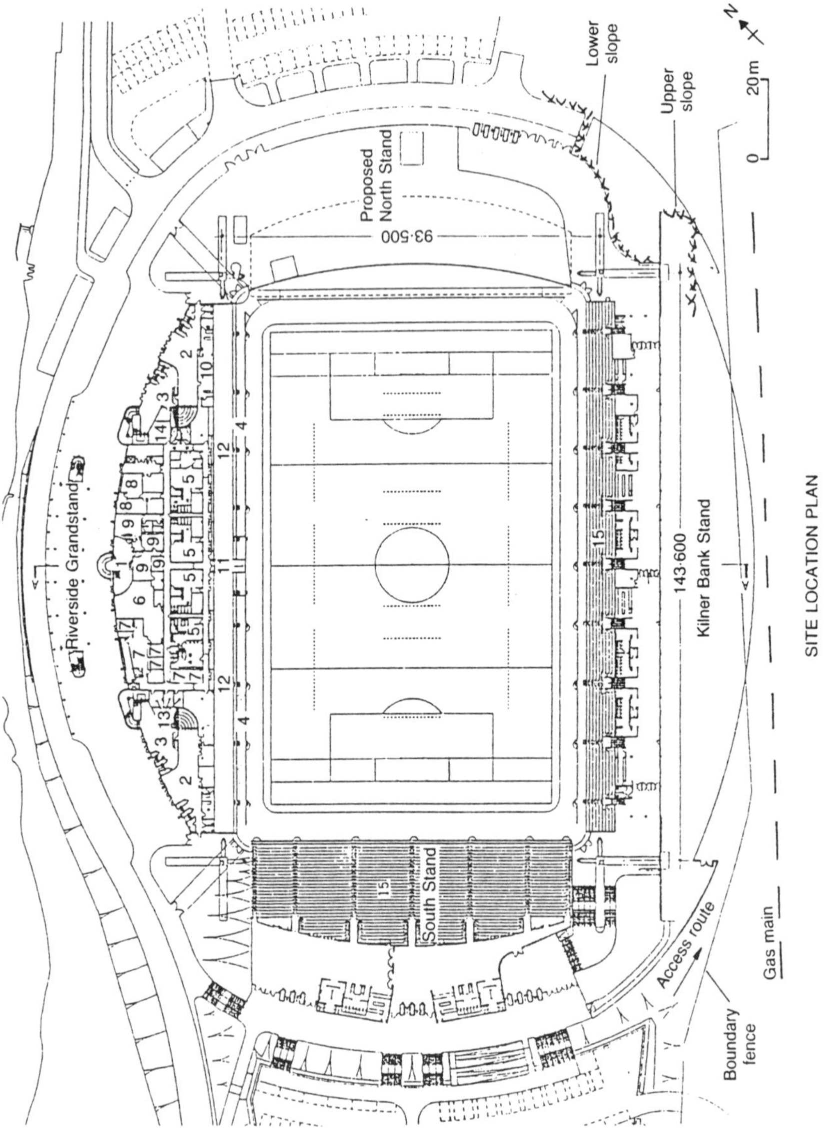

Riverside Grandstand
Proposed North Stand
93·500
South Stand
Kilner Bank Stand
143·600
Lower slope
Upper slope
0
20m
N
Gas main
Boundary fence
Access route
SITE LOCATION PLAN

Fig. 1

THE ENGINEERS PROPOSED SLOPE STABILITY WORKS

The consulting engineer for the project YRM Anthony Hunt had formulated a scheme to support the slopes. The works proposed a gabion solution at high level and a reinforced concrete king post supported wall immediately in front of the lower slopes. The low level works involved boring holes and installing in them the 37 king posts at 2 m spacings followed by the construction between each of a horizontally spanning reinforced concrete panel retaining wall. One aspect of this work required placing quantities of fill material behind the king post wall on the lower slopes to add weight and improve the stability. E C Civil Engineering Ltd (ECCE) was invited, by the client's representative, to offer an alternative solution for stabilization works based on our wide experience in the reinforced earth design and build field. ECCE were originally contacted by the client's representative Spring and Co., this then became a formal approach through the main contractor.

ASSESSMENT OF THE SCOPE OF WORKS

From the site inspection the following constraints of such works at such a late stage in the project were soon appreciated:

1   The stadium had been in use for some time and therefore all works had to be phased around both football and rugby fixture lists.

2   Extensive block paving had been laid in the area of the lower works, the blocks had been laid for light duty use, and services underlaid the block paviours. Therefore plant would have to be small, or protection measures would be needed.

3   Turnstiles and gates had been erected, these limited the size of plant.

4   Access to the upper area, the former piling bench, was extremely difficult. Access could be gained from the east end only by constructing a 350 m long temporary road across and along a slope. Access from the west would be along the rear of the completed Kilner Stand. However this access was very narrow as a rear security fence had already been erected and raking struts from the stand roof encroached into the access. Consideration was given to removing part of the fence near the works but this raised security questions. Access from outside the fence meant this route would pass along the line of the gas main.

5   These access difficulties would be reduced if the imported material quantity for the chosen solution could be reduced.

6   The programme for the works including design, checking, and construction had to be completed by 14 December 1994 the Main Contract completion date. This gave a total period from conceptual design through completion of only 9 weeks.

7   Winter was fast approaching, limiting hours and raising the probability of working in bad weather.

It quickly became apparent that a soil nailing solution, in combination with some conventional reinforced soil, would overcome many of the construction difficulties. This technical combination would address many of the constraints above, it would be quick, require minimal bulk material movements and would reduce the affect of the limited access on programme and cost.

Having settled on the appropriate technical solution, work began on the facing solution. It would have to be permanent, be able to be securely fixed to the soil nails to transfer loads from the slope face to the nail and be acceptable aesthetically to the Architect and Client. It was opted to use galvanised steel mesh as a facing set at angle of 1 to 4. The main structural mesh element comprised 10 mm bars on a 200 mm square grid with a smaller 50 mm grid spacing mesh behind to retain the facing materials. It was decided that the slope face treatment would be a geotextile in contact with the mudstone as a drainage membrane with a 200 mm layer of clean rock serving to both place weight on the mudstone and give a gabion like appearance, Figure 2.

These ideas were developed into engineering details in conjunction with Soil Nailing Limited, a firm specialising in ballistic nails. A set of standard details for the reinforced soil wall element was formulated using the same facing aesthetics as for the soil nailed area, Figure 3. On 14 October a preliminary alternative proposal was submitted to the main contractor specifying a 43 day program from receipt of order, Figure 4. A final proposal was submitted on 24 October and a meeting of all interested parties attended on 27 October at which ECCE were awarded the subcontract, and given the go ahead to commence working.

DESIGN AND PROCUREMENT

The design was coordinated with Soil Nailing Limited who used the software package Talren to analysis the slope stability and for the design of nail diameter, spacing and length, Figure 5. These parameters being computed as 38 mm diameter, 1.0 m centre to centre spacing and with a penetration of 3 m. In parallel ECCE designed the reinforced soil based on the coherent gravity method as set out in draft BS 8006 which

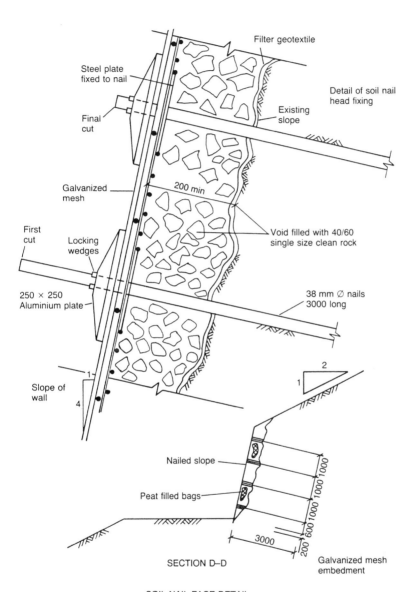

Filter geotextile

Steel plate
fixed to nail

Detail of soil nail
head fixing

Final
cut

Existing
slope

Galvanized
mesh

200 min

First
cut

Void filled with 40/60
single size clean rock

Locking
wedges

250 × 250
Aluminium plate

38 mm Ø nails
3000 long

Slope of
wall

Nailed slope

Peat filled bags

3000

SECTION D–D

Galvanized mesh
embedment

SOIL NAIL FACE DETAIL

Fig. 2

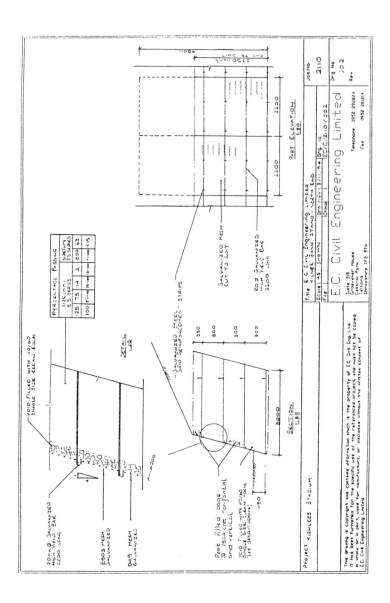

Fig. 3

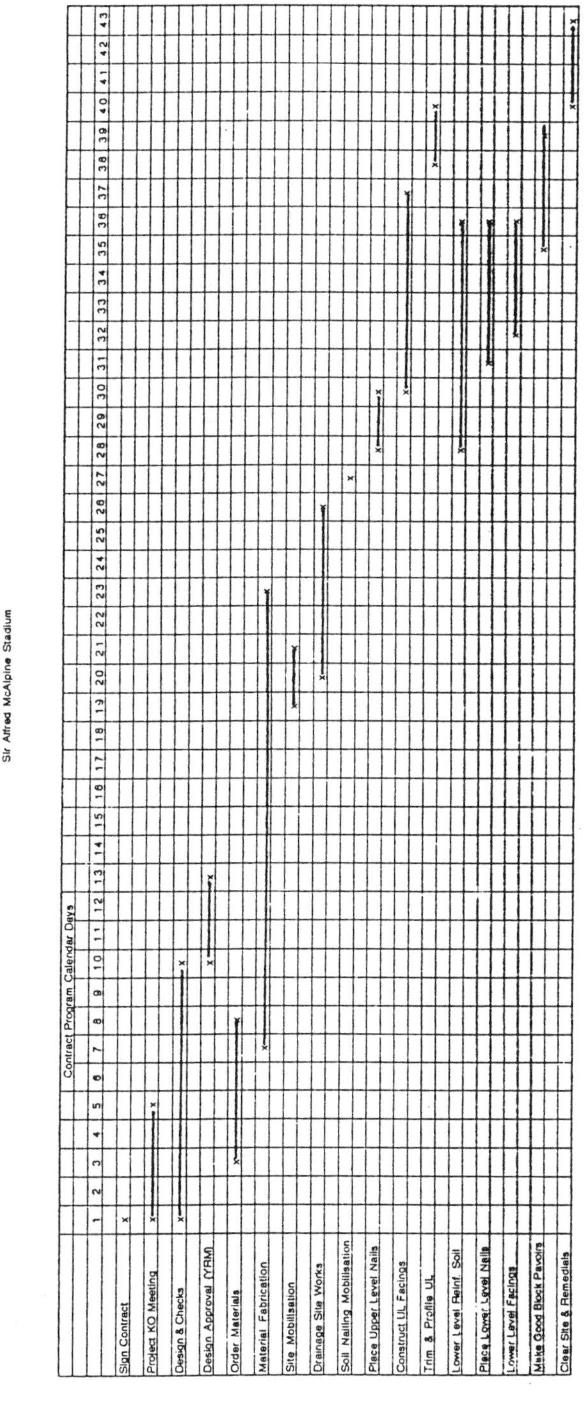
Sir Alfred McAlpine Stadium
Contract Program Calendar Days
1 2 3 4 5 6 7 8 9 10 11 12 13 14 15 16 17 18 19 20 21 22 23 24 25 26 27 28 29 30 31 32 33 34 35 36 37 38 39 40 41 42 43
Sign Contract
Project KO Meeting
Design & Checks
Design Approval (YRM)
Order Materials
Material Fabrication
Site Mobilisation
Drainage Site Works
Soil Nailing Mobilisation
Place Upper Level Nails
Construct UL Facings
Trim & Profile UL
Lower Level Reinf. Soil
Place Lower Level Nails
Lower Level Facings
Make Good Block Pavoirs
Clear Site & Remedials

Fig. 4

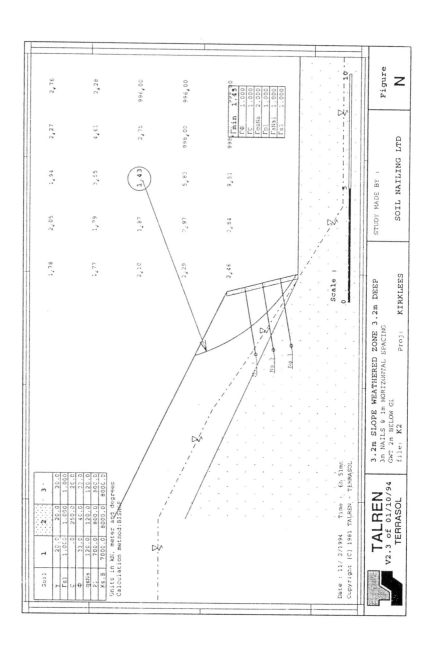

Fig. 5

is in use world wide. The necessary formulae were set up in an Excel spreadsheet. Contract drawings were produced and the design package submitted to the main contractor for checking. British Gas also carried out an independent check in addition to YRM carrying out their check for the Client. During the checking process orders were placed for the steel mesh and soil reinforcing strips. Full design approval was issued in due course.

SOIL NAILING OPERATIONS

ECCE mobilised to site on 9 November to begin preparations for access and preliminary items. The rear access behind the stand was improved and facing rock was moved along this access using a 2 tonne dumper. The nailing equipment arrived on site on 15 November by low loader. The nailing gun was mounted on a 15 tonne hydraulic excavator. The nail gun, originally developed for military applications by Ferranti, was fitted to the end of the excavator arm and operated by compressed air from a separate power pack mounted on the machine. Plywood sheeting was spread over the existing block paviours to provide protection. The machine was unloaded and prepared for work, Figure 6.

The nails were supplied 6 m long with conical groves at the tip. A plastic assembly was fitted to the nail tip. During the firing sequence the compressed air charge is applied to the plastic fitting accelerating the nail into the soil from its tip. The machine was immediately set to work on the lower slope with work progressing quickly firing all 108 nails in 2½ days. The nails penetrating 4.5 m on average, exceeding the minimum embedment of 3 m, Figure 7.

It had been planned to move the machine by low loader to the opposite end of the stadium to gain access to the upper slope area by tracking it behind the Kilner Bank Stand. This was always going to be a confined operation. In the event it became apparent that it would not fit into the required clearance envelope and would foul the rear raking supports to the stand roof. An alternative solution was adopted by suspending the gun from a crane. Due to the access situation, a 50 tonne rough terrain short wheelbase unit was hired, Figure 8. A head member had to be temporarily removed from an access gate through which the crane had to pass. The crane had to cross the block paviours on 3 layers of plywood protection. It was quickly set up with the excavator controlling the gun in tandem with the crane via a banksman.

The upper bench area was nailed in a single day, using temporary floodlights to allow work to continue until completion at 8 pm that night.· A total of 72 nails were placed in the upper area in 9 hours. Due to the proximity of the high pressure gas main at the top of the slope a member of staff from British Gas attended these operations.

With nailing completed, work started on the construction of the permanent face starting with the low level structures. The sequence of work followed to construct the face is set out below :

Fig. 6

Fig. 7

Fig. 8

Fig. 9

1   The nails, which protruded an average of 1.5 m out of the slope face were trimmed with a disc cutter to give both a uniform line and a minimum extension of 300 mm.

2   Heavy grade needle punched geotextile was fixed to the mudstone face with 100 mm woodwork nails.

3   Steel plates 200 mm square were welded to the soil nails such that they were positioned at least 200 mm from the mudstone embankment along the design plane of the structure. The plate positions defined the final face profile.

4   A galvanised steel mesh with a grid size of 50 mm was fixed to the plates followed by the galvanised structural mesh made of 10 mm diameter steel bar at a 200 mm grid.

5   Cast aluminium cotter plates were fitted to the protruding nail heads to permanently fix the mesh to the nail. Tension in the joint caused the assembly to be permanently tight.

6   A 75 mm single size clean limestone was dropped between the geotextile and the rear of the steel mesh. The stone had to be tipped by the road lorries into a storage area some 50 m from the work area. A 2 tonne dumper was used to transport the stone to the work area where a telehoist fitted with a wide front bucket carried out the placement operation. Planting bags were placed in the face on a 1.5 m grid.

7   Finally the remaining soil nail protrusions (100 mm) were trimmed back in line with the cotter assemblies and all exposed steel given two coats of zinc rich paint. This lower area of face included two right angle corners one internal and one external. The abutting faces were sloping each at 1 in 4. The mesh face was fabricated on site to fit by cutting and welding the standard mesh units, all areas of bare metal were then painted with zinc rich paint.

The upper slope face was constructed in the same manner except that the facing stone was placed using a concreting skip on a 50 tonne crane.

REINFORCED SOIL WALL

The lower slope improvement works measured 75 m long in plan. Some 60 m was constructed using soil nailing as described above, the remaining

15 m being in the form of a reinforced soil wall. For aesthetic reasons the appearance of this area of wall needed to match the soil nailed section since from the front view both types of construction appear as one structure.

The formation was struck and proved. Next the two types of mesh, the 50 mm and 200 mm grids, were propped with timber to a 1 in 4 slope to match the adjacent soil nailed structure. The flat steel soil reinforcement strips, of 75 mm by 4 mm section, were produced with a 180° bend of a 20 mm radius at one end to give a short return of 500 mm. The reinforcement element being 3 m in plan length and galvanised. This hook detail allowed rapid connection to the mesh face using a 20 mm diameter galvanised steel bar placed horizontally in front of the mesh.

The bottom row of reinforcement was laid on the formation and connected to the facing mesh as described above. Due to access difficulties a mini excavator had to be used to spread and level the imported granular backfill material. A small pedestrian roller was employed to provide the necessary compaction. The fill material, crushed limestone, had to be tipped by road transport some 100 m from the work location due to the finished state of the area adjacent to the retaining wall. The fill had to be transported to the wall location by a telehoist with a large front bucket which also placed the fill in the required position for the mini excavator.

This small area of reinforced soil wall with a face area of 60 m² took 3 days to construct. The finished appearance matching the nailed area

Fig. 10

very closely with single size rock and planting bags evenly spaced behind the mesh face, Figures 9 and 10. Figure 9 shows the reinforced soil wall and the adjacent lower nailed slope. The upper nailed slope can be seen in the top part of the photograph. Figure 10 shows a long view of the upper and lower nailed slopes in relation to the end of the Kilner Bank Stand. The telehoist lifted out the mini excavator and roller on completion.

A small amount of ancillary drainage work in the form of a gulley pot and a dished drainage channel formed in paviour blocks was constructed. The site was cleared on 16 December 1994.

CONCLUSIONS

This alternative engineering solution for stabilising the Kilner Bank allowed the main contractor to substantially complete the project on time. The conforming bid would have required an extension of the contract period by several weeks. The Client also benefitted from substantial cost savings for this work.

With its innovative nature the project proved very successful. Good planning, tight monitoring on site, flexibility during construction as well as excellent cooperation between the Client, the Main Contractor, the Engineer, the Architect and British Gas allowed this difficult project to be completed 8 days inside the 43 day programme.

A rapid technique for soil nailing slopes

B MYLES, Soil Nailing Limited, United Kingdom

INTRODUCTION

Reinforced soil has been established for over 20 years, however, the *dig out and replace with reinforced soil* solution on unstable slopes can produce a stability condition during the construction sequence more precarious than that existing in the original slope. Conventional in-situ soil reinforcement by drilling, grouting or piling is often too expensive and time consuming to be applied to unstable slopes. The development of technologies to directly install long reinforcing elements with small sections to depths of 5 m should allow in-situ soil reinforcement to be more widely applied to slopes with shallow zones of instability.

REINFORCEMENT OF EXISTING GROUND

The technique of reinforcing existing ground without excavation involves some form of insertion of a reinforcement. This method is generally applicable to walls and slopes. In some projects the reinforcement will be installed during a staged excavation whilst in other instances the reinforcement will be required to improve the stability of an existing slope or earthworks.

A widely used technique for such reinforcement is ground anchors, however, this technique is regarded as an active reinforcement in which a stress is induced and transferred to the soil. The techniques to be discussed relate to passive reinforcement in which soil movement is needed to active the reinforcement. The most common techniques of passive reinforcement are:

- Soil nailing
- Reticulated root or micro-piles
- Soil dowels

The major emphasis of this note will be directed to soil nailing although references will be given to the other techniques.

A soil nailed structure has many common features with conventional reinforced fill in which the reinforcing members primarily provide tensile resistance. Most reinforcements used in fill have little or no stiffness and therefore the orientation of the reinforcement is simple and often dictated by the method of construction.

THE HISTORY OF SOIL NAILING

The first use for soil nailing in Europe was in 1972 when the French railways undertook the stabilization of an 18 m high battered face and cemented sand. The success of this project encouraged others and soil nailing was adapted for use in the Paris underground extensions.

However, in the late seventies there were two notable failures in France which highlighted the need for a much more thorough examination of the design mythology and execution of soil nailing. These difficulties gave impetus to the Clouterre programme which will be mentioned later in more detail. At about the same time a major research programme was being undertaken at the University of Karlsruhe in Germany which also involved extensive full-scale trials which were loaded to failure. Both government and private industry participated in these two large research projects, the total cost of which was in excess of $6 million. The impact of this research work is quickly being shown, particularly in France where the annualized production of soil nailed facing exceeds 150,000 m^2 per year with a growth rate in the teens percent.

THE LIFETIME OF SOIL NAILS

The division between the use of soil nails for temporary and permanent structures is somewhat blurred. An example can be the soil nailing of a basement excavation, in many cases the support provided by the soil nails is rendered redundant by the building structure when completed, however, increasingly the contribution of the soil nails is being partially taken into account when assessing the total stability. Another aspect which is affecting the concept of the soil nailed structure's lifetime are the developments taking place in road widening. The rapid development of transportation technology means that many of the traditional lifetime concepts of transportation structures are called into question. If a three-lane highway has to be extended into a four-lane highway in less than 10 years, the question must be asked "How many years will elapse before the demand is for a five-lane highway?"

THE NATURE OF SOIL NAILS

Soil nails often possess a degree of stiffness and therefore the inclination of installation relative to the critical failure surface is of importance. Another significant difference between conventional reinforced fill and reinforcement by soil nails is the construction process. In soil nailing the excavated face commences from the top and proceeds down thus placing the force in the upper nails first, in conventional reinforcement the lower levels are loaded first. This difference in the distribution of load can be critical during construction, particularly when considering the deformation profile of the face.

THE TYPE OF SOIL NAILS

Even within soil nails there are different types, sometimes referred to as flexible nails and stiff nails. Flexible nails are generally nails with a diameter less than 25 mm which is installed in a drilled and grouted hole and orientated to mobilise tension. Stiff nails are often directly inserted without the addition of grout and are orientated to generate both shear and bending in the nail as well as tension. The geometry of directly inserted nails may, in some cases, be considered as soil dowelling where the influence of tension can be disregarded.

While it is common to ignore the effect of shear on flexible nails, it is always wise to ascertain the shear forces in all soil nails as these should be taken into account in assessing the permissable tensile load on the nail. A similar argument applies to the tensile force on nails that are primarily used in shear.

Steel nails should have properties that tend to ductile rather than be brittle. This is particularly relevant as at the ultimate condition the nail must retain its ability to carry tensile forces whilst deformed. Yield stresses in excess of 500 N/mm^2 should be avoided. The other advantage of using low yield stress is that corrosion will be more uniform and the tendency to pit will be less.

The use of stainless steel is not generally recommended unless soil conditions are highly aggressive. The use of synthetic nails, as yet, is not widespread and while there are several commercially available products these either suffer from brittle behaviour and poor performance under bending or have a high initial deformation prior to full uptake of load. In all cases existing synthetic nails should be orientated into a tension mode and any bending and shear should be avoided.

DESIGN PROCEDURES

The existing design procedures fall into two categories: those that take into account shear bending and tension and those that recognise only tension as a contributing restraint mechanism. As in all soil reinforced structures there is a requirement to analyze the reinforced mass for an external failure. These procedures follow standard accepted geotechnical practice and will not be commented upon further.

The internal stability mode of the soil nailed structure can be considered as having several mechanisms, however, in most procedures the failure surface is regarded as a log spiral or circular arc. The exception is Germany where a bi-linear wedge analysis is used.

The simplified only tension approach will not be considered further as the full-scale trials in Germany and France have shown that shear and bending do exist in the nails and as most analysis procedures are computer controlled there seems little reason why all the contributing resistances should not be utilised.

Using the French Talren program, which is based on the classical Bishop slope stability method, an example can be constructed to illustrate the contribution made by the nail stiffness.

A soil with a friction angle of 30° and a cohesion of 2 kPa is cut at a gradient of 1:1 to a depth of 4 m. The slope is just stable and has therefore been reinforced with three 2.5 m long, 38 mm diameter soil nails. The nails are inserted at 30° to the horizontal. A thin, high cohesion surface is included in the analysis to deter the computer program from seeking failure slips between the nails. The difference in factors of safety in the tension only and tension with shear analysis are illustrated in Figure 1 and Table 1.

Table 1 Calculated factors of safety

Talren Analysis	Factor of Safety
Unreinforced	1.00
Soil nails tension only	1.21
Soil nails tension and shear	1.31

FACTORS OF SAFETY

Table 2 shows a summary of the safety of load factors that are in common use. The experience of the comprehensive work of the Clouterre project, particularly the monitoring of the extensive trials, gives confidence in the Clouterre recommendations for nailed walls. The partial factors for slopes is a proposal from the United Kingdom which is applied to conventional reinforced fill slips and nailed slopes.

NAIL INSTALLATION

Drilled and Grouted - Most small track mounted drill rigs can be adapted for the installation of soil nails. Larger hydraulic powered rigs tend to be clumsy and their capacity under-utilised. Wherever possible open drilling should be attempted as case hole methods are expensive and time consuming. The inclination of the nail is 10° - 15° to allow gravity grouting. The normal diameter of holes drilled for grouted nails is 100 mm although a hole size of 150 mm is not uncommon in North America while Japanese technology often utilises bore holes below 75 mm. The use of centralizers is important as is the connection detail to the facing. The size of nail in grouted constructions varies typically between 12 mm and 32 mm, although the majority of nails tend to be below 19 mm. The practice of secondary fracture grouting can be used in different soil conditions but it is not common.

Directly inserted - The installation of conventionally head driven nails is difficult due to length to radius of gyration ratio which reduces the

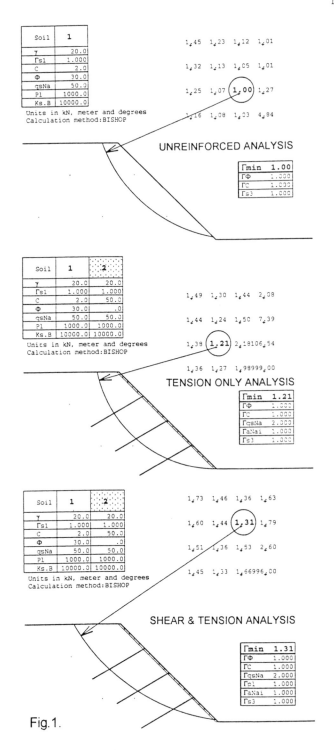

Fig.1.

Table 2 Load and safety factors for permanent nail wall design

Global	Yield	Pull-out	Load Static	Load Imposed	Soil Friction	Soil Cohesion	
1.0	1.7	2.0	1.0	1.0	1.0	1.0	Germany
1.5	1.5	2.0	1.0	1.0	1.0	1.0	France
1.5	1.5	1.5	1.0	1.0	1.0	1.0	France
1.125	1.15	1.4	0.95-1.05	0.9-1.2	1.2	1.5	Clouterre recommenda-tions

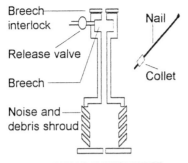

1. NAIL BEING PRESENTED
FOR LOADING

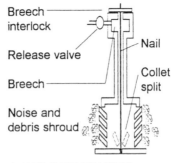

4. NAIL IMPACT WITH
COLLET RELEASE

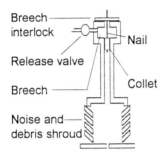

2. NAIL LOADED IN
LAUNCHER

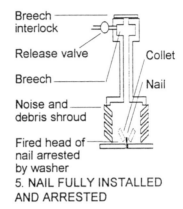

5. NAIL FULLY INSTALLED
AND ARRESTED

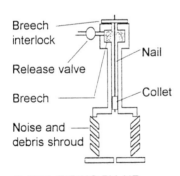

3. NAIL FIRING BY AIR
PRESSURE RELEASE

Fig. 2.   THE SEQUENCE OF INSTALLING A SOIL NAIL BALLISTICALLY

obtainable length to about 3 m. Another complication is that the small repetitive percussive impacts that the Euler load demands disturb the soil and reduces the available skin friction. A more rapid and efficient method of installing driven nails is achieved by ballistic penetration which overcomes the buckling problem and the swift single impulse inserts the nail in less than one fifth of a second resulting in a uniform annulus of displaced soil whilst minimising the disturbance of the soil structure.

Ballistic nailing - With ballistically installed nails the nail is propelled by compressed air from its tip to which the force of the air pressure is transferred via a disposable plastic collet, in this way the nail is placed in tension in flight. The tension, induced by the tip firing ensures that the nail does not buckle on impact. Once the nail enters the ground it is supported by the earth and its straightness maintained. The mechanism that fires the nails is known as the *launcher*. This is mounted on a wheeled or tracked vehicle with attachments capable of positioning the nail precisely at the required inclinations. The launching sequence is controlled by a microprocessor ensuring correct and safe operation. The launcher makes a sharp boom on firing but the noise is reduced by a baffled shroud which also captures the disposable collet and any surface debris as shown in Figure 2. The steel nails fired by the present air launcher, as seen in Figure 3, are 38 mm in diameter with nail lengths of up to 6 metres.

Figure 3 Soil nailing machine strengthening failed road shoulder

Future developments include larger nail diameters up to 80 mm and different shaped cross sections, increasing the perimeter/area ratio and the cross sectional stiffness. The head of the nail can be located at the surface or at specific depths by means of an arresting steel collar. The ballistic nail may also be a perforated tube for drainage or gas extraction. The head of the nail can be threaded to allow the attachment of facings, nail extensions or soil reinforcing strips and geotextiles.

NAIL ANCHORAGE

Anchorage within the active zone is ignored in vertical or near-vertical slopes as these are furnished with a facing into which the nail is connected. In the nailing of unstable slopes where no facing is envisaged, anchorage in the active zone should be carefully analyzed and the use of faceplates is often recommended, particularly the toe region of the slope.

NAIL SPACING

The spacing of the nails will depend on many considerations such as, soil type, type of nail, height of structure, etc., but as a guideline: for grouted nails the spacing will vary between one nail per 1.5 m^2 of face for vertical cuts to one nail per 3 m^2 for existing slopes. On some existing slopes there will be a limitation in utilising the strength of the grouted nail due to the effect of "combing" or instability between nails. For driven nails the spacing can be one nail per 0.8 m^2 of face for vertical or near vertical structures to one nail per 2 m^2 for existing slopes.

CORROSION PROTECTION

Steel nails are protected by galvanising, epoxy coating, plastic sheathing or cement grout or a combination all three. The use of a sacrificial thickness, particularly with mild steel, is regarded as good practice and often external protected coatings, such as galvanising, are not taken into account when calculating the sacrificial thickness.

The use of protective sheathing is only relevant to grouted nails and the protective effect of grout should be regarded as a contribution rather than a full protection.

Care should be taken not to confuse the corrosion protection requirements of stranded anchor cables and the like to the requirements of lowly stressed soil nails. The sacrificial thickness loss of 1 mm on a 38 mm nail reduces the cross section by about 12%; the same corrosion on a strand in a cable would be catastrophic.

Table 3 shows a comparison of the recommended sacrificial thicknesses in United Kingdom and France together with the practical range used commercially for driven galvanised nails.

SOIL REINFORCING IN EUROPE

Table 3 Sacrificial thickness in mm applicable to soil nails

	Years	1.5→	5→	10→	30→	40→	50→	70→	100→	120→
France	Slight corrosive	0		2				4		
	Medium corrosive	0		4				8		
	Very corrosive	2		8						
United Kingdom	Out of water		0.25	0.35	0.95		1.15			
	In water (fresh)		0.25	0.4	1.3		1.55			
France & United Kingdom	Highly corrosive	Special protective measures needed								
Soil Nailing Ltd Driven nails	Slight to medium corrosive, out of water	700 g/m² galvanizing								
		0.25	1	1.5	3.5	4	4.5	5.5		

A range of synthetic nails has been developed but until there is a demand for significant production they are likely to be prohibitively expensive compared with steel nails.

SOIL CONDITIONS
The ground conditions for cut and nailed construction can be critical. For drilled and grouted nails a vertical or steeply sloped face should be capable of standing unsupported for a period of one or two days. For driven nails this can be reduced by half due to the speed of installation. In difficult conditions non-continuous excavation can be adopted but this often has severe cost implications. Non-cemented sand and gravels can be pre-treated to enhance their cohesion but this can add greatly to the cost. Care should be taken if there are known to be considerable variations in soil conditions occasional large stones will not restrict the installation of driven nails, however, any abundance of boulders or zones of cobbles, will make driven nails inapplicable. Any variation in water table or subsequent imposed loads should also be taken into account. Particular care should be taken if the gradient above the cut is within 5% of the soil angle of friction. Soil nailing is not recommended in soft clays with a PI > 20.

DEFORMATION
Soil nails are by their nature and method of installation initially passive and are only mobilized by soil movement. For this reason deflections which are often referenced to the upper part of the cutting or slope are greater than those occurring in anchored and tie back walls. The size of deflection is somewhat mitigated by the density of nails compared with anchors. The normal range of deflections of both horizontal and vertical will be within the range of 0.1 to 0.3 percentile of the wall height. Theoretically the deformation of driven nails should be greater than those for grouted nails as the pullout is much less but this is not seen to be the case. One of the reasons for the equivalents of deformation between the two methods could be the period of time between excavation and the nail becoming active, particularly as the curing time of the grout must be added to the installation period for grouted nails.

CONSTRAINTS OF SOIL NAILING
As in all technologies advantages are offset by constraints and problems. The limitation of the types of soil, particularly in vertical structures, sometimes restricts the use of soil nails. Variations and obstructions in soil often make the installation of driven nails difficult or is impossible and those of drilled and grouted nails unduly expensive. The passive nature of the reinforcement brings about deformations which in turn can induce soil movements that are unacceptable, particularly where adjacent properties are affected. Facings of vertical and near-vertical structures often require rapid installation of shotcrete which

makes it difficult to achieve an acceptable finish requiring further facing works to realise an aesthetic appearance.

ADVANTAGES OF SOIL NAILS

Soil nails are cost effective in reinforcing soil, particularly for limited height structures or where they can be combined with other retaining techniques such as anchors. They are extremely effective in stabilizing existing slopes or where slopes have to be steepened. Even in Northern European climates vegetation can be established on nail slopes in excess of 50 degrees. The installation of soil nails in existing slopes is often achieved with minimal disruption to the environment, particularly compared with an excavated or replacement solution.

The ballistic nailing machine has two further benefits; it is very quick installing nails with installation rates for 4.5 m long nails exceeding 12 nails per hour and the ability to detach the air launcher section of the machine and position it by crane while slaving the air and control line from the main machine allowing working in inaccessible locations without staging or platforms.

Discussion on Session 2

C.G. JENNER, Netlon Limited, United Kingdom - Discussion Reporter

Professor Jones, Chairman of the afternoon session, opened the discussion with three brief presentations.

Dr Bush, Highways Agency, commented that the Highways Agency has heard that soil reinforcement is widely used in Europe and that it is cheap, quick to construct and reliable. In the UK however reinforced soil has faced resistance to its use. Problems of lengthy approval procedures and the lack of design standards have been cited as causing part of this resistance.

Over the last 12 months the approval procedures have been streamlined and clear guidelines have been issued to Highways Agency project managers. HA 68/94 has been issued to give guidelines on reinforced soil slope design and, later in the summer, BS 8006 is expected to be published giving guidance on the design of foundations as well as slopes, walls and abutments. It is hoped that these remarks will enable the Highways Agency to take advantage of these lower cost solutions.

Dr Barley, Keller Colcrete stated that in the UK there have been about a dozen large soil nail contracts carried out in the last two years. This includes contracts with slope heights up to 18 m with 16 rows of nails and a total number of drilled and grouted soil nails in excess of 5000.

For stabilising slopes, geogrids have been used in the form mentioned earlier by Professor Gässler but these have been retained in place by the nail heads. Where the slopes have been steep and the soil particularly likely to spall heavily, prior to vegetation growth, strong Maccaferri mesh has been incorporated to prevent the grid bursting where retained by the nail heads. When the growth of vegetation is achieved the root matrix supplements or replaces the mesh retention in provision of surface stability.

The installation of upward sloping drains is essential on the majority of slopes. There have been cases where the soil nail holes themselves have relieved the slope mass of water by acting as drains. This makes it even more important to fully grout the soil nails, and within the soil nail, incorporate an efficient corrosion protection system to isolate the steel tendon from attach for its full life span.

The first major contract in the UK involving soil nailing and shotcreting of a high vertical face is being carried out near Bournemouth. After shotcreting and nailing, during progressive excavation to a depth of 10 m in granular materials, a reinforced concrete wall is constructed with nail head plates cast in.

To date some 90% of the soil nails installed in UK are of the drilled and grouted type, in which effective corrosion protection can be easily installed. The diameter of the drilled hole is designed to ensure that adequate ground-grout bond can be mobilised over half the nail length generally to equate to or exceed the tensile capacity of the bar. This usually requires bore hole diameters of 100 mm in stronger and granular materials to 200 mm in weaker clays. Within bores of this size range it is appropriate and economic to install and grout a single plastic corrugated duct which surrounds and protects the steel tendon. This system has been developed from ground anchor practice and protection capacity, groutability and bond capacity have all been well proven, subject to the soil nailing contractor having the appropriate experience and method.

The alternative to the use of corrosion protected steel bars is glass reinforced plastic bars. The 22 mm diameter rough faced GRP bars have a tensile capacity in excess of 400 kN and have been proven to be satisfactory in bond with both resin and cement grout. Although the capacity of the plastic thread is of the order of 100 kN, this is generally more than adequate in restraining the nail head plate.

With regard to nail testing we have to date been heavily influenced by the reinforced soil systems where the external length of the geotextile may be wrapped around the facing element. This means that there is no problem with bond at the external end and thus only the embedded length is in question and may require testing. In the soil nail system there is a section of nail, *proximal*, within the active soil and a section of nail, *distal*, within the passive soil.

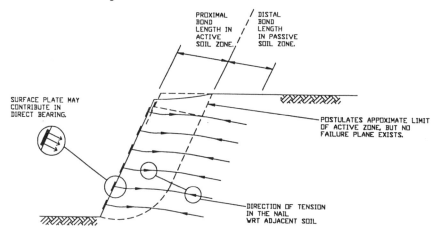

Figure 1 Schematic of slope movement to mobilise load in soil nails

To date it has been normal practice to carry out pullout test on the nail length embedded in the passive soil only, *eg* reinforced soil, and to neglect any testing of the proximal half of the nail within the active soil. In certain instances this proximal bond capacity may be supplemented by the bearing capacity of the nail head plate. Thus, as indicated in Figure 1, there are generally three separate working load components of a soil nail which should be independently tested by pullout, *eg* the distal half of nail, push-in, *eg* the proximal half of nail, and bearing test, *eg* the plate component. The push-in test, to establish bond capacity in the active zone, would simulate the direction of loading induced by the active soil as it tends to flow past the nail, albeit a pullout test on this half nail length may be an appropriate alternative.

In the design of a soil nail there must be values of grout-ground bond stress and possibly plate bearing capacity considered, thus it is appropriate to test them all on the site, preferably in the same direction of passive loading. Soil varies, drilling techniques vary, construction techniques vary and thus every site should carry out tests to substantiate the critical design assumptions.

Mr Lawson, Terram Limited, referring to high, steep slopes, with particular reference to slopes over 20 m high and greater than 60 degrees, dealt with some of the practicalities of constructing such reinforced soil slopes and the implications this has on design.

In many instances the existing soil lies at its natural slope angle. The base of the new reinforced slope is cut into the existing soil deposit. In many instances the width of the base of the reinforced slope is controlled by the extent to which the base of the reinforced slope can be extended. Instability of the excavated soil face or the occurrence of bedrock limits the width of the base of the reinforced soil slope. For high slopes this limitation on base width can result in low base width to slope height ratios - approaching 0.5 in some cases. In this instance the possibility of forward sliding should be checked closely.

All reinforced slope design methods assume a firm, incompressible foundation. In practice, this may not be the case especially if the front part of the base of the high slope lies on existing fill material. Compaction of the surface of the fill on which the slope is to be constructed may be carried out, although its effect with regard to foundation depth is limited. Consequently, when high slopes are constructed with limited base width the eccentricity of the high slope loading may cause compression of the slope foundation and some rotation of the reinforced slope can occur. Depending on the degree of rotation and the type of soil behind the reinforced mass a tension crack may become evident at the reinforced soil-backfill interface during the construction of the slope. The important lesson here is not to panic if this occurs. Significant movements of the structure are likely to occur during construction of slopes of this magnitude and geometry. If tension cracks do occur during construction they should be quickly filled in and sealed to prevent possible water ingress.

Good quality of construction is essential for high reinforced slopes of limited base width, especially when movements of the structure occur during construction. In addition, good drainage is also essential to enable the quick and efficient release of groundwater.

General discussion opened with a statement from Mr McNichol, Wardell Armstrong. I am dealing with eight or nine cases of soil nailing and in two of them we have had a little bit of deflection at the crest, more than we expected. This is a bi-planar slope, with a lower slope and an upper slope. I discussed one of these cases with Dr Love and we decided that it is very important to get the top line of soil nails right in at the crest. We had also put a dowel in behind and found that helped. In the other case we did have the top row of nails quite high and we still got a little bit of deflection, more than expected, and I am asking if anyone else has experienced this.

There is something in the Guidance Note about another T_{max} mechanism and although we had allowed for that we got slightly more movement than we expected. The final thing to say is that on every one of these jobs you are working off three boreholes. When I was working in Hong Kong I would have maybe twenty or thirty boreholes but working back in England you are lucky to get three and you never get effective stress parameters.

Professor Gässler, FH München, responded by stating that the first excavation stage is the most critical one, this is also my experience. There are some reasons for this. Very often you have a weathered top layer and the top 1 or 2 metres is weak or loose, and therefore the first excavation stage is critical. Another reason is that the nails need a certain minimum overburden pressure that we call the critical depth. The mechanism of constrained dilatancy works only in a certain depth, at about 2.5 m and between 0 and 2.5 m the nails will not be very resistant to pull-out.

I would recommend that you should be very careful when excavating the first excavation step, maybe 1 m but not more. The further excavation steps might then be 1.5 m and so on and the first nails should be installed at 0.5 m to 0.8 m depth, not deeper. If you are very anxious then use longer nails in the first two rows than in subsequent rows. It is my experience that if you have managed the first two excavation stages the rest will go quite well. The first stage is critical.

Mr French, MMG Civil Engineering Systems, noted that there is an awful lot of black plastic structures out there, both in this country and elsewhere. Should more attention be paid at the very early stage of design as to the *greening up* of these structures. Should we not, as I know happens sometimes, involve landscape architects at the beginning of these projects, rather than perhaps at the end. Careful looking at seed mixtures and, as was said this morning, the maintenance of the finished project. Without maintenance these structures do not get the acclaim that perhaps they should get. That was my first comment.

The other comment I wanted to make was as a result of Mr Rimoldi's presentation about the excellent creep properties of polyester and one of the ways that this has been solved in woven fabrics is by using a straight warp-weave.

Dr Sembenelli, Piero Sembenelli Consultant, added to Mr Lawson's observations about tensile stresses developed in reinforced soil. If we go back some forty years, Professor Terzaghi carried out experiments with gelatine and found that in cohesive soils the maximum tensile stresses develop at 0.4 to 0.5 times the height. I think we can apply the same rules also in reinforced soil and so we need a proportional relationship between height and length which does not depend on the reinforcement but depends essentially on the fill and the backfill materials. So in many cases when we are building a structure the maximum tensile stress is moving backward through the structure and if the reinforcement is not long enough we have a crack at the rear of the top surface and then the structure starts moving forward. We must pay a lot of attention to this problem.

Another point is that the structures must always be well seated, the reinforcement should be inside and there should, if possible, be a berm at the toe. There should also be drainage, deep drains and horizontal drainage.

Mr Myles, Soil Nailing Limited, I would just like to add to that very good point made by Mr Lawson concerning short reinforcement at the base of an excavation since this is important to widening of existing carriageways. There is a tendency now to install soil nails in the lower area until you have sufficient room to use reinforced soil. If the shape of the new section has two parallel faces this does tend to undermine the existing structure. So there is an opportunity to strengthen the lower section with soil nails but still keep it narrow.

Mr Rudd, Howard Humphreys, posed a general question regarding the Department of Transport Advice Note. I have made some use of the document for soil nail design and it does not seem to cover reinforced soil slopes where more than one soil stratum is involved. If, in the case of soil nailing, you want to widen or steepen an existing slope then it is probable that more than one stratum is involved and likewise if you are wanting to stabilise an existing slope which has slipped material with shear surfaces parallel to the slope then you may want to model more than one stratum. This seems to be something lacking in the Advice Note and I wondered if there was any intention to rectify this.

One other small point, in the Advice Note it recommends for high plasticity materials such as London Clay where the plasticity index is greater than 25, in that case much greater than 25, that critical state or fully softened parameters are used in design. This is presumably on the assumption of large strain occurring and if you do this in soil nail design it can result in, what appear to me to be, excessive lengths of nails. By adopting a c' of zero, since $c' + \sigma_n \tan\phi$ the overburden is involved in the analysis, if you do not have much overburden or you do not have much gain in overburden with depth then you end up with extremely long nails. I don not know if anybody would like to comment on the appropriateness of using c' = zero in soil nail design.

Dr Love, Geotechnical Consulting Group, responded to Mr Rudd by commenting on three aspects of the Advice Note HA 68/94, namely, multiple soil layers, residual angles of friction in overconsolidated clays and calculation of pullout lengths of soil nails in clay.

In a multiple soil layer situation, the user may split up the various parts of the mechanism and apply the appropriate values of soil strength at the relevant locations since general form versions of all the equations are provided in the Advice Note for the two-part wedge mechanism which make this possible. However, as a first step for preliminary design, it would be reasonable to assume that all the soil layers have the same strength as the worst layer.

Regarding the use of residual angles of friction for overconsolidated clays, the design method in the Advice Note adopts the approach that if *large displacement* soil parameters are assumed, then no further factor of safety on soil strength is required; the implication being that the soil strengths cannot be worse than this. Normally this equates to taking *critical state* soil parameters or the *post-peak* strength. However, in the case of overconsolidated clays, the Advice Note flags up a warning that this may not be enough, since in these soils it is possible to develop much lower residual strengths, ϕ'_r, on planes of continued displacement, either due to pre-existing surfaces or a progressive type of failure. This does not mean that the value of ϕ'_r should be used on all surfaces of the mechanism, however. In the case of pre-existing shear planes, the likely orientation and depth of surfaces on which residual strength has already developed, may usually be anticipated either from observation in trial pits or from a general appreciation of the geology, and so some judgement is required.

Regarding calculation of pullout resistance, in the absence of reliable long term, site specific pullout test data in clays, the normal situation at design state, the Advice Note provides a method of estimating pullout resistance of soil nails based on effective stress theory. This means that the shallower the nail, the longer the necessary nail length. Two speakers today have already made supporting comments. Mr Voskamp showed that pullout capacity was governed by the magnitude of the effective stress acting on the reinforcement, and Professor Gässler pointed out that the top rows of nails, up to a critical depth of around 2.5 m, will often have to be much longer than the rest. However, in order to keep nail lengths to the minimum in the calculation, the Advice Note provides an option for playing off nail lengths against a reduced horizontal spacing. Alternatively the first row of nails could be inclined more steeply. The other alternative of adopting empirical blanket values of skin friction without carrying out effective stress calculations or individual site pullout tests, is not recommended. The Clouterre document itself reports a case history where the long term pullout resistance in a clayey soil was greatly overestimated in this way - see page 62 referring to a slope failure.

In closing the discussion the Chairman, Professor Jones, commented that it is a sign of a good symposium that you have to curtail discussion. We have had a very interesting and a very good symposium. During today we have looked at the fundamentals, material properties, analysis, design and construction technologies. We have seen those from right across Europe. Applications over a whole range from soil nailing, conventional applications and dormant structures.

This seminar has been truly European and from the UK delegates point of view I would like to say thank you very much, we are very grateful for those people from Europe who have attended, either giving papers, participating in the discussion, or just attending. Thank you very much indeed. Also thank you very much to the organisers, particularly Dr Terry Ingold and Dr Shiram Dikran.

The development of reinforced soil design methods - European and worldwide practice

P.K. WORRALL, Reinforced Earth Company Limited, United Kingdom

SYNOPSIS

Substantial harmonisation of design processes has taken place over the past fifteen years. This has resulted in design methods, evolved from the classical Rankine and Coulomb approaches, which provide safe, economical structures. To date some 25,000 reinforced soil structures have been constructed worldwide and the overwhelming majority of these have used the coherent gravity method of design. Reinforced soil continues to be used increasingly in lieu of more conventional forms of construction and is indeed now the norm in many countries.

INTRODUCTION

When Henri Vidal built the first Reinforced Earth wall in the Pyrenees in 1966 he based its design on classical methods of soil mechanics extended by the results of his research and development work. Other walls followed notably at Incarville, Schlosser (1968), and Vigna, Pasturel & Besnard (1968). Subsequent work led to the development of the coherent gravity method which is today the most widely used method for the design of reinforced soil structures both in Europe and worldwide.

EARLY DEVELOPMENT

The early design work of Vidal was essentially based on the two classical concepts of Rankine and Coulomb as applied to conventional retaining walls. The Rankine approach allowed for the estimation of horizontal pressure at any depth below the upper surface of the wall. At each layer of reinforcement the load within the reinforcement was assumed to be that corresponding to the lateral stress imposed on its contributing facing area. The stresses within the reinforcing strips were kept below the normal working stress for the metal used. The strip length was at this time set at not less than 80% of wall height although it was checked that the required bond length was half of the actual strip length. The use of strips of length equal to 80% of wall height came from observations of early model tests and it was considered at the time that the use of long strip lengths would ensure that the reinforcements passed beyond the classical Coulomb potential rupture surface.

At this time the coefficient of friction between the strip and soil was measured by shear box and was usually found to be a proportion of tanϕ. In 1969 Vidal & Schlosser (1969) published their work on reinforced earth. Shortly afterwards the *La Terre Armee* company was formed and the volume of research work increased with much of this involving collaboration between La Terre Armee and the Laboratoire Central des Ponts et Chaussees (LCPC). Notable amongst early structures built are:

- ♦ Dunkerque in 1970
- ♦ Pont de Sevres 1971
- ♦ Sete 1971
- ♦ Palarseum 1971
- ♦ Highway 39, Los Angeles 1971
- ♦ Granton, Edinburgh 1972
- ♦ Thionville Abutment 1972

Most of these were closely monitored by Vidal, the owner authority and the LCPC. Vidal played host to many engineers who visited France to see the first structures. Many national highway authorities, including the Transport and Road Research Laboratory and Department of Transport were represented at these site visits.

DEVELOPMENT OF DESIGN METHODS

By this time, La Terre Armee had established the first practical design rules from a combination of model tests, the first full scale structures and classical soil mechanics. This work was extended by the LCPC who began to compare the theoretical assumptions with the monitoring data from these early structures. The designs, while being found to be safe, were in part seen to be at variance with actual behaviour. In particular the friction stresses along the reinforcements were seen to divide the mass into two zones, but not along the classical Coulomb plane. The vertical stresses within the mass were found to be less than those calculated. In 1973 collaboration between La Terra Armee and LCPC resulted in the publication of a note, LCPC (1973), which briefly presented the main aspects of the concept, design and construction. However, very little space was given to detailed review of the internal design and it was acknowledged in the document that, in the main, the responsibility for this aspect lay with the specialist designer and supplier.

In the UK, following the success with the technique at Edinburgh, two further structures were constructed at Widnes and Huntingdon. The Department of Transport, following the successful projects in France and the UK, carried out an examination of the technique including the design and construction of a few structures.

This experience led to the preparation of a set of draft design rules and specifications. Several structures including those at Oldham and Bournemouth were designed using these draft rules. These rules were consolidated into Technical Memorandum BE3/78, DoT (1978).

From 1973 to 1979 dozens of structures, many instrumented, were built including several abutments and walls of significant height. Results from monitoring were systematically reviewed and many items prompted further research. Consequently design methods were refined and allowed a more accurate prediction of the forces in the reinforcements. This period marked the evolution of the coherent gravity method for reinforced soil design and this was the method subsequently used for the design of the majority of reinforced soil structures worldwide. Some key developments included the location of the line of potential rupture which was noted to be practically vertical in the upper part of the structure and to lie on the Coulomb wedge line in the lower part.

The phenomenon of soil-reinforcement friction was better understood and had lead to the development in 1976 of the *high adherence strip* by which the incorporation of transverse ribs during strip manufacture created higher frictional bond due to dilation of the soil.

Five major conferences were held between 1977 and 1979, ASCE (1978), ENPC/LCPC (1977, 1979), NSWIT (1978), TRRL (1979), and all this work was formalised in recommendations, MdT (1979), produced by a working party which included LCPC, SETRA, SNCF, CNRS and RECo. These recommendations set out the coherent gravity method which has subsequently become the principal design document used in most European countries in either its limit state form or working stress form. Worldwide, around 90% of all reinforced soil structures are designed to this method. Since publication of these recommendations further research work and full scale monitoring in many countries has shown the basic concept to be realistic and to produce safe designs. The continuing refinement of the design methods, particularly for abutments, carried out in France during the early eighties resulted in the first, and to date only, national standard covering reinforced soil design, AFNOR (1992). This standard is now being adopted by more and more European countries, particularly those within the European Union.

Current practice in the UK continues to be BE3/78 for trunk road applications. This document is presently under revision and also the new draft British Standard BS 8006 for reinforced soil is in its final stage prior to publication. This standard also includes the coherent gravity method for inextensible reinforcements as a move to bring UK practice in line with the rest of Europe. Since the publication of the first design code in 1979, other materials have been developed and used in reinforced soil walls. These materials are predominantly polymeric and hence are generally classed as extensible materials. BS 8006 also addresses these materials and is distinctive in so far as it includes a separate design method for extensible materials.

CONCLUSIONS

Current design methods have evolved from classical approaches which have been refined to varying degrees by research and monitoring data available to drafters of various documents. To date some 25,000 structures have been constructed worldwide and the vast majority have used the coherent gravity method of design. Substantial harmonisation of design processes has taken place over the past fifteen years and has resulted in well tried and tested methods which provide safe, economical structures. The technique continues to be used increasingly in lieu of more conventional structures and is now the norm in many countries.

REFERENCES

Schlosser F, 1968, *Mur experimental en Terre Armee d'Incarville*. Bull. des Laboratoires des Ponts et Chaussees No. 33, Aout-Sept.

Pasturel L.D. & Besnard S., 1968 *Mur en Terre Armee d'Incarville*. Compte rendu des mesures, Rapport Interne, Dec.

Schlosser F. & Vidal H., 1969, *La Terre Armee*, Bull, de Liaison LRPC, No. 41, November.

LCPC, 1973, *La Terre Armee*. Note d'Information Technique, Avril.

NSWIT, 1978, *Soil reinforcing and stabilising techniques in engineering practice*. New South Wales Institute of Technology/University of NSW.

ASCE, 1978, *Earth reinforcement*. American Society of Civil Engineers.

ENPC/LCPC, 1979, *Soil reinforcement, reinforced earth and other techniques*. Int. Conf., ENPC & LCPC.

ENPC/LCPC, 1977, *Use of fabrics in geotechnics*. Int. Conf., ENPC.

MdT, 1979, *Les ouvrages en terre armee - recommendations et regles de l'art*. Ministere des Transport, Direction des Routes et de la Circulation Routiere.

DoT, 1978, *Reinforced earth retaining walls and bridge abutments for embankments*. Tech. Memorandum BE3/78, Department of Transport.

AFNOR, 1992, *Design of backfilled structures with inextensible and flexible reinforcing strips or sheets* Standard NF-P-94-220.

TRRL, 1979, *Reinforced earth and other composite soil techniques*. TRRL/Heriot-Watt University Symp. 1977, TRRL Supp. Report 457.

THE DURABILITY OF GEOGRIDS FOR SOIL REINFORCEMENT APPLICATIONS

D. CAZZUFFI, ENEL SpA - CRIS, F. MONTANELLI, Tenax SpA and P. RIMOLDI, Tenax SpA, Italy

SYNOPSIS

This paper deals with the major factors affecting the long-term performance of geogrids for soil reinforcement applications by comparing the published results of several durability test on different types of products. In particular, the following tests are presented: mechanical tests, including tensile strength, junction strength, long term design strength, and construction damage, chemical resistance and UV resistance evaluations.

INTRODUCTION

The durability of geogrids is a very complex issue because the factors which can affect the long term performances of these particular geosynthetics are many and diversified. As a first consideration, the geogrids presently available on the market can be produced using different polymers, the main ones being high density polyethylene (HDPE), polypropylene (PP) and polyester (PET), and different production processes, the main ones being extrusion, weaving, bonding. Moreover each brand of geogrids is produced in several qualities, differing in mesh, mass per unit area and tensile properties. The present universe of geogrids may well include more than a hundred different products.

The application of geogrids to reinforcement is probably among the most technical since geogrids always play a structural role in providing a reinforcing function. Hence the design engineer is usually very concerned about the long term performances of such products, since the failure of the geogrids may easily bring about failure of the whole structure.

It is therefore important to address the fundamental issue of the durability of geogrids by first listing the factors affecting the performances of each type of geogrid and then carrying out a full range of tests to assess the resistance of the products to each potentially damaging agent.

The Authors have been involved for many years in geogrids testing and are presently involved also in the preparation of the European standards for the durability of geosynthetics. This paper presents the summary of such experiences, particularly related to geogrids, together with the results of several tests performed on various types of geogrids as listed in Table 1.

Table 1   Geogrid types considered in this paper

Type	Description
A	integral extruded, cold punched, uniaxially or biaxially drawn, in PP or HDPE
B	integral extruded, hot formed, uniaxially or biaxially drawn, in PP or HDPE
C	woven PET yarns covered with PVC or other types of sheeting
D	PET strips sheeted in LDPE, thermally bonded at the strips intersections

MECHANICAL TESTS

Geogrids are composed of longitudinal and transversal ribs, connected by junctions. Hence the mechanical properties of geogrids stem from the strength of the ribs, of the junctions and of the overall structure of the product. The determination of suitable test methods to assess the resistance of ribs and junctions also allows evaluation of the variation of properties caused by the physical, chemical, biological agents.

Tensile strength

For geogrids it is important to compare different products on the base of common testing methods and to select testing methods that are representative of the behaviour of the whole product and not of its constituents *eg* raw polymers or yarns or strips. For example, polyester yarns have higher strength and modulus than corresponding HDPE yarns, but when PET yarns are woven into a geogrid, the strength and modulus of the geogrid are affected both by the polymer and by the weaving process. A longitudinal yarn, when is tensioned, has to crimp over the transversal yarns; this means that a structural elongation occurs in addition to the polymer elongation.

On the other hand, HDPE integral geogrids have higher polymer elongation, but almost zero structural elongation. The combination of the two mechanisms is illustrated in Figure 1 which compares the published tensile curves from wide width tensile test for geogrid types A, B, C and D. It is clear that integral geogrids present much higher tensile modulii than woven and bonded geogrids for the same peak tensile strength. This means that in the working range of strains, $\varepsilon < 5\%$, integral geogrids provide much higher tensile forces for the same elongation. Similar results have been shown by several authors *eg* Bathurst & Cai (1994).

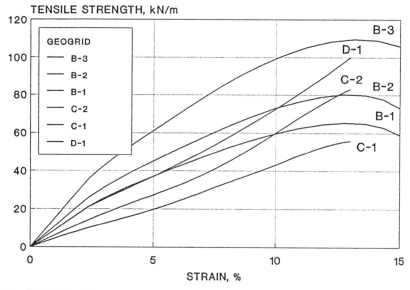

Source: Published data
Test Method: Wide Width Tensile Test

Figure 1 Geogrid wide width tensile strength

The two main internationally recognised standards bodies, ASTM in North America and CEN/ISO in Europe, are presently discussing the mechanical testing of geogrids. The determination of the tensile strength can be made according to two basic methods; the Wide Width Tensile Test (WWTT) and the Single Rib Tensile Test (SRTT). The WWTT is based on a specimen of 200 mm minimum width and has been standardised by ASTM D 4595 and CEN 30319 / ISO 10319. These three standards are very similar, but the CEN/ISO includes specific provisions for testing geogrids while the ASTM does not. The main features of these standards are listed in Table 2.

The integral geogrids do not show appreciable transverse contraction during the WWTT, hence for these geogrids the SRTT yields results very close to the WWTT, at a considerably lower cost and time. ASTM is presently discussing the standardisation of the SRTT, based on the GRI-GG1 test proposed by the Geosynthetic Research Institute. The features of this test are also reported in Table 2 .

Table 3 lists the results of tests performed according to these three standards on several types of geogrids. It is possible to note the excellent agreement of the results yielded by the three methods. The slight difference in results between the WWTT and the SRTT is due mostly to the different rates of strain. Therefore both the WWTT and the SRTT can be considered as very reliable and suitable test methods for geogrids.

Table 2 Features of ASTM D 4595, ISO 10319 and GRI-GG1 tests

Features	ASTM D 4595	ISO 10319	GRI-GG1
Specimen width	200 mm	200 mm	1 rib
Specimen length	100 mm	3 junctions	3 junctions
Clamp distance	100 mm	3 junctions	3 junctions
Clamp type	wedge	wedge, capstan, roller	wedge
Type of test	Constant rate of strain	Constant rate of strain	Constant rate of extension
Rate of strain	10% / min	20% / min	50 mm / min
Preloading	1.25%	1.00%	-
Extensometers distance	-	60 mm	-

Table 3 Tensile strengths in kN/m from different testing standards

Product		Geogrid Type	ASTM	ISO	GRI
Tenax TT 301	MD	B-1	68	68	70
Tenax TT 401	MD	B-2	85	88	88
Tenax TT 701	MD	B-3	112	118	120
Tenax LBO 303	MD	B-4	21	-	24
Tenax LBO 303	TD	B-4	38	-	42
Tensar SR 55	MD	A-1	55	55	53
Tensar SR 80	MD	A-2	86	84	88
Tensar SS2	MD	A-3			19
Tensar SS2	TD	A-3			34
Fortrac 55	MD	C-1	52	52	56
Fortrac 80	MD	C-2	75	78	85
Raugrid 6/6-15	MD	C-3	62	-	-
Paragrid 100/155	MD	D-1	105	-	-

JUNCTION STRENGTH

The strength of the junctions is a fundamental parameter for the evaluation of the lateral confinement provided by the geogrid and of its pullout properties. Moreover, whenever a connection of adjacent layers of geogrid or of a layer of geogrid to a wall face has to be made, the junction strength also assumes a structural importance, since the junctions must allow for the transmission of the stresses from one layer to another and from the structure to the ribs. Since geogrid structures are designed on the basis of their Long Term Design Strength (LTDS), they will never be subject to tensile forces greater than the LTDS multiplied by a proper Factor of Safety (Fsj):

Junction Strength > LTDS x Fsj

Typically, Fsj is taken as 1.50 and the geogrid LTDS is 40% of the peak tensile strength, so, the junction strength should always be greater than 60% of the peak tensile strength or it should withstand the long term loading by mean of creep testing with *through-the-junctions* type clamps.

As far as junction strength tensile methods are concerned, discussion is still very open both in ASTM and CEN/ISO committees. Montanelli and Rimoldi (1994b) proposed some test methods to evaluate both the shear strength and the brittleness of geogrid junctions. Figure 2 shows the schemes of these tests, while Table 4 reports some of the test results.

Table 4 Results of junction tests (after Montanelli and Rimoldi, 1994b)

Geogrid Type		Shear Strength (kN/m)	Shear (kN/m) (normal load 600 kPa)	Diagonal Strength (kN/m)	Impact Strength (J)
B-2	MD	76.5	-	-	15.5
B-4	MD	24.4	-	19.3	-
B-4	TD	31.0	-	21.5	-
A-2	MD	81.8	-	-	10.1
A-3	MD	19.2	-	16.5	-
A-3	TD	32.3	-	24.2	-
C-2	MD	3.1	6.6	2.3	3.5
C-2	TD	3.3	7.0	2.4	-

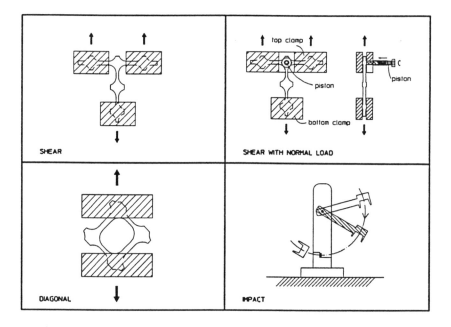

Figure 2 Scheme of the junction tests (after Montanelli and Rimoldi, 1994b)

It can be seen from Table 4 that the strength and the brittleness (from the impact test) of the different types of geogrids can vary quite widely. While the junction shear and the junction diagonal tests provide an indication of the ability of the geogrid structure to provide strong interlocking and transfer of load between longitudinal and transversal ribs, the impact test provides an index of the resistance of the geogrids to construction damage.

LONG-TERM DESIGN STRENGTH (LTDS)

The determination of the LTDS of geogrids is based on extensive creep and creep rupture testing. The creep test has already been standardised by ASTM D5262-92, while the CEN/ISO standard is still under discussion. The principle of the test is that specimens of geogrids are subjected to a constant load at constant temperature and humidity for a period of time of 10,000 hours or more. The elongation versus time is measured and time to rupture is also recorded. The geogrids are tested under the same loads at different temperatures, typically 10, 20 and 40°C.

This procedure makes application of the principle of time-temperature superposition valid for polymeric materials; hence mathematical methods allow extrapolation of behaviour to about 100 years. Montanelli & Rimoldi (1993) provides a comprehensive presentation of the applicable extrapolation techniques. In this way the LTDS is defined on the basis of creep strain criteria: the LTDS is the load that yields a total elongation of 10% at 10^6 hours ($\sim$ 120 years) at 20°C. The long-term extrapolation is based upon the determination of the geogrid creep modulus at 35% of applied load ratio. This level of load is ideal since it is very near to the actual design loads at 10, 20, 30 and 40°C. The 35% creep modulus curves for 10, 20, 30 and 40°C are shifted to superimpose the one at 20°C curves, Figure 3. In this way it is possible to predict the creep modulus at 10, 20, 30°C without extrapolation. The predicted creep modulus is statistically defined by a bilogarithmic curve with associated lower and upper 95% confidence limits. The predicted and 95% L.C.L. values are then analitically defined. The ratio of the 35% load and the 35% creep modulus gives the predicted strain.

$$\varepsilon\,(t) = M_{35\%}(t) \,/\, F_{35\%}$$

If the predicted strain $\varepsilon(t)$ is with $\pm$ 10% of the design strain ε_d, the long term design strength is given by the 35% creep modulus times the design strain.

$$LTDS = M_{35\%}(t) \times \varepsilon_d$$

Since typically ε_d is 10%, the long term design strength is given by 10% of the 35% creep tensile modulus.

Presently there are concerns that the creep strain criterion may not be the most conservative for some geogrids, since creep rupture can occur at a lower strain than 10%. Therefore CEN is also discussing the standardisation

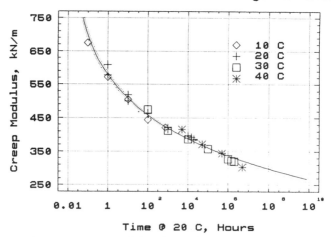

Figure 3 Creep modulus time shifting for geogrid B-2
(Bilogarithmic curve fitting model)

of a creep rupture testing procedure. The procedure is similar to the traditional creep test, but the applied loads are higher, so as to produce rupture of the specimen in a relatively short time (10,000 hours). Several loads are applied to the geogrid specimens and only the time to rupture is recorded, without any reference to the strains. Tests are performed at three temperatures and then mathematical techniques are applied to the test data to yield the load that will induce creep rupture at 10^6 hours at 20°C. Ingold et al. (1994) report extensively on creep rupture testing.

As for the tensile strength, the long term tensile properties must be compared on the base of a common testing method which represents the behaviour of the geogrid and not just its components. Hence creep tests on yarns are unacceptable and misleading: Figure 4 shows the creep data, published in trade literature, the PET yarns of a type A and C geogrids while Figure 5, Montanelli and Rimoldi (1993), shows the creep behaviour of the same geogrid tested on a three ribs wide specimen. From the first tests the producer infers that the LTDS of this geogrid, but in reality only the yarns, is equal to 60% of the tensile strength, while in contrast Figure 6 indicates that the LTDS of this PET woven geogrid. product C-1, is about 40% of the tensile strength which a similar figure for the integral HDPE geogrids. Similar behaviour while testing fibres instead of full geogrid products has been indicated by Greenwood (1990) and here reported in Figure 7. Greenwood (1990), shown in Figure 8, also indicates that also for bonded geogrids type D a LTDS of about 40% can be assumed when considering 10% creep strain after 120 years. Therefore, based on creep strain criteria, all the types of geogrids present a similar long term tensile behaviour, and it seems that no one of them shows a distinctive advantage over the others. Figure 9, from Ingold et al. (1994), reports the extrapolated creep rupture data for geogrid B-2 and A-2. A comparison with Figure 6 shows that, for the integral geogrid B-2, the creep strain criterion yields a lower, more conservative LTDS than the creep rupture criterion. On the other hand Figure 8 shows that for integral geogrids A-2 the creep rupture criterion yields a lower LTDS than the creep strain one. Therefore both creep tests and creep rupture tests are required to define the LTDS of geogrids.

CONSTRUCTION DAMAGE

When soil, especially crushed gravel, is spread on geogrids and compacted, the geogrids may suffer damage. Every type of geogrid suffers a different degree of damage and the degree can be assessed by tensile tests performed on both damaged and undamaged products. An extensive program of full scale compaction damage trials was carried out by the TRL (Transport Research Laboratory), following the procedure described by Watts & Brady

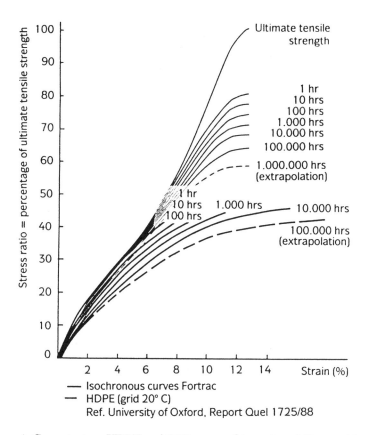

Figure 4 Creep test on HDPE and PET yarns of type A and C geogrids (from commercial brochure)

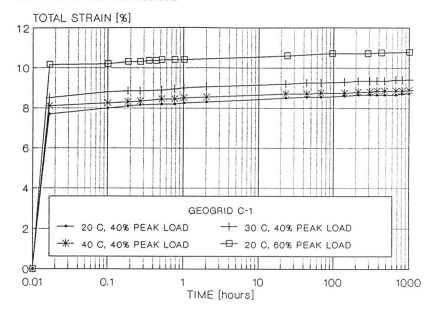

Figure 5 Creep test on PET geogrid type C (Montanelli and Rimoldi, 1993)

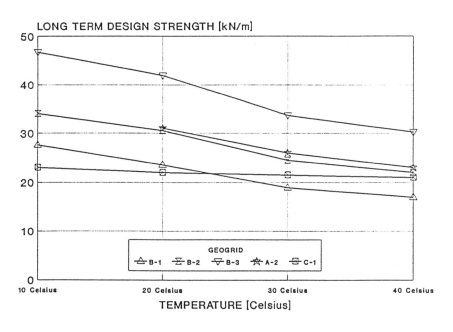

Figure 6 Long-term design strength of several geogrids (Montanelli and Rimoldi, 1993)

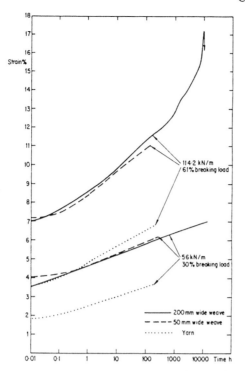

Figure 7 Comparison of creep tests on weave and yarn for a polypropylene fabric (from Greenwood, 1990)

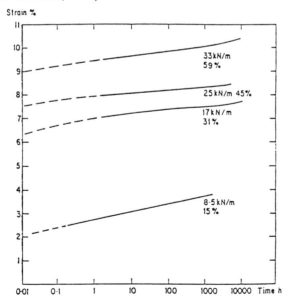

Figure 8 Creep curves for polyester strip: percentages are of breaking load (from Greenwood, 1990)

273

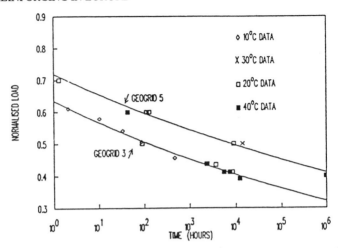

Figure 9 Normalized rupture loads versus time, shifted to 20°C, for geogrid 3 (A-2) and geogrid 5 (B-2)

(1990), in which tensile tests were performed both on the original and damaged specimens. The results of these tests for several geogrids are summarised in Table 5 which also contains some results of tests performed by TRL and reported by Wright and Greenwood (1994), and Watts and Brady (1994), together with results of additional tests performed by Montanelli and Rimoldi (1994a) using the procedure described by Watts and Brady (1990).

With limestone gravel, geogrid C-1 retains around 60% of its original tensile strength and geogrid A-2 around 80%, while geogrid B-2 retains its entire original strength. Similar behaviour is reflected in the results of impact tests on junctions. From Table 4, geogrid B-2 is seen to damp around four times

Table 5 Results of compaction damage tests with crushed limestone gravel

Product	Data Source		Original strength (kN/m)	Damaged strength (kN/m)	Strength Retention (%)
B-1	b	MD	76.15	71.23	93.54
B-2	a	MD	83.43	83.63	>100
B-2	c	MD	80.00	80.00	100
B-3	b	MD	111.11	112.65	>100
B-4	b	MD	24.96	24.83	99.48
B-4	b	TD	42.65	42.13	98.79
A-2	b	MD	95.92	73.61	76.74
A-2	c	MD	79.00	64.00	81.01
A-3	b	MD	21.34	20.88	97.83
A-3	b	TD	34.45	32.87	95.41
C-1	c	MD	57.00	33.00	57.89

a) Wright and Greenwood;   b) Montanelli and Rimoldi;   c) Watts and Brady

the energy damped by geogrid A-2 and some 50% more than geogrid C-2 before breaking. The impact test results, taken as a measure of the brittleness of the junctions, may be considered to reflect the results of the damage tests in which geogrid B-2 appears to be less affected by impact loads than the other geogrids.

CHEMICAL RESISTANCE

Geogrids may be exposed to chemically aggressive environments, which may affect their long term behaviour to different degrees depending mainly on the polymer composition. The HDPE polymer used for integral geogrids is inert and resistant to chemical attack. Results of test performed on geogrids B, exposed according to US EPA 9090 Standard, are shown in Figure 10, Tisinger, 1990. The results of exposure of geogrid B to aggressive synthetic leachate clearly show that this geogrid is unaffected by these chemicals.

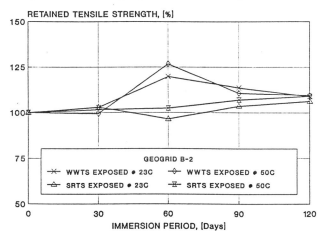

Figure 10 Retained strength after EPA 9090 exposure at 23°C and 50°C

For PET geogrids a loss of strength of 9% may be expected after 20 months exposure to an environment of PH=9, Enka (1982). In comparison, in an environment of neutral water hydrolysis causes a loss of strength of 3% in the same period. Insufficient data are presented to extrapolate these effects.

UV RESISTANCE

Mostly geogrids are buried in the soil and are only exposed to sunlight for few days during the installation period, but in some cases they may be permanently exposed without any external protection. Polymers are all susceptible to attacked by light, oxygen, heat and water, resulting in product brittleness, cracking, crazing, colour change, ageing, strength loss and sometimes failure of a product to perform its functions, Tisinger (1991). The accelerated test methods using artificial light sources provide the advantages of reducing the testing period and of providing repeatable results thus allowing an easy quality control and assessment.

When a geosynthetic is exposed outdoors, it is subjected to cycles of sunlight exposure, wet and dry conditions, and temperature changes. These conditions may have a synergetic effect, thus leading to more severe ageing and deterioration. To simulate these conditions in laboratory, a QUV fluorescent condensation tester equipped with UV-B type lamps is a cost effective and technically sound option. The UVB-313 fluorescent lamps simulate the shortest wave lengths found in the sunlight at the earth's surface that are responsible for most polymer damages, having however minimal emission below 290 nm. The typical spectral irradiance of the fluorescent UV-B lamps compared is shown in ASTM G53. Cazzuffi et al. (1994) have performed extensive testing on geogrids to evaluate the influence of atmospheric conditions: the cycles for performing the tests have been selected in accordance to ISO 4892-3 and ASTM G53 test methods and consisted in 4 hours UV exposure at 60°C and 4 hours of condensation at 50°C.

To verify the correct interpretation of the environmental conditions, the results obtained by exposure in the UV-B device have been compared those from outdoor ones exposure at the 45° parallel in Milan, Italy. At this location the typical annual solar irradiance is 120 Kcal/cm^2/year. Specimens were

Table 7   Results of UV testing (after Cazzuffi et al., 1994)

Product direction	Virgin sample		After 3000 hours UVB exposure		After 1 year sun exposure	
	Tensile strength kN/m	Elongation at peak %	Tensile strength kN/m	Elongation at peak %	Tensile strength kN/m	Elongation at peak %
B-2 MD	87.64	13.30	86.72	16.60	87.94	15.37
B-3 MD	126.45	12.60	-	-	127.68	16.10
B-4 MD	20.52	16.40	-	-	22.15	13.90
B-4 TD	40.14	12.30	37.08	9.5	40.07	11.20

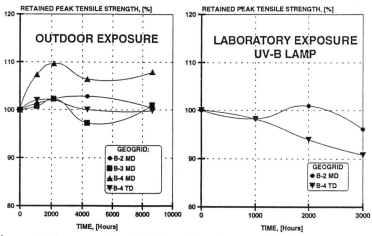

Figure 11   Some results of UV-B and outdoor exposure tests on geogrids type B (after Cazzuffi et al., 1994)

deliberately installed flat on a gravel bed to simulate a typical geosynthetic application. The horizontal position of the specimens allows them to be exposed all the day long and ensured temperature and humidity conditions similar to those encountered during the service life. It has been decided to test the geogrids using a single rib specimen (GRI-GG1) since it is not practicable to perform laboratory weathering tests on wide width specimens due to space limitation in the testing apparatus. The tests results are reported in Table. 7 and Figure 11. It can be seen that the UV resistance of integral geogrids is excellent, in fact even a 3000 hours UV-B exposure, equivalent to at least 6 years of real continuous exposure in temperate climates, did not produce appreciable alterations of the tensile properties.

REFERENCES

ASTM D4595-86, 1986, *Standard test method for tensile properties of geotextiles by the wide-width strip method.* ASTM, Philadelphia.

ASTM D5262-92, 1992, *Standard test method for evaluating the unconfined tension creep behaviour of geosynthetics.* ASTM, Philadelphia.

Bathurst, R.J. and Cai, Z., 1994, *In-isolation cyclic load-extension behaviour of two geogrids.* Geosynthetics International, Vol. 1, No. 1, pp. 1-19.

Cazzuffi, D., Fede, L., Montanelli, F. and Rimoldi, P., 1994, *Outdoor and UV-B laboratory weathering resistance of geosynthetics.* Proc. 5th Int. Conf. on Geotextiles, Geomembranes and Related Products.

Enka, 1982, *Mechanical properties of Stabilenka reinforcing fabrics subjected to long term loads.* Stabilenka, IEN 94/27, RH/AT, Enka Industrial Systems.

Greenwood, J.H., 1990, *The creep of geotextiles.* Proc. 4th Int. Conf. on Geotextiles, Geomembranes and Related Products.

GRI-GG1, 1987, *Geogrid rib tensile strength.* Geosynthetic Research Institute, Philadelphia.

GRI,-GG2, 1987, *Geogrid junction strength.* Geosynthetic Research Institute, Philadelphia.

Ingold, T.S., Montanelli, F. & Rimoldi, P., 1994, *Extrapolation techniques for long term strengths of polymeric geogrids.* Proc. 5th Int. Conf. on Geotextile, Geomembranes and Related Products.

ISO 10319-92, 1992, *Geotextiles wide width tensile test.* ISO .

Montanelli, F. and Rimoldi, P., 1993, *Creep and accelerated creep testing for geogrids*. Proc. Geosynthetics '93 Conference, Vancouver.

Montanelli, F. and Rimoldi, P., 1994a, *The construction damage resistance of geogrids*. Tenax Internal Document, Viganò, Italy.

Montanelli, F.and Rimoldi, P., 1994b, *The development of connection strength tests for geosynthetics*. Proc. 5th Int. Conf. on Geotextiles, Geomembranes and Related Products.

Small, G.D. and Greenwood, J.H., 1992, *A review of the phenomenon of stress rupture in HDPE geogrids*. GEO Report No. 19, Civil Engineering Dept., Hong Kong.

Tisinger, L.G., 1990, *Chemical compatibility testing of drainage net and geogrid*. Geosyntec Report G 123-002, Boynton Beach, Florida.

Tisinger, L.G., Peggs, I.D., Dudzik, B.E., Winfree, J.P. and Carraher, C.E., 1991, *Microstructural analysis of a polypropylene geotextile after long-term outdoor exposure*. Geosynthetic testing for waste containment applications, ASTM STP 1081, Philadelphia

Watts, G.R.A. and Brady, K.C., 1990, *Site damage trials on geotextiles*. Proc. 4th Int. Conf. on Geotextiles, Geomembranes and Related Products.

Watts, G.R.A. and Brady, K.C., 1994, *Geosynthetics - installation damage and the measurement of tensile strength*. Proc. 5th Int. Conf. on Geotextiles, Geomembranes and Related Products.

Wright, W.C.A. and Greenwood, J.H., 1994, *Interlaboratory trials on installation damage in geotextiles and comparison with site trials*. ERA Report 93-0915. Leatherhead, UK.

Texsol - Origin, properties and application

R.R.W. HARRIS, Bachy Limited, United Kingdom and
Y. CLAQUIN, Societe d'Application du Texsol, France

SYNOPSIS
Texsol is a composite system of sand and polyester fibre which was developed by the Laboratoire Central des Ponts et Chaussees for use in slope retention and protection. It has been applied on more than 200 sites in the past decade and the extensive empirical record, together with an exhaustive series of laboratory tests, resulted in the publication of a technical guide, LCPC/SETRA (1990). This paper reviews the development and application of the technique.

INTRODUCTION
Texsol is derived from the development of geotextile materials commonly used in layer or strip form to enhance the geotechnical properties of soils. The constituent element of the geotextile, namely the synthetic thread, or yarn, is intimately mixed with soil to form a reconstituted mass visually indistinguishable from the original soil, but with greatly enhanced strength and deformation characteristics which do not deteriorate with time.

COMPOSITION
The system is a two component material mixed at the point of placement. The components are:

> Polyester thread formed by the continuous spinning of melted polymer and supplied on bobbins.

> Sand which falls within the general envelope given in Figure 1. Sandy soils and crushed aggregates having a high angle of internal friction are particularly suitable, while the limitations on the fines content is required to avoid balling and blocking during conveyance to the point of placement.

The proportion of yarn to sand is usually in the range of 0.1 % to 0.2 % by weight. However, so light and thin is the thread that the above

The practice of soil reinforcing in Europe. Thomas Telford, London, 1995

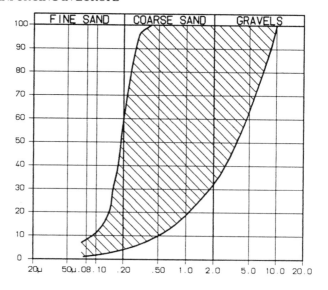

Figure 1 Grading envelope for base material

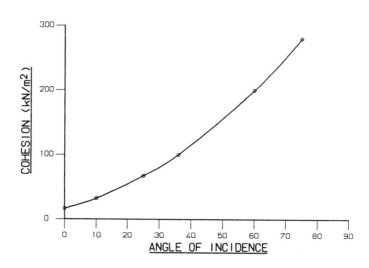

Figure 2 Cohesion variation with angle between shear and thread planes

proportion is equivalent to between 100 and 200 kilometres of thread per cubic metre of the composite mix. It is this interlaced mesh of fibre which provides the reconstituted soil mass with the exceptional mechanical characteristics discussed below.

PROPERTIES
The properties of the mix will be influenced by :

the characteristics of the soil and fibre used

the mix proportions of fibre and soil

the efficiency of the mixing process

anisotropy arising from any preferential orientation inherent in the placement process

An extensive programme of field and laboratory trials was commissioned to evaluated the above influences and these, together with continuously enhanced knowledge based on site experience, led to the publication of the LCPC-SETRA Technical Guide in May 1990. This guide forms the present basis for the design of retaining structures and provides the basis for the following summary of characteristics.

Friction angle - Triaxial tests have demonstrated that the angle of internal friction of the mix is always greater than that for the base soil. However, for design purposes, the friction angle of the base soil is used in order to produce conservative assessments.

Cohesion - When the mix deforms under stress, the textile threads are placed in tension thereby bestowing an apparent cohesion to the essentially granular base material. For an equivalent section area, the polyester thread commonly used has a tensile strength greater than that of steel. This strength, together with the continuous nature of the thread, provides a cohesion to the mass of approximately 100 kN/m^2 for each 0.1 % increment of thread content by weight.

Deformation - The failure strain in granular soils varies typically between 2 % and 6 % depending on relative density. The incorporation of polyester fibre can increase the strain to 10 % at failure.

Compressive strength - The compressive strength of the

mix increases in linear proportion to the fibre content. Unconfined compression tests show this to be approximately 500 kN/m² for each 0.1% increment of thread content by weight compared with 100 kN/m² per 0.1 % for cohesion.

Shear strength - During the simultaneous placement of soil and thread the latter is laid from front to back as the height of the deposit is increased. The general orientation of the thread therefore tends more toward a horizontal than vertical plane. It follows that the angle of incidence between this preferred planar orientation and the shear plane will result in variations in the measured cohesion and internal friction angles of the reinforced mass. Shear box tests results are presented in Figures 2 and 3.

The enhancements in geotechnical properties are augmented by the following advantages :

Permeability - The mixture retains the permeability of the base soil.

Erodability - The Japanese Ministry of Construction submitted a 5 m high wall, without vegetation, to continuous artificial rain having an intensity of 30 mm/hour. The result, represented in Figure 4, indicates a face loss limit of 18 mm. Monitoring of actual projects confirms this finding and is explained by the increasing concentration of thread at the face as the loose surface sand is removed.

Impact and blast resistance - Under the auspices of the French Ministry of Defence, tests were performed on reinforced embankments to assess the effects of shell splinter penetration and resistance to blast shock waves.
An instrumented embankment was subjected to a blast of 3000 kN/m² generated by the detonation of 400 kg of TNT at a distance of 10 m. The embankment with a free height of 2.2 m and front face slope of 50°, was keyed in to the in-situ soil to a depth of 1.5 m and showed only minor distortion. Furthermore, the presence of the textile filaments held the base material in place resulting in minimal blast erosion. In further tests, 55 mm artillery shells were fired at a wall from a distance of 3 m. Splinter penetration did not exceed 200 mm and gouging was minimal.

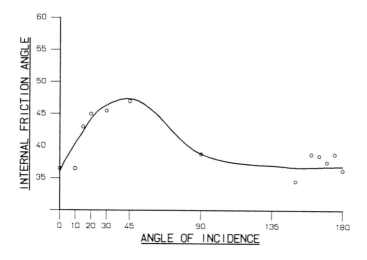

Figure 3 Friction angle -v- angle between shear and thread planes

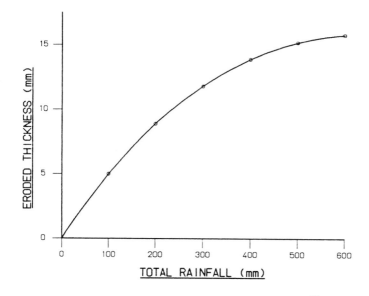

Figure 4 Face erosion against rainfall

Seismic behaviour - Texsol demonstrates the ability to absorb and dissipate dynamic loads. Laboratory tests have been performed in France and Japan which subjected samples, and model structures, to simulated seismic loading. In addition, an instrumented 10 m high wall was built to evaluate behaviour under actual earthquake loading which occurred three months after construction, February 1989, with an earthquake measuring 5.7 on the Richter scale.

Creep - The necessary longevity was investigated by exhaustive creep tests performed on both synthetic fibres and the composite mix. Tests performed by both the Laboratoire Regional de Ponts et Chaussees and the Centre d'Experimentation Routiere resulted in the selection of polyester as the preferred thread. It was concluded that the system exhibits no creep at temperatures less than 70° C centigrade, the glass transition temperature for polyester, and there was no strength loss over time.

Chemical resistance - Synthetic geotextiles have been in use for more than 25 years and, in this time, have demonstrated their inertness under normal ambient conditions. In exceptional circumstances where contact with aggressive landfill or groundwater is possible, site specific testing will be required.

USES

Texsol is able to simultaneously exploit the friction angle of a granular soil and the cohesion of a stiff clay while demonstrating resilience to impact loading. These properties have led to its use as an alternative to conventional retaining structures. It contains no corrodible elements and is maintenance free. In addition to these long term advantages, considerable economies can be obtained by reducing the extra volumes of cut required to install tie back or concrete retaining structures and eliminating the subsequent back filling of the over cut required by traditional techniques.

The stabilisation of natural slopes or embankments which have been steepened beyond their natural angle of repose, and slender section environmental protection barriers, further exploit the geotechnical properties of the system whereas military requirements have led to its use as cladding for blast containment or protection to hangers bunkers and explosive stores. Figures 5 to 8 illustrate the versatility of application.

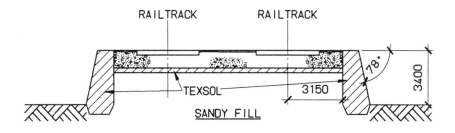

Figure 5 Retaining wall - RATP Croix de Berny

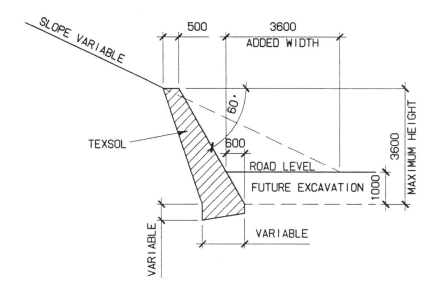

Figure 6 Slope stabilisation - design for M25 widening in cut

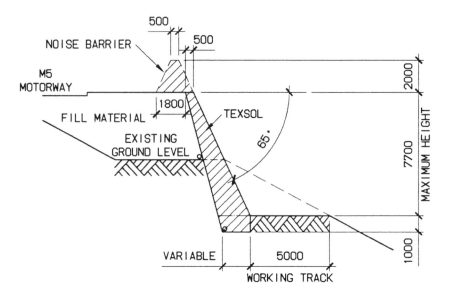

Figure 7 Slope stabilisation - design for M5 widening in fill

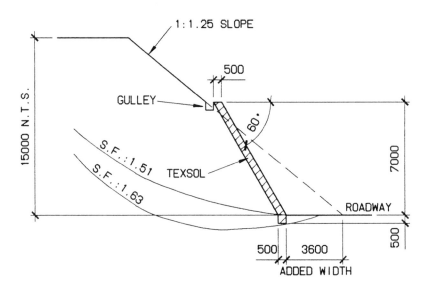

Figure 8 Frost protection and greening of stable chalk cuts on M25

DESIGN

The LCPC Technical Guide is the basis for design. It applies two design methods depending on the angle of the face; where the face angle is 65°, or less, a conventional slope stability analysis against circular, or non circular, failure is carried out, however, where the face angle is greater than 65°, two stability analyses should be carried out. One as above, and the other as a gravity wall which considers both the external and internal stability as well as the active earth pressure against the rear face.

Further considerations at design stage include the depth and section profile of a toe trench which is generally required to key in a retaining structure. Although, with appropriate granular fill, the system is free draining, the effects of piping or erosion caused by concentrated flows of water must be avoided. Consideration must therefore be given to crest interceptor drains and any requirement necessity for built in drainage measures.

PREPARATION AND PLACEMENT

The design for a particular application will determine the initial preparation measures required prior to placement. These would include the trimming of the natural slope, the excavation of the toe trench and the grading of a working platform for the production equipment.

The extent of the preparation work will sometimes be constrained by the short term stability of the slope being retained and it may be necessary to carry out the placement in alternating cuts of limited length.

The mobile production unit integrates the sand conveyancing system and the thread dispenser. Both the sand and thread are delivered to the point of placement in regulated quantities and deposited to a controlled width in lifts of approximately 300 mm. The lifts are compacted by plates, tampers or rollers to 95% Proctor, or greater, with final trimming carried out manually. With unobstructed access placement rates of 100 m³ per day, per production unit, can be exceeded. The product requires no curing period and so follow on works can be continued without delay. After placement the slope can be hydroseeded or treated with Texsol Vert, a greening process incorporating polyester thread and binder to fix vegetation on even the steepest slopes.

QUALITY CONTROL

The quality of the base material delivered to site is verified against the design requirement by establishing that the particle size distribution falls within the required envelope. In addition water content and cleanliness must be such that the sand is conveyed to the point of placement without undue aggregation. To assure placement of the correct mix two sampling methods are used. First discharge volumes of the two components are collected for a specified time period and then weighed to obtain a thread to soil weight ratio, second a sample of the mixture is produced and the constituents are then separated and weighed. The density of the in situ mix is measured by a gamma logger in preference to diaphragm or sand replacement techniques.

CONCLUSIONS

By devising an economical means of integrating synthetic thread with soil, the Texsol system is able to greatly enhance the mechanical properties of the original soil without changing either its appearance, permeability or density.

The enhancements allow significant economies to be made in earth structures by increasing the angle of stability and thereby reducing volumes of cut and fill. It requires no artificial support, neither does it require over-excavation to tie it into position. These characteristics make the system suited to the upgrading of communication corridors where increased width can be obtained from within the confines of the original cut, or embankment, plan area.

This system presents the geotechnical designer with an environmentally friendly means of limiting, and subsequently hiding, the extent of earthworks. Recent research has broadened its usage to include blast limitation and control.

REFERENCES

LCPC-SETRA, 1990, *Technical Guide*

Fukuoka M et al., 1990, *Stability of retaining wall reinforced by continuous fibers during earthquakes*. Proc. IV Int. Conf. on Geotextiles, geomembranes & related products, The Hague, Vol. 1, 27-32.

Kutura K et al., 1989, *Behaviour of prototype steep slope embankment having soil walls reinforced by continuous threads*. Proc. IV Geotextile Symposium, Tokyo.

Leflaive E & Liausa P, 1986, *Le renforcement des sols par fils continus*. Proc III Int. Conf. on Geotextiles, Vienna, Vol. 2, 523-528.

Gigan J P et al., 1987, *Proprietes mecaniques du Texsol applications aux ouvrages de soutenement*. Proc XXII ICSMFE Rio, 1251-1252.

The use of reinforced soil structures in landfill

S.S. DIKRAN, Tenax Plastics Limited, United Kingdom.
P. RIMOLDI, Tenax SpA, Italy

SYNOPSIS

This paper considers the some uses and functions of geosynthetics in the development of landfills. Emphasis is on reinforcements in particular but drainage, containment, erosion control, separation and protection are considered in general. Applications are illustrated by reference to different structural elements such as poor subsoil and subgrade, reinforcement of waste to increase stability and storage capacity, side slopes, dykes and embankments around landfills. Finally a case in the UK is presented, where geosynthetics were widely used to solve several problems during the design and construction stage of a landfill.

INTRODUCTION

The demand for landfill sites has increased dramatically in the last few years and, as a corollary, so has the cost of disposal, with this running at some a £100 per tonne for some refuse in the UK.

Recent changes in environmental legislation have also pressed for safe landfill sites. Therefore landfill design technology has also improved and probably one of the most important improvements is the use of geosynthetics in collection of leachate, prevention of contamination of groundwater, stability of landfill slopes, separation of different layers of the lining and construction of access roads.

The siting of waste landfills is known to be sensitive and the *not-in-my-backyard* syndrome seems to confront every landfill development. Often, the reasons for opposing a siting are not technical but are political or social. When considering a new, or greenfield, site a situation can arise where technical reasons are often ignored during the decision making process. Thus an alternative location is often investigated and often it is the site of an existing, or abandoned landfill. Such sites rarely have state-of-the-art liners beneath them and frequently have no liner at all, Figure 1. This practice is known as *piggy-backing*, Koerner (1994). This practice raises some important issues which must be addressed by the design engineer on a site specific basis are as follows:

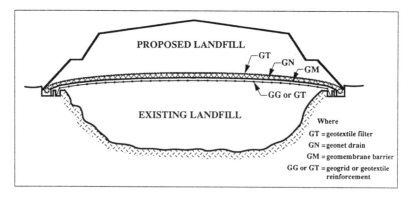

Figure 1 Typical vertical expansion of a landfill

♦ A state-of-the-art liner and leachate collection system must be placed beneath the proposed landfill which will act simultaneously as a cover for the old landfill. A major use of geosynthetics is often considered.

♦ With a large mass of solid waste placed above the old landfill, large total settlements of the existing landfill should be anticipated. Slopes above and below the proposed landfill must be designed accordingly.

♦ Differential settlement of the old landfill might occur so requiring a reinforcing system placed beneath the new liner system.

♦ Gases rising from existing landfill will accumulate at the bottom of the new liner and should be vented. This is a difficult design issue and either uniformly sloped grading or extraction wells should be considered.

♦ Leachate may be expelled from the existing landfill due to the high surcharge load of the proposed landfill. This problem is potentially solved by extraction wells drilled from the perimeter of the site.

Several examples are presented here in which geosynthetics were widely used in the development of landfill sites. Emphasis is given to reinforcement in particular but other applications, such as drainage, containment and erosion control, are also considered briefly. Soil reinforcement in landfill is categorized in four areas as follows:

♦ Landfills on poor subsoil and subgrade

♦ Increasing storage capacity and slope stability by reinforcing waste

♦ Side slopes, dykes and embankments around the landfill

♦ Landfill top capping

LANDFILL ON POOR SUBSOIL AND SUBGRADE

It is often the case that poor subsoil conditions are encountered at the base of a landfill. Large settlements may occur due to the weight of the waste, causing damage to the bottom lining system with the result of environmental hazards due to leachate seeping into groundwater. Ground investigation is necessary to assess the geotechnical properties of the weak soils. Traditional soil improvement techniques available include soft soil replacement by granular material, compaction, dynamic compaction, preloading with the installation of vertical drains such as sand piles and geocomposite strip drains. A reinforced subgrade is highly recommended in this case to reduce tensile stresses in the bottom lining system. Biaxially oriented geogrids can be used as reinforcing elements within a multilayer subgrade, as shown in Figure 2.

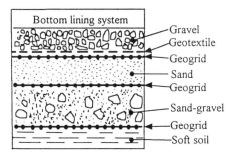

Figure 2 Reinforced subgrade at the base of a landfill

Where an existing landfill is expanded vertically as shown in Figure 1, and due to the poor bearing capacity of the existing waste, a structural lining system is generally used as shown in Figure 3. The reinforcing element in this case is a biaxially oriented HDPE geogrid.

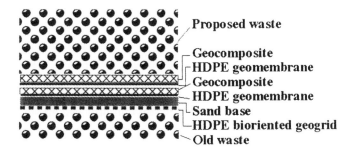

Figure 3 Vertical expansion of a landfill with geogrid reinforced base

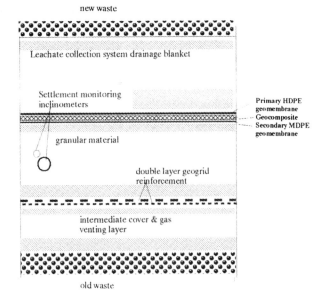

new waste

Leachate collection system drainage blanket

Settlement monitoring
inclinometers

Primary HDPE
geomembrane
Geocomposite
Secondary MDPE
geomembrane

granular material

double layer geogrid
reinforcement

intermediate cover & gas
venting layer

old waste

Figure 4 Example of a double lining system

Another case of an expansion of an existing landfill is where the old waste is highly compressible. The design would include a double lining system which could be placed over the existing solid waste as shown in Figure 4. A major design consideration is the large differential settlements, due to loads from the new waste, resulting in the yielding of the geomembrane beyond the 12% maximum strain normally associated with HDPE geomembranes. To provide a safety factor against rupture a maximum system strain of 5% can therefore be established. Two methods are usually adopted to predict deformations in the old waste, namely the soil arching tensioned membrane method and the finite element method. Details of these analyses are described by Beech et al. (1988, 1990) and Badie and Wang (1985).

The soil arching tensioned membrane method assumes that a void of a given diameter, with rigid side walls, develops in the underlying waste after the waste overburden has been placed. The analysis further assumes that the vertical loads above the void are transferred to the rigid side walls through an arching mechanism. From this analysis a computation is made of the vertical stresses that must be carried by the reinforced overliner support system assuming the soil and/or waste above the liner and void have reached a limit state.

The finite element method requires that the actual properties of the waste mass be determined to allow for the response of the waste to the applied loading. This is a very detailed approach which necessitates in situ measurement of the waste properties and modelling of the waste mass. The result of the FEM analysis is a close approximation of the predicted waste settlements and the subsequent overliner tensile strains.

The above analyses predict the tensile strain in the geogrids with a specified long term modulus. The differential settlement can then be predicted in any area where weak zones could occur. In order to monitor the relative movement of the overliner system a network of horizontal inclinometers are installed during project construction, Figure 4.

INCREASING STORAGE CAPACITY BY REINFORCING WASTE

A classic waste management method is to fill in the waste in small areas at a time to minimize leachate production due to rain. Separation dykes constructed from clay are usually made in the form of cells, but this solution is economically not viable because of the large space occupied by the dykes. At Pontailler landfill, France, the waste material was used as reinforced fill material to form vertical walls around the cells as shown in Figure 5. The reinforcement used was a nonwoven polyester needlepunched geotextile. This example explains how a reinforced structure can be constructed by using any fill material including refuse.

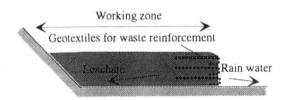

Figure 5 Internal separation dyke with waste reinforced by geotextiles

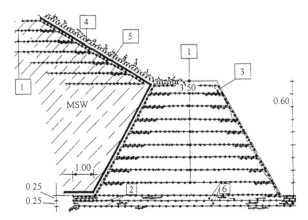

Figure 6 An HDPE geogrid reinforced waste slope and soil embankment
1-Uniaxially oriented geogrid, 2-Biaxially oriented geogrid,
3-Biomat, 4-Geocells, 5-Geomembrane, 6-Sand & gravel.

Figure 6 shows a second example. The left part represents geogrid reinforcing of the landfill slopes, by means of 4 m long uniaxially oriented HDPE geogrids at 0.6m vertical centres, Rimoldi and Togni (1991). This allowed steepening of the outer slope of the waste mass to increase capacity and prevent slope failure. The slope surfaces were covered by geocells for erosion protection. A central embankment was constructed to divide the landfill into two separate cells and the embankment was reinforced with geogrids to steepen both sides to 60°.

An important aspect when analyzing the stability of a landfill mass is to check the failure mechanism along the bottom lining system. The low friction interface between the geomembrane and the drainage geocomposite may be a potential failure surface when the waste height becomes large, Figure 7. Delmas et al. (1993) and Artieres et al. (1994) carried out a numerical study to evaluate the influence of several parameters on the stability of waste over a typical lining system comprising clay-HDPE geomembrane-nonwoven needlepunched geotextile-gravel-waste. They showed that the most critical surface passes through the geomembrane and geotextile, and that the efficiency of the drainage over the geomembrane is of great importance to stability.

The use of reinforcement in the body of the waste, either near the lining system or inside the waste, seems to be a solution which allows on the one hand an increase in global stability during the filling stage, until such time as consolidation of the waste is nearly completed, and on the other hand a steepened slope gives greater storage capacity.

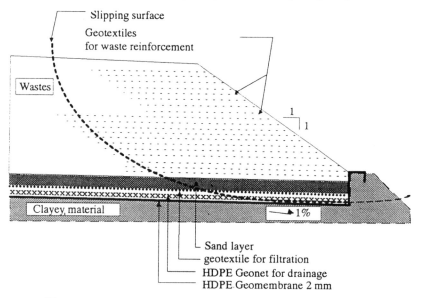

Figure 7 Section through Torcy landfill, France

An example of waste reinforcement at the base of a landfill is at Gallenbach, Germany, where two layers of uniaxially oriented geogrid were used to increase the global stability of the 42 m high waste. The side slopes were increased from 5H:1V to 3H:1V, thus increasing the waste storage capacity.

At the Torcy landfill, France, the maximum height of waste was 40 m with an external side slope of 45°, Figure 7. The critical surface passes through the lining system between the geomembrane and the geonet. The total tensile force required to maintain global stability was calculated to be 2800 kN/m, Artieres et al (1994). The reinforcement consisted of 31 layers of high strength geotextile with a tensile strength of 200 kN/m and a modulus of 1400 kN/m, spaced 1 m vertical centres, with lengths varying from 25 to 70 m. The geotextile was a needlepunched nonwoven polypropylene knitted with polypropylene yarns. The design however seems too conservative.

SIDE SLOPES AND DYKES AROUND THE LANDFILL

Geosynthetics are commonly used in earthworks to provide reinforced embankment slopes; an approach used in landfills to increase storage capacity. This technique was applied to the external dyke of the municipal landfill in Modena, northern Italy, Rimoldi et al. (1988). The geogrid reinforced embankment, 5 m high and 600 m long, was built directly on existing waste to contain additional waste material, Figure 8. Large settlements were expected due to the highly compressible existing waste, therefore a geogrid reinforced soil *beam* was designed using Winkler theory as shown in Figure 8b. The body of the embankment was reinforced with horizontal layers of HDPE uniaxially oriented geogrid.

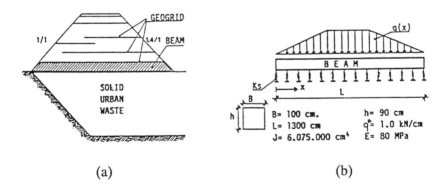

(a)   (b)

Figure 8   a) Cross section through Modena landfill; b) Winkler model

Reinforced soil embankments at the toe of a waste body are becoming a common solution to increase the disposal capacity of a landfill. An example can be seen in the right of Figure 6. The embankment, 5.4 m high was constructed using 9 layers of uniaxially oriented HDPE geogrids and the foundation was prepared using two layers of biaxially oriented geogrid. The outer slopes were covered by biodegradable natural matting to allow a vegetative growth, Rimoldi and Togni (1991).

Design procedures, DoT (1994), Jewell (1990), are available as are computer programs for analysis of reinforced soil structures, associated slope stability and foundation problems, Morrison and Dikran (1995).

LANDFILL TOP CAPPING

The top capping of a landfill is usually a multi-layer system and an important element in a modern landfill design. It has two main functions; first it serves to avoid the escape of harmful contaminants into the environment; and second, it acts as a barrier against water infiltration into the waste, in order to minimise the production of leachate. Therefore, important design considerations to be taken into account are stability, erosion control and the ability to perform as a barrier to both liquids and gases throughout the design life. A typical example of a top capping system is shown in Figure 9. When considering the stability of a capping layer, two criteria must be checked; first, stability against slumping and cracking due to settlement of the waste; and second, slope stability of the several layers which constitute the system.

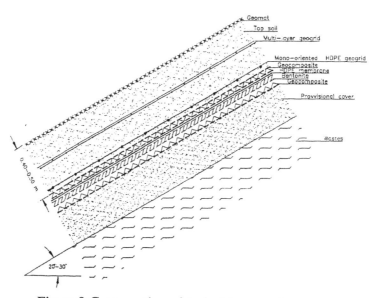

Figure 9 Cross section of typical top capping system

The former generally causes a tension failure of the system, and the latter a sliding problem due to the low friction between the different layers of the system. Design procedures for the capping layers generally adopt basic soil mechanics and structural theories and are explained in several references such Koerner and Hwu (1991) and Koerner (1994).

CLOCKHOUSE LANDFILL CASE STUDY

The landfill at Clockhouse, UK, typifies the range of application of geosynthetics in landfills. The site consists of a void awaiting some 600,000 m³ of household waste. The development of the site from initial concept, through the design to construction took place over 4-5 years. Due to the prolonged pre-construction phase of the site and the rapidly changing legislation and viewpoints of statutory authorities, the initial design was vastly altered to achieve the final product. Several problems had to be tackled during the design and construction stages:

♦ Stability of the side slopes

♦ Control of porewater pressures behind the slope faces

♦ Leachate collection

♦ Protection of leachate collection system from ingress of soil/refuse

♦ Site access roads

Figure 10 Slope failures during construction of Clockhouse landfill

During the construction of the 18° side slopes, several slips had occurred, Figure 10, the main cause being the build up of porewater pressure behind the face of the slopes caused by water seeping through the permeable layers of the Weald Clay.

To prevent this build up of porewater pressure it was decided to use horizontal drainage blankets to collect water from the Weald Clay. The design included the use of geocomposites placed at 2 m vertical spacings. Collector drains were constructed with a fall of 1:300 in order to carry the water from the geocomposites to a collection sump. The drainage geocomposite is composed of a sandwich of two filter fabrics thermally bonded to a HDPE geonet core. The fabric is a nonwoven geotextile which functions like a filter, allowing water to enter the geonet core but preventing the ingress of soil into the core. This product is manufactured in several sizes and is designed according to the volume of water that can be in contact at any time with its surface. The leachate collection system comprised a geonet, sandwiched between two filter fabrics. A general view of the leachate collection system is shown in Figure 11.

Slope stability analysis confirmed low factors of safety against slip failure and so the consultants decided to reinforce the slopes using geogrids. The design included the use of HDPE geogrids with a long term tensile strength of 23.5 kN/m. The reinforcement was placed at 1 m vertical centres with 3 m wide benches provided to interlock the original Weald Clay with the compacted fill facing, Figure 12.

Figure 11 View showing leachate collection system at Clockhouse

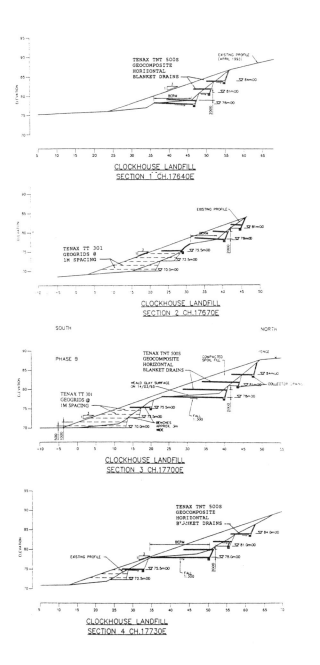

Figure 12 Face stabilization at Clockhouse landfill

Temporary site access roads were required for the heavy construction plant and by using reinforcement under the road construction, it was possible to prevent rutting during trafficking. The access roads design included high strength biaxially oriented polypropylene geogrids.

CONCLUSIONS

Landfill engineering is a very recent innovation, has a very short history, and many solutions are rapidly evolving. Wide application of geosynthetics in landfill design and construction were described in this paper. With respect to reinforcing applications, the main structural elements considered, can be categorised as:

♦ Landfills on poor subsoil and subgrade

♦ Increasing storage capacity and slope stability by reinforcing waste

♦ Side slopes, dykes and embankments around the landfill

♦ Landfill top capping

REFERENCES

Artieries, O. Delmas, P. Correnoz, M. & Oberti O., 1994, *New concepts in waste disposal improved by geosynthetics*. Proc. Fifth Int. Conf. on Geotextiles, Geomembranes & Related Products, Vol. 3, 1069-1072.

Badie, A. & Wang, M.D., 1985, *Effect of an underground void on foundation stability*. ASCE Jrnl of Geotechnical Engrg, 111,8:1008-1019.

Beech, J.F., Bonaparte, R., Giroud, J.P. & Cross, B.A., 1988, *Load bearing capacity of a soil layer supported by a geosynthetic overlying a void*. Theory & Practice of Earth Reinforcement, Balkema, 185-190.

Beech, J.F., Bonaparte, R., Giroud, J.P. & Cross, B.A., 1990, *Design of soil layer geosynthetic systems overlying voids*. Geotextiles & Geomembranes, Vol. 9, 11-50.

Delmas, P., Soyes, B., Berche, J.C. & Artieres, O., 1993, *Stability of wastes on lining systems - models and analysis*. Proc. Int. Symp. Geoconfine 93, Montpellier, Balkema, 505-510.

DoT, 1994, *Design methods for the reinforcement of highway slopes by reinforced soil nailing techniques*. Advice Note HA68/94, Design Manual for Roads and Bridges, Department of Transport.

Jewell, R.A., 1990, *Revised design charts for steep reinforced slopes*. Reinforced Embankments Theory and Practice, Thomas Telford, 1-30..

Koerner, R.M., 1994, *Piggybacking of landfills*. Geosynthetics World, Vol. 5, No 1.

Koerner, R.M., 1994, *Designing with geosynthetics*. 3rd ed., Prentice-Hall.

Koerner, R.M. & Hwu, B.L., 1991, *Stability and tension considerations regarding cover soils on geomembrane lined slopes*. Geotextiles and Geomembranes, Vol. 10, 335-355.

Morrison, I.M. & Dikran, S.S, 1995, *A review of methods of slope stability analysis*. Proc. Symposium on The Practice of Soil Reinforcing in Europe, London, Thomas Telford.

Rimoldi, P. & Togni, S., 1991, *Soil-geosynthetic interaction through direct shear and pullout tests*. Proc. Sardinia 91 - Third Int. Landfill Symposium, Cagliari, Vol. 1, 605-624.

Rimoldi, P., Pagotto, A. & Cazzuffi, D., 1988, *Behaviour of a geogrid reinforced embankment over waste material*. Proc. 2nd Int. Conf. on Case Histories in Geotechnical Engrg., St Louis.

An application of ballistic soil nailing

T.S. INGOLD, Consulting Engineer, United Kingdom

SYNOPSIS

A commercial development, started in 1994 and completed early in 1995, required reduction of the existing ground level within the site boundary by up to 6.3 m. Since space within the site was at a premium, it was not economically viable for the cut slope to be formed as a conventional earthwork. Consequently it was planned to retain the higher ground, outside the site boundary, by use of a reinforced soil modular block faced slope with a batter of 2½:1, (68°). In the event, construction of the reinforced soil slope gave rise to stability problems and the modular block slope was replaced by a nailed slope. The engineering factors involved are explored.

INTRODUCTION

In 1994 work commenced on the construction of a commercial development in southern England. An early requirement was grading of the site which involved the formation of cut slopes up to 6.3 m deep. To minimise land take these cut slopes needed to be as steep as possible and so it was decided to construct reinforced soil slopes faced with a modular block system. Figure 1 indicates a typical cross section in which the original ground profile is shown in light line and the reinforced slope in heavy line. The site boundary is at the crest of the natural slope which falls towards the centre of the site.

SOIL PARAMETERS

The site comprised an over-consolidated clay, with frequent sand partings, overlying chalk at a depth of typically 4.5 m below the invert level of the cut slope. Effective stress shear strength design parameters were given as $\phi' = 23°$, $c' = 10$ kN/m² and $\phi' = 35°$, $c' = 5$ kN/m² for the clay and chalk respectively. Total stress peak shear strength for the clay was typically 100 kN/m² falling to around 30 kN/m² on remoulding. In all cases the unit weight was taken as 20 kN/m³. The phreatic surface in the natural slope was typically 2.5 m below ground level and on construction of the slope was drawn down approximately one metre below the reduced site level at the toe of the slope.

The practice of soil reinforcing in Europe. Thomas Telford, London, 1995

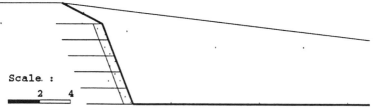

Figure 1 Cross section of modular block slope

ANALYSIS OF MODULAR BLOCK SLOPE

The required design life was 60 years and in addition to self weight loading the reinforced soil modular slope was required to support four 2.2 m square foundation pads for an electricity pylon. The pad nearest the slope was at a depth of approximately 2.5 m below original ground level and some 3 m back from the crest of the slope. Under normal conditions the vertical design load imposed by each pad was 20 tonnes combined with a horizontal load of 6 kN as indicated in Figure 2. For this loading condition the minimum required factor of safety on overall stability was 1.5. Analysis of the slope returned a minimum calculated factor of safety of 1.4 but this was not considered to be problematical since the required minimum value could have been obtained readily by lowering the groundwater table slightly further, Figure 2.

Under abnormal pylon loading, once in 50 years, the vertical design load increased to 57 tonnes combined with a horizontal load of 19 kN. For this case the minimum required factor of safety on overall stability was relaxed to 1.3. This loading lead to a minimum calculated factor of safety of 1.1 which could not be improved adequately by enhancing the reinforcement or lowering the groundwater table.

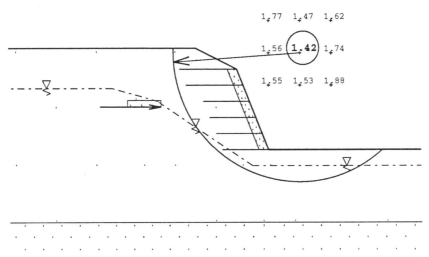

Figure 2 Modular block slope under normal pylon loading

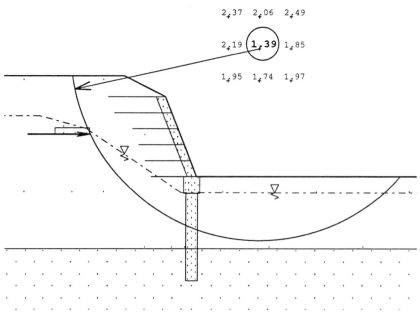

Figure 3 Piled modular block slope under abnormal pylon loading

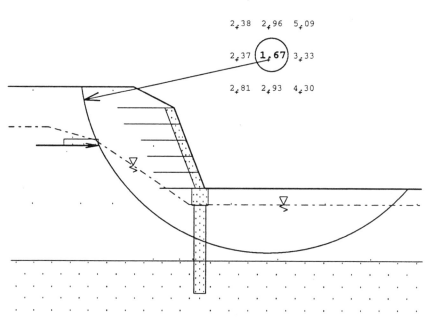

Figure 4 Piled modular block slope under normal pylon loading

In the event, others decided to found the modular block slope facing on a reinforced concrete ground beam, 1.05 m wide by 1.05 m deep, supported by 750 mm diameter bored piles, at 2.25 m centres, taken down some 6.5 m from the cut invert level to toe into the underlying chalk. As indicated in Figure 3, this foundation configuration returned a minimum calculated factor of safety of 1.39 for abnormal pylon loading rising to 1.67 for normal loading so exceeding the minimum required values of 1.3 and 1.5 respectively, Figure 4.

CONSTRUCTION OF MODULAR BLOCK SLOPE

Reinforcement to the modular block facing extended up to 3 m back from the rear of the facing and to install the reinforcement required the formation of a temporary works slope a corresponding distance back from the final line of the face. Short term analysis indicates a minimum factor of safety in excess of 4 decreasing to less than unity in the long term, Figure 5. Intermediate term stability is difficult to predict in cohesive soils but, with the presence of frequent sand partings, it was probable that the long term condition would be attained in a shorter time than for a homogeneous clay.

Shortly into construction, signs of failure were manifested and it seemed that the clay, over stressed by the temporary works, was reducing in shear strength from a peak to a residual value. Consequently a cantilever sheet pile wall was installed in the cut slope, to the rear of the reinforcement line, with a view to regaining stability in the area affected. In light of the instability associated with the temporary works it was decided, by others, that a permanent continuous sheet pile wall should be installed along the length of the modular block slope prior to slope construction.

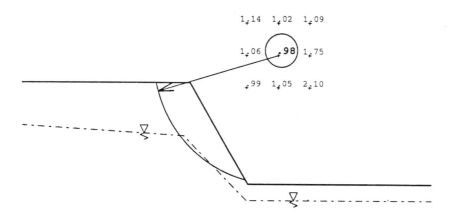

Figure 5 Long-term stability of temporary works for modular block slope

ANALYSIS OF NAILED SLOPE

The installation of soil nails into natural ground is achieved from the face of the cut slope to be formed. Additionally, soil nails may be installed from the top of the cut, downwards to the bottom of the cut, as construction proceeds. As a corollary to this, the cut slope may be permanently reinforced at all stages of construction in which case no temporary works are necessary. In contrast, the construction of a reinforced soil, more aptly a *reinforced fill*, cut slope requires the removal of natural ground, behind the line of the final slope, to accommodate the reinforced fill mass which eventually forms the finished slope. Such a construction procedure introduces the necessity, and risk, of temporary works. In view of this, along with the resulting saving in time and cost, the client opted for soil nailed slopes rather than continuing with reinforced soil slopes.

The nailed slopes were designed at a batter of 1½:1, (56°), and at the design stage the 6.3 m nailed slope was assessed assuming use of 38 mm diameter steel nails with 5 nails, spaced evenly up the slope, at 1 m lateral spacings. Without the ground beam and pile foundation, as proposed for the modular block slope, the nailed slope returned a minimum factor of safety of 1.18 under abnormal pylon loading as indicated in Figure 6. This value was only marginally higher than the value of 1.1 calculated for the modular block slope, without the pile foundation, and in both cases was associated with deep seated overall rotational failure. However, rather than reverting to a piled foundation, it was decided to assess the use of mass concrete counterfort buttresses installed at the toe of the slope and extending downwards sufficiently into the clay foundation soil to raise factors of safety to the target values.

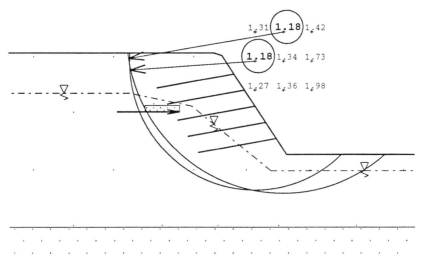

Figure 6 Nailed slope under abnormal pylon loading

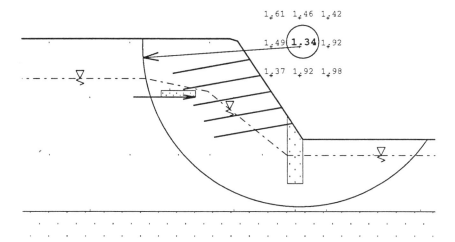

Figure 7 Nailed slope, with counterfort, under abnormal pylon loading

A 1 m thick mass concrete counterfort buttresses, installed to 2.7 m below the cut invert level, was calculated to raise the factors of safety to 1.51 for the normal pylon loading and 1.34 for the abnormal loading so attaining the target values, Figure 7.

CONSTRUCTION OF NAILED SLOPE

In situ pullout tests confirmed the magnitude of the ultimate pull out stress and that, using a firing pressure of 17 MPa (2500 psi), the average achievable penetration was 3.2 m as opposed to the 5.0 m used in the preliminary design. Consequently the number of rows of nails was increased from 5 at 5 m long to 8 at an average length of 3.2 m. Analysis of this revised nail configuration returned minimum factors of safety of 1.51 and 1.29 for the normal and abnormal pylon loadings respectively, Figure 8.

The slope was constructed by excavating and nailing incrementally down the slope to the required invert level where the mass concrete counterfort buttresses were installed. Prior to installing the nails the currently exposed face of the slope was covered with a lightweight biaxially oriented geogrid, with a 20 mm square mesh size, which was in turn overlain by a 150 mm by 100 mm steel mesh. These meshes were secured to the face by cruciform locking plates, attached to the protruding nail heads by collets, and the excess lengths of nail heads cut flush with an angle grinder, Figure 9. Some 261 nails were installed, at nominally 1 m spacings laterally and up the face of the slope, at a rate of typically 5 minutes per nail. As can be seen from Figure 10, careful excavation and nailing produced a neat, planar slope ready for taking the final finish which is usually shotcrete or vegetation. In this particular case the slope was finished by hydroseeding.

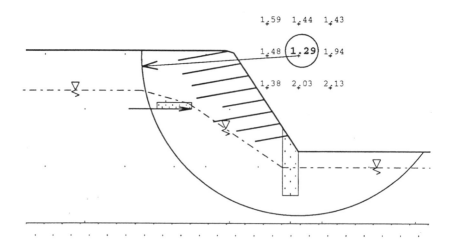

Figure 8 As built nailed slope under abnormal pylon loading

Figure 9 Securing of face mesh

Figure 10 A section of slope awaiting hydroseeding

COMPARATIVE COSTS

Ballistic soil nailing is well suited to reinforcing slopes formed in insitu soil *eg* steep cut slopes formed in natural ground or fill, steep embankment slopes requiring strengthening or remedial works, and natural slopes requiring strengthening or remedial works. The same end objective can be achieved by use of reinforced fill but this requires the removal of soil, to make way for the reinforced mass, and thereby the additional cost, and risk, of temporary works. Ignoring these costs, ballistic soil nailing is typically 80% of the cost of reinforced fill. In the case of the particular project described above the soil nailing solution cost something less than 50% of the originally proposed solution.

CONCLUSIONS

At the onset of a commercial development requiring steep cut slopes it was planned to use a reinforced fill modular block faced slope founded on a ground bean supported by 6.5 m long piles. Slope stability problems were encountered during construction of the reinforced fill slope temporary works. Subsequently the modular block slope was replaced by a nailed slope with 2.7 m deep mass concrete counterforts.

ACKNOWLEDGEMENT

The author wishes to thank Soil Nailing Limited for their permission to publish this paper.